SUGGESTED RETAIL PRICE
1025 992 71
OUR PRICE
922

ELEMENTARY LINEAR ALGEBRA

ELEMENTARY LINEAR ALGEBRA

PAUL C. SHIELDS

DEPARTMENT OF MATHEMATICS

WAYNE STATE UNIVERSITY

WORTH PUBLISHERS, INC.

70 FIFTH AVENUE, NEW YORK, N.Y. 10011

LIBRARY OF CONGRESS CATALOG NUMBER 67-31678

AMS 1968 SUBJECT CLASSIFICATIONS 1501, 1505, 1510, 1515, 1520,

1525, 1530, 1535, 1570, 3420, 4760

DESIGNED BY MALCOLM GREAR/GORDON BRETT

FIFTH PRINTING JANUARY 1971

Printed in the United States of America

TABLE OF CONTENTS

PREFACE

The trend toward early courses in linear algebra has received impetus from the recommendations of the Committee on the Undergraduate Program in Mathematics (CUPM) of the Mathematical Association of America.* CUPM recommends that linear algebra be taught as part of the two-year calculus program to bridge introductory calculus and the more sophisticated calculus of several variables. In attempting to implement this recommendation at Wayne State University, we encountered an immediate problem — the lack of a text in linear algebra suitable for the average underclassman. Consequently, I prepared a set of notes for such a course, and these notes have proved very successful at Wayne State. Since many other schools have expressed interest in this work, I decided to develop a more complete and polished version of my notes. This book is the result.

The text is designed to introduce some of the basic concepts and techniques of linear algebra and to make them accessible to freshmen and sophomores, many of whom are not mathematics majors. With this audience in mind, I have not stressed sophisticated proof technique, which can be left to later courses for mathematics majors. Instead, the emphasis is on interpretation and on the development of computational tools. Systems of equations and matrices are used as vehicles for the introduction and interpretation of vector spaces, subspaces, independence, and dimension. My experience indicates that this enables the student to move easily from familiar material into new ideas and, furthermore, provides him with techniques for problem solving while absorbing subsequent abstractions. This interplay is continued in the discussions of linear transformations, similarity, and linear differential equations, where students are again provided with computational tools as the general theory is presented. Discussions are generally confined to low-dimensional coordinate spaces, often omitting general proofs of the more technical results. Geometric interpretations are frequently given as a further aid to conceptual development.

Elementary differentiation and integration techniques and some vector geometry are used throughout the book. Therefore, a short introduction to calculus (such as the Math. 1 course in the CUPM recommendations) is a prerequisite. An appendix on vector geometry is included which may be used to supplement the student's background.

*"A General Curriculum in Mathematics for Colleges," a report to the Mathematical Association of America by the Committee on the Undergraduate Program in Mathematics, 1965.

The book is explicitly designed for classroom use on the basis of my own experience with beginning students. With only a few exceptions, the material has been divided into sections which can be discussed in one or two lectures. Each section consists of short theoretical discussions with numerous examples and a large number of exercises, most of which are extensions of the examples. *The examples and exercises are the most important part of the book.* My experience indicates that beginning students progress most easily via careful explication of examples combined with homework which further illuminates the concepts and techniques. Wherever possible answers to the exercises are given at the back of the book. This method of presenting material by examples and exercises allows for considerable flexibility of use, the instructor being able to select those parts of the discussion in each section which he finds most relevant while insuring the student's development of conceptual understanding and technique.

The first three chapters also contain interpretations of independence, subspaces, and linear operations as applied to vector spaces of functions. In addition, extensions to the complex case are given in the exercises. The fourth, and final, chapter is on the theory of constant-coefficient linear differential operators. This material, which uses only elementary-calculus results, is accessible to beginning students and provides a significant application of linear algebra. Such concepts as independence, null spaces, operator multiplication, and operator polynomials are further illuminated in this context.

An appendix on dimension theory has been included to introduce the basic techniques of advanced linear algebra. It can be used as a supplement for the better students or in a parallel honors course. The short annotated bibliography will direct interested students to further topics in linear algebra. For ease of reference, I have also included at the back of the book a list of the basic theorems used.

The arrangement of the book allows for a number of possible uses. These include:

> *A one-quarter course*, using the first three chapters and omitting the "optional" material (which is denoted by □)
>
> *A one-semester course*, using (1) the first four chapters less optional material, (2) the first three chapters with optional material, or (3) most of the first three chapters plus Appendix 1 or 2
>
> *A parallel honors course*, using the material of Appendix 2 where appropriate

A supplement for other courses, using various parts of the book. Material from Chapters 1 and 2 can be used to supplement a calculus program. Chapter 4 provides a useful supplement on linear differential equations.

I owe considerable thanks to my colleague and friend, Prof. David Jonah, who read the manuscript at each stage of its development and whose criticisms and suggestions have resulted in major improvements in both content and style. Prof. Vincent Celeste also read the manuscript and suggested a number of additions and changes. I am also grateful to Ted Cary, who assisted me in teaching this material, corrected many errors, and worked all the problems. Thanks are also due to Mrs. Elizabeth Surzyn, who typed the manuscript with her usual accuracy and speed, and to my wife Dorothy, who provided an ear for conversations as well as assistance in the proofreading.

This, my second book, is for Betsy, my second daughter.

Paul C. Shields
Palo Alto, California
October, 1967

CHAPTER 1

MATRICES AND VECTORS

This book is an introduction to some of the elementary concepts and results of linear algebra. Linear algebra provides a basic framework and language for the study of calculus of several variables, differential equations, and modern algebra. In addition, many problems in engineering and the physical and social sciences are now treated using linear concepts.

The most important concept in linear algebra is that of a linear operator. Linear operators are defined on vector spaces. In this chapter we introduce the basic properties of vectors and vector spaces. The name vector space is given to any collection of objects which can be added together or multiplied by numbers, these operations being subject to some of the same laws which hold for ordinary arithmetic. This terminology is an extension of the terminology used in physics, where vectors are quantities that possess both magnitude and direction and can be manipulated subject to some obvious algebraic rules.

Systems of linear equations can be used to illustrate many vector space ideas, and also provide a useful framework for treating computational questions. We therefore devote the first three sections of this chapter to the discussion of a general method for solving such systems. The method involves the use of a special device known as a matrix. We then introduce the concepts of vector and vector space in Section 4. In Sections 5 and 6 we show how linear systems can be rewritten as matrix-vector equations, a procedure that leads to a description of the solutions in terms of subsets of vector spaces, known as subspaces. The fundamental concepts of independence, spanning, basis, and dimension are discussed in Sections 7, 8, and 9, where it is often found useful to express these concepts in terms of matrix equations. The remaining sections of Chapter 1 introduce some geometric considerations that further illustrate these concepts.

SECTION 1 The Elimination Method

We shall often find it necessary to solve systems of linear equations such as

1

$$\begin{aligned} x - y + 2z &= 0 \\ 3x + y - z &= 0 \\ 2x + 2y - 3z &= 0 \end{aligned}$$

Such a system, in which the constant terms are all zero, is called a **homogeneous** system, and several different methods can be used to solve it. We shall describe a procedure known as **elimination** or **reduction** for determining the solutions.

The trick of the elimination method is to add to one equation a suitable multiple of another, chosen so as to eliminate one of the variables. For example, if we add to the second equation of the above system -3 times the first equation, and then add to the third equation -2 times the first equation, we obtain

2
$$\begin{aligned} x - y + 2z &= 0 \\ 4y - 7z &= 0 \\ 4y - 7z &= 0 \end{aligned}$$

We see that x has been eliminated from all except the first equation. System **2** has the same solutions as system **1**. A formal proof of this will be given in Chapter 2. We can now proceed to eliminate y from the first and third equations by adding multiples of the second equation to each to obtain

3
$$\begin{aligned} x \qquad + \tfrac{1}{4}z &= 0 \\ 4y - 7z &= 0 \end{aligned}$$

We have now proceeded as far as necessary to find solutions, for we can assign an arbitrary value to z and easily calculate x and y from system **3** to obtain a solution to system **1**. For example, if $z = 1$, equations **3** give

$$x = -\tfrac{1}{4} \qquad y = \tfrac{7}{4}$$

Thus
$$x = -\tfrac{1}{4} \qquad y = \tfrac{7}{4} \qquad z = 1$$

is a solution to system **1**.

We can express the dependence of the solutions on z by rewriting system **3** as

4
$$\begin{aligned} x &= -\tfrac{1}{4}z \\ y &= \tfrac{7}{4}z \\ z &= z \end{aligned}$$

The student should observe that there is little reason to continue writing down the variables x, y, and z. All we need to do is keep track of the coefficients that belong to each variable in each equation. The standard device for doing this is called a **matrix**, which is a rectangular array of numbers.

The **matrix of coefficients** for system **1** is

5
$$\begin{bmatrix} 1 & -1 & 2 \\ 3 & 1 & -1 \\ 2 & 2 & -3 \end{bmatrix}$$

Note that the numbers in each row are the coefficients of x, y, and z (in that order) in the corresponding equation of system **1**. For example, the numbers in the *second* row are 3, 1, and -1, which are the coefficients of x, y, and z in the *second* equation.

The operations used to reduce system **1** to system **3** can now be described as operations on the rows of matrix **5**. For example, if we add to the second row -3 times the first row and then add to the third row -2 times the first row we obtain

$$\begin{bmatrix} 1 & -1 & 2 \\ 3+(-3)(1) & 1+(-3)(-1) & -1+(-3)(2) \\ 2+(-2)(1) & 2+(-2)(-1) & -3+(-2)(2) \end{bmatrix} = \begin{bmatrix} 1 & -1 & 2 \\ 0 & 4 & -7 \\ 0 & 4 & -7 \end{bmatrix}$$

which is the matrix of coefficients of system **2**.

If we now add to the first row $\frac{1}{4}$ times the second row and then add to the third row -1 times the second row we obtain the matrix

$$\begin{bmatrix} 1 & 0 & \frac{1}{4} \\ 0 & 4 & -7 \\ 0 & 0 & 0 \end{bmatrix}$$

The bottom row of zeros shows that the third equation has been eliminated, while the zeros in the first and second columns indicate that x has been eliminated from all except the first equation and y from all except the second equation. The first two rows are just the coefficient matrix of

$$\begin{aligned} x \qquad + \tfrac{1}{4}z &= 0 \\ 4y - 7z &= 0 \end{aligned}$$

from which, as we have seen, the solutions are easy to determine. The following examples illustrate this procedure of matrix elimination.

EXAMPLE 1 The above matrix method will be used to solve

6
$$\begin{aligned} 3x + y &= 0 \\ x - 2y &= 0 \end{aligned}$$

Form the matrix of coefficients

$$\begin{bmatrix} 3 & 1 \\ 1 & -2 \end{bmatrix}$$

Add to the first row -3 times the second row; then add to the second row $\frac{2}{7}$ times the first row. This procedure first gives

$$\begin{bmatrix} 0 & 7 \\ 1 & -2 \end{bmatrix} \quad \text{then} \quad \begin{bmatrix} 0 & 7 \\ 1 & 0 \end{bmatrix}$$

The latter matrix is the coefficient matrix for

$$\begin{aligned} 0 \cdot x + 7 \cdot y &= 0 \\ 1 \cdot x + 0 \cdot y &= 0 \end{aligned} \quad \text{that is} \quad \begin{aligned} 7y &= 0 \\ x &= 0 \end{aligned}$$

Clearly the only solution is

$$x = y = 0$$

This is therefore the unique solution to system **6**.

EXAMPLE 2 The coefficient matrix of

7
$$\begin{aligned} 2x - y + z &= 0 \\ -7x + \tfrac{7}{2}y - \tfrac{7}{2}z &= 0 \\ 4x + y - 2z &= 0 \end{aligned} \quad \text{is} \quad \begin{bmatrix} 2 & -1 & 1 \\ -7 & \frac{7}{2} & -\frac{7}{2} \\ 4 & 1 & -2 \end{bmatrix}$$

Add to the second row $\frac{7}{2}$ times the first row; then add to the third row -2 times the first row. The result is the matrix

8
$$\begin{bmatrix} 2 & -1 & 1 \\ 0 & 0 & 0 \\ 0 & 3 & -4 \end{bmatrix}$$

Note the row of zeros, which indicates that the second equation has been entirely eliminated, as it is superfluous. We now add to the first row $\frac{1}{3}$ times the third row to obtain

9
$$\begin{bmatrix} 2 & 0 & -\frac{1}{3} \\ 0 & 0 & 0 \\ 0 & 3 & -4 \end{bmatrix}$$

which is the coefficient matrix (after dropping the second row) of

10 $$\begin{aligned} 2x \quad\quad - \tfrac{1}{3}z &= 0 \\ 3y - 4z &= 0 \end{aligned}$$

This system is easy to solve. For example, with $z = 2$, we have the solution to system **7**:

$$x = \tfrac{1}{3} \qquad y = \tfrac{8}{3} \qquad z = 2$$

The dependence of the solutions on z can be expressed by rewriting system **10** as

11 $$\begin{aligned} x &= \tfrac{1}{6}z \\ y &= \tfrac{4}{3}z \\ z &= z \end{aligned}$$

We could, of course, eliminate in the matrix **8** in a different fashion, obtaining other forms for the solutions. For example, if we add $\frac{1}{4}$ times the third row of matrix **8** to the first row we obtain

$$\begin{bmatrix} 2 & -\frac{1}{4} & 0 \\ 0 & 0 & 0 \\ 0 & 3 & -4 \end{bmatrix} \quad \text{which gives} \quad \begin{aligned} 2x - \tfrac{1}{4}y &= 0 \\ 3y - 4z &= 0 \end{aligned}$$

This system can be rewritten as

12 $$\begin{aligned} x &= \tfrac{1}{8}y \\ y &= y \\ z &= \tfrac{3}{4}y \end{aligned}$$

thus expressing the dependency of the solutions upon y.

EXAMPLE 3 The coefficient matrix of

13 $$\begin{aligned} 2x - y + z &= 0 \\ -4x + 2y + z &= 0 \end{aligned} \quad \text{is} \quad \begin{bmatrix} 2 & -1 & 1 \\ -4 & 2 & 1 \end{bmatrix}$$

Adding 2 times the first row to the second row gives

$$\begin{bmatrix} 2 & -1 & 1 \\ 0 & 0 & 3 \end{bmatrix}$$

Thus, in the process of eliminating x from the second equation we have also eliminated y. We now add to the first row $-\frac{1}{3}$ times the second row to obtain

$$\begin{bmatrix} 2 & -1 & 0 \\ 0 & 0 & 3 \end{bmatrix}$$

which is the matrix of coefficients of

$$\begin{aligned} 2x - y &= 0 \\ 3z &= 0 \end{aligned}$$

We see that z must be zero, while y can be assigned arbitrary values and x calculated in terms of y. Rewriting this to express the dependence on y, we have

14
$$\begin{aligned} x &= \tfrac{1}{2}y \\ y &= \phantom{\tfrac{1}{2}}y \\ z &= 0y \end{aligned}$$

as the general form of the solutions to system **13**.

DISCUSSION The elimination method is not always the easiest or fastest way to solve a system, but it does have the advantage of being a systematic procedure. We shall also later find that this process of reducing a matrix is useful in other situations. The student may want to work some of the exercises at this stage to make certain that he understands the procedures given in the above examples.

As shown in equations **11** and **12** there may be several ways to describe the form of the solutions, depending upon the way we eliminate in the matrix. For convenience in stating results it is helpful to obtain a uniform form of the solutions. The kind of matrix that will give this form will be called a reduced matrix.

A **reduced matrix** is a matrix such that

15
- **a** *The first nonzero entry in each row is 1; all other entries in that column are zeros.*
- **b** *Each row that consists entirely of zeros is below each row which contains a nonzero entry.*
- **c** *The first nonzero entry in each row is to the right of the first nonzero entry of each preceding row.*

For example, matrix **9**

$$\begin{bmatrix} 2 & 0 & -\frac{1}{3} \\ 0 & 0 & 0 \\ 0 & 3 & -4 \end{bmatrix}$$

is *not* in reduced form, for it violates **a** and **b**. We can, however, put it in reduced form by multiplying row one by $\frac{1}{2}$, row three by $\frac{1}{3}$, and then interchanging rows two and three to obtain

$$\begin{bmatrix} 1 & 0 & -\frac{1}{6} \\ 0 & 1 & -\frac{4}{3} \\ 0 & 0 & 0 \end{bmatrix}$$

This matrix *is* reduced. It is the coefficient matrix of (omitting the superfluous row)

$$\begin{aligned} x \quad\quad - \tfrac{1}{6}z &= 0 \\ y - \tfrac{4}{3}z &= 0 \end{aligned}$$

which can be rewritten in the form of **11**.

It can be shown that by adding multiples of various rows to other rows, by multiplying rows by nonzero numbers, and by interchanging rows a given matrix can be reduced to one and only one reduced matrix. (*See* the bibliography for a reference.) Thus by reducing we obtain a uniform form for the solutions. The next three examples indicate further the use of the reduced form in describing solutions.

EXAMPLE 4 The matrix of coefficients of

16
$$\begin{aligned} 4x - 2y + 2z + w &= 0 \\ 2x - y - 3z - w &= 0 \end{aligned} \quad \text{is} \quad \begin{bmatrix} 4 & -2 & 2 & 1 \\ 2 & -1 & -3 & -1 \end{bmatrix}$$

We proceed to reduce this as follows: first multiply row one by $\frac{1}{4}$; then add to row two -2 times row one. This gives first

$$\begin{bmatrix} 1 & -\frac{1}{2} & \frac{1}{2} & \frac{1}{4} \\ 2 & -1 & -3 & -1 \end{bmatrix} \quad \text{then} \quad \begin{bmatrix} 1 & -\frac{1}{2} & \frac{1}{2} & \frac{1}{4} \\ 0 & 0 & -4 & -\frac{3}{2} \end{bmatrix}$$

Now multiply row two by $-\frac{1}{4}$; then add to row one $-\frac{1}{2}$ times row two. We have first

$$\begin{bmatrix} 1 & -\frac{1}{2} & \frac{1}{2} & \frac{1}{4} \\ 0 & 0 & 1 & \frac{3}{8} \end{bmatrix} \quad \text{then} \quad \begin{bmatrix} 1 & -\frac{1}{2} & 0 & \frac{1}{16} \\ 0 & 0 & 1 & \frac{3}{8} \end{bmatrix}$$

The latter matrix is reduced, for the first nonzero entry in each row is a 1, all other entries in that column being zeros; the zero rows are below the nonzero rows (for there are no zero rows); and the leading nonzero entry in the second row is to the right of the leading nonzero entry in the first row. The reduced matrix gives

$$\begin{aligned} x - \tfrac{1}{2}y \qquad + \tfrac{1}{16}w &= 0 \\ z + \tfrac{3}{8}w &= 0 \end{aligned}$$

which can be rewritten to express the dependence of the solutions to system **16** upon y and w in the following manner:

$$\begin{aligned} x &= \tfrac{1}{2}y - \tfrac{1}{16}w \\ y &= 1 \cdot y + 0 \cdot w \\ z &= 0 \cdot y - \tfrac{3}{8}w \\ w &= 0 \cdot y + 1 \cdot w \end{aligned}$$

EXAMPLE 5 The method of reduction can be used for systems with more equations than unknowns such as

$$\begin{aligned} x - y + z &= 0 \\ x + y - z &= 0 \\ -x \qquad + z &= 0 \\ x + 2y + z &= 0 \end{aligned}$$

The coefficient matrix is

$$\begin{bmatrix} 1 & -1 & 1 \\ 1 & 1 & -1 \\ -1 & 0 & 1 \\ 1 & 2 & 1 \end{bmatrix}$$

Subtract the first row from the second and fourth rows and add it to the third row to yield

$$\begin{bmatrix} 1 & -1 & 1 \\ 0 & 2 & -2 \\ 0 & -1 & 2 \\ 0 & 3 & 0 \end{bmatrix}$$

Multiply the fourth row by $\frac{1}{3}$; add the fourth row to the first and third rows; and add -2 times the fourth row to the second row. After interchanging the fourth and second rows we have

$$\begin{bmatrix} 1 & 0 & 1 \\ 0 & 1 & 0 \\ 0 & 0 & 2 \\ 0 & 0 & -2 \end{bmatrix}$$

Now multiply the third row by $\frac{1}{2}$; subtract the third row from the first; and add twice the third row to the fourth row. We now have

$$\begin{bmatrix} 1 & 0 & 0 \\ 0 & 1 & 0 \\ 0 & 0 & 1 \\ 0 & 0 & 0 \end{bmatrix}$$

This matrix is reduced and gives the system

$$\begin{aligned} x \quad\quad &= 0 \\ y \quad &= 0 \\ z &= 0 \end{aligned}$$

The unique solution to our original system, then, is $x = y = z = 0$.

EXAMPLE 6 The method we have illustrated works even if there is a large number of equations with a large number of unknowns. Of course, the process of elimination is much longer. Consider the system (subscripts, rather than separate letters, have been used on the unknowns)

$$\begin{array}{rcrcrcrcrcl} x_1 & + & x_2 & - & x_3 & + & x_4 & & & = & 0 \\ & & & & x_3 & + & x_4 & + & x_5 & = & 0 \\ 2x_1 & + & 2x_2 & - & x_3 & & & + & x_5 & = & 0 \\ x_1 & + & x_2 & - & 2x_3 & & & - & x_5 & = & 0 \\ & & & & 2x_3 & - & 4x_4 & + & 2x_5 & = & 0 \\ -x_1 & - & x_2 & + & 2x_3 & - & 3x_4 & + & x_5 & = & 0 \end{array}$$

17

Form the matrix of coefficients:

$$\begin{bmatrix} 1 & 1 & -1 & 1 & 0 \\ 0 & 0 & 1 & 1 & 1 \\ 2 & 2 & -1 & 0 & 1 \\ 1 & 1 & -2 & 0 & -1 \\ 0 & 0 & 2 & -4 & 2 \\ -1 & -1 & 2 & -3 & 1 \end{bmatrix}$$

One possible sequence of steps for reducing this matrix is

1 Add to the third row -2 times the first row.

2 Add to the fourth row -1 times the first row.

3 Add to the sixth row 1 times the first row.

We have thus finished eliminating in the first column. Notice that in this case we have also eliminated as much as we can in the second column, for we now have

$$\begin{bmatrix} 1 & 1 & -1 & 1 & 0 \\ 0 & 0 & 1 & 1 & 1 \\ 0 & 0 & 1 & -2 & 1 \\ 0 & 0 & -1 & -1 & -1 \\ 0 & 0 & 2 & -4 & 2 \\ 0 & 0 & 1 & -2 & 1 \end{bmatrix}$$

Proceed to eliminate in the third column:

4 Add to the first row 1 times the second row.

5 Add to the third row -1 times the second row.

6 Add to the fourth row 1 times the second row.

7 Add to the fifth row -2 times the second row.

8 Add to the sixth row -1 times the second row.

We now have

$$\begin{bmatrix} 1 & 1 & 0 & 2 & 1 \\ 0 & 0 & 1 & 1 & 1 \\ 0 & 0 & 0 & -3 & 0 \\ 0 & 0 & 0 & 0 & 0 \\ 0 & 0 & 0 & -6 & 0 \\ 0 & 0 & 0 & -3 & 0 \end{bmatrix}$$

Proceed to eliminate in the fourth column by adding multiples of the third row to the fifth and sixth rows.

9 Add to the fifth row -2 times the third row.

10 Add to the sixth row -1 times the third row.

For ease of further elimination,

11 Multiply the third row by $-\frac{1}{3}$.

We now have

$$\begin{bmatrix} 1 & 1 & 0 & 2 & 1 \\ 0 & 0 & 1 & 1 & 1 \\ 0 & 0 & 0 & 1 & 0 \\ 0 & 0 & 0 & 0 & 0 \\ 0 & 0 & 0 & 0 & 0 \\ 0 & 0 & 0 & 0 & 0 \end{bmatrix}$$

The reduction to reduced form is completed as follows:

12 Add to the first row -2 times the third row.

13 Add to the second row -1 times the third row.

The student should check definition **15** to see whether the matrix we now have is a reduced matrix.

$$\begin{bmatrix} 1 & 1 & 0 & 0 & 1 \\ 0 & 0 & 1 & 0 & 1 \\ 0 & 0 & 0 & 1 & 0 \\ 0 & 0 & 0 & 0 & 0 \\ 0 & 0 & 0 & 0 & 0 \\ 0 & 0 & 0 & 0 & 0 \end{bmatrix}$$

This is the matrix of coefficients of

$$\begin{aligned} x_1 + x_2 \qquad\qquad + x_5 &= 0 \\ x_3 \qquad + x_5 &= 0 \\ x_4 \qquad\quad &= 0 \\ 0 &= 0 \\ 0 &= 0 \\ 0 &= 0 \end{aligned}$$

We can now assign arbitrary values to the unknowns x_2 and x_5 and compute x_1, x_3, and x_4 from these equations to obtain a solution to system **17**. For example, if we put $x_2 = 0$ and $x_5 = 0$, we obtain the solution

$$x_1 = x_2 = x_3 = x_4 = x_5 = 0$$

If we put $x_2 = -1$ and $x_5 = 2$, we obtain the solution

$$x_1 = -1, \quad x_2 = -1, \quad x_3 = -2, \quad x_4 = 0, \quad x_5 = 2$$

We can express the dependence of these solutions upon x_2 and x_5 by rewriting the system as

$$\begin{aligned} x_1 &= -x_2 - x_5 \\ x_3 &= -x_5 \\ x_4 &= 0 \end{aligned}$$

EXERCISES

1 Each of the matrices on the right is the coefficient matrix for one or more of the systems on the left. Match them.

a $\begin{aligned} 3x + 2y - z &= 0 \\ 2x - y + 2z &= 0 \end{aligned}$

b $\begin{aligned} 2x - y &= 0 \\ x + 4y &= 0 \\ 0x - 0y &= 0 \\ 3x - 3y &= 0 \end{aligned}$

c $\begin{aligned} 3x_1 + 2x_2 - x_3 &= 0 \\ 2x_1 - x_2 + 2x_3 &= 0 \end{aligned}$

d $\begin{aligned} 2x - y &= 0 \\ x + 4y &= 0 \\ 3x - 3y &= 0 \end{aligned}$

e $x + 2y + 3z + w = 0$

f $\begin{aligned} 4x_1 + x_2 + 2x_3 + 6x_5 &= 0 \\ x_1 - x_3 + x_4 + 2x_5 &= 0 \\ \tfrac{1}{2}x_1 + \tfrac{1}{3}x_4 + x_5 &= 0 \\ 2x_1 + 2x_2 + 2x_3 + x_4 &= 0 \\ 2x_1 - 2x_3 + 2x_4 + 4x_5 &= 0 \end{aligned}$

g $\begin{aligned} 2x - y &= 0 \\ 3x - 3y &= 0 \\ x + 4y &= 0 \end{aligned}$

A $\begin{bmatrix} 2 & -1 \\ 1 & 4 \\ 3 & -3 \end{bmatrix}$

B $\begin{bmatrix} 4 & 1 & 2 & 0 & 6 \\ 1 & 0 & -1 & 1 & 2 \\ \frac{1}{2} & 0 & 0 & \frac{1}{3} & 1 \\ 2 & 2 & 2 & 1 & 0 \\ 2 & 0 & -2 & 2 & 4 \end{bmatrix}$

C $[1 \quad 2 \quad 3 \quad 1]$

D $\begin{bmatrix} 2 & -1 \\ 3 & -3 \\ 1 & 4 \end{bmatrix}$

E $\begin{bmatrix} 2 & -1 \\ 1 & 4 \\ 0 & 0 \\ 3 & -3 \end{bmatrix}$

F $\begin{bmatrix} 3 & 2 & -1 \\ 2 & -1 & 2 \end{bmatrix}$

2 Form the matrix of coefficients and use the elimination method to find one description of the solutions to each of the following (as in Examples 1, 2, and 3).

a $$\begin{aligned} x - 3y &= 0 \\ 2x + y &= 0 \end{aligned}$$

b $$\begin{aligned} 7x - 2y &= 0 \\ 2x + y &= 0 \end{aligned}$$

c $$\begin{aligned} 2x - \tfrac{1}{2}y &= 0 \\ 4x - y &= 0 \end{aligned}$$

d $$\begin{aligned} 3x - 2y + 7z &= 0 \\ 3x + 2y - 7z &= 0 \end{aligned}$$

e $$\begin{aligned} 6x + y - z &= 0 \\ x + \tfrac{1}{6}y + 2z &= 0 \end{aligned}$$

f $$\begin{aligned} 2x - y &= 0 \\ x + 2y &= 0 \\ 3x - 2y &= 0 \end{aligned}$$

g $$\begin{aligned} 6x - y + 2z &= 0 \\ -x + 3y - z &= 0 \\ 2x + 7y &= 0 \end{aligned}$$

h $$\begin{aligned} 2x + y + 2z &= 0 \\ -x - \tfrac{1}{2}y - z &= 0 \\ 2x + y &= 0 \end{aligned}$$

i $$\begin{aligned} 10x + 12y - z &= 0 \\ 3x - 7y + 6z &= 0 \end{aligned}$$

j $$\begin{aligned} 6x - 3y + 4z &= 0 \\ x + 6y - 7z &= 0 \\ 5x - 5y &= 0 \end{aligned}$$

k $3x - 2y + z = 0$

3 For the system

$$\begin{aligned} x - 2y + z &= 0 \\ 2x - y - 3z &= 0 \end{aligned}$$

form the matrix of coefficients. Reduce to express the solutions in a form showing the dependence upon z. Reduce in a different manner to show the dependence upon y. Then reduce in a third way to show the dependence upon x. (*See* Example 2.)

4 Find the form of the solutions to each of the systems of Exercise 1 by reducing the coefficient matrix to a *reduced* matrix.

5 Find the form of the solutions to each of the systems of Exercise 2 by reducing the coefficient matrix to a *reduced* matrix.

6 Proceed as in Exercise 5 for each of the systems

a $$\begin{aligned} x + y + z + w &= 0 \\ x - y + z + w &= 0 \\ x - y - z + w &= 0 \\ x - y - z - w &= 0 \end{aligned}$$

b $$\begin{aligned} 2x_1 + x_2 + 3x_3 + x_5 &= 0 \\ 2x_1 - 2x_2 - 6x_4 + x_6 &= 0 \\ x_1 - x_2 - 3x_4 - x_5 &= 0 \\ -2x_1 + 4x_2 - x_3 + 6x_4 + x_5 + x_6 &= 0 \end{aligned}$$

c $$\begin{aligned} 3x_1 + 2x_2 - 7x_3 + 2x_4 + x_5 &= 0 \\ -x_1 + x_2 - 7x_4 + x_5 + 3x_6 &= 0 \end{aligned}$$

7 Does a homogeneous system always have at least one solution? If so, what is this solution?

8 Which of the following matrices are reduced matrices?

a $\begin{bmatrix} 0 & 0 \\ 0 & 0 \end{bmatrix}$ **b** $\begin{bmatrix} 1 & 2 & 1 \end{bmatrix}$

c $\begin{bmatrix} 0 & 1 & 1 \\ 0 & 0 & 1 \end{bmatrix}$ **d** $\begin{bmatrix} 0 & 1 & 1 \\ 1 & 0 & 0 \end{bmatrix}$

e $\begin{bmatrix} 1 & 0 & 1 \\ 0 & 1 & 0 \\ 0 & 0 & 1 \end{bmatrix}$ **f** $\begin{bmatrix} 1 & 2 & 0 & 0 \\ 0 & 0 & 0 & 0 \\ 0 & 0 & 1 & 0 \\ 0 & 0 & 0 & 1 \end{bmatrix}$

9 List all possible reduced matrices with two rows and two columns; with two rows and three columns; with three rows and three columns. For example, every reduced matrix with two rows and two columns which has one zero row must be of the form

$$\begin{bmatrix} 0 & 1 \\ 0 & 0 \end{bmatrix} \quad \text{or} \quad \begin{bmatrix} 1 & a \\ 0 & 0 \end{bmatrix}$$

10 Suppose $A = \begin{bmatrix} a & b \\ c & d \end{bmatrix}$ and that A can be reduced to $\begin{bmatrix} 1 & 0 \\ 0 & 1 \end{bmatrix}$

Find the solutions to
$$\begin{aligned} ax + by &= 0 \\ cx + dy &= 0 \end{aligned}$$

11 Show that $A = \begin{bmatrix} a & b \\ c & d \end{bmatrix}$ reduces to $\begin{bmatrix} 1 & 0 \\ 0 & 1 \end{bmatrix}$

if $ad - bc \neq 0$. Show that if $ad - bc = 0$, then A reduces to a matrix with one row consisting of zeros.

12 Show that if the second row of A is a sum of multiples of the third, fifth, and sixth rows of A, then we can reduce A to a matrix with a row of zeros.

13 Suppose we interchange two *columns* of A to obtain B. How is the system whose matrix of coefficients is B related to the system whose matrix is A?

14 Show that if by a sequence of row operations A is reduced to B, then there is a sequence of row operations that reduces B to A.

15 Suppose R_1 and R_2 are each reduced matrices with two rows and two columns such that the corresponding systems have the same solutions. Show that $R_1 = R_2$.

16 Show that if

$$c_0 + c_1x + c_2x^2 + c_3x^3 = 0$$

for all x then $c_0 = c_1 = c_2 = c_3 = 0$. (Hint: Put $x = 0, 1, 2, 3$ to obtain a system of four equations in the unknowns c_0, c_1, c_2, c_3. By reduction show that this system has only one solution.)

17 Show that if $c_1 \sin x + c_2 \sin 2x + c_3 \sin 3x = 0$ for all x, then $c_1 = c_2 = c_3 = 0$.

□ **18** The method of elimination given also works for systems with complex coefficients. Find the matrix of coefficients and use this to find the form of solutions to

a
$$\begin{aligned} ix + (1 + i)y + 2z &= 0 \\ 2x - (1 - i)y + iz &= 0 \end{aligned}$$

b
$$\begin{aligned} (1 + i)x - iy + 2iz &= 0 \\ (1 - 2i)x + y \qquad &= 0 \end{aligned}$$

(Hint: Remember that $1/(a + ib) = (a - ib)/(a^2 + b^2)$.)

SECTION 2 Nonhomogeneous Systems

Matrix elimination methods can also be used to solve systems in which the constants are not all zero such as

1
$$\begin{aligned} 3x + y &= 4 \\ x - y &= 2 \end{aligned}$$

Such a system is called a **nonhomogeneous linear system**. We now need to carry the constant terms along in the computations, using some device that will keep track of the constants that go with each equation. The usual way to do this is to form the so-called **augmented matrix** of the system.

2
$$\left[\begin{array}{cc:c} 3 & 1 & 4 \\ 1 & -1 & 2 \end{array}\right]$$

The first two columns of this system consist of the coefficient matrix of system **1**, while the *final* column consists of the corresponding constants. Now we need only apply the row operations of Section 1 to this matrix until we obtain the augmented matrix of a simpler system. We therefore proceed to reduce matrix **2**. One possible sequence of operations is to add to the first row -3 times the second row. This gives

$$\left[\begin{array}{cc:c} 0 & 4 & -2 \\ 1 & -1 & 2 \end{array}\right]$$

Multiply the first row by $\frac{1}{4}$; then interchange the first and second rows. We now have

$$\left[\begin{array}{cc:c} 1 & -1 & 2 \\ 0 & 1 & -\frac{1}{2} \end{array}\right]$$

Add to the first row 1 times the second row. We now have obtained the reduced matrix

$$\left[\begin{array}{cc:c} 1 & 0 & \frac{3}{2} \\ 0 & 1 & -\frac{1}{2} \end{array}\right]$$

which is the augmented matrix of

$$\begin{aligned} x &= \tfrac{3}{2} \\ y &= -\tfrac{1}{2} \end{aligned}$$

We conclude that this is the only solution to system **1**.

A homogeneous system always has at least one solution (namely, the one in which all the variables are equal to zero). It is possible, however, that a nonhomogeneous system may have no solution. This situation will be made evident during the process of reduction of the augmented matrix by the occurrence of a row in which all entries, *except* the last entry are zeros. The next example illustrates this.

EXAMPLE 1 The augmented matrix of

3
$$\begin{aligned} 3x - y + z &= 1 \\ 7x + y - z &= 6 \\ 2x + y - z &= 2 \end{aligned} \qquad \text{is} \qquad \left[\begin{array}{ccc:c} 3 & -1 & 1 & 1 \\ 7 & 1 & -1 & 6 \\ 2 & 1 & -1 & 2 \end{array}\right]$$

which can be reduced by using the following sequence of row operations: multiply row one by $\frac{1}{3}$; then add to row two -7 times row one; and then add to row three -2 times row one. We now have

$$\left[\begin{array}{ccc:c} 1 & -\frac{1}{3} & \frac{1}{3} & \frac{1}{3} \\ 0 & \frac{10}{3} & -\frac{10}{3} & \frac{11}{3} \\ 0 & \frac{5}{3} & -\frac{5}{3} & \frac{4}{3} \end{array}\right]$$

and can use the second row to eliminate. To continue the row operations, multiply row two by $\frac{3}{10}$; then add to row three $-\frac{5}{3}$ times row two. The result is

$$\left[\begin{array}{ccc:c} 1 & -\frac{1}{3} & \frac{1}{3} & \frac{1}{3} \\ 0 & 1 & -1 & \frac{11}{10} \\ 0 & 0 & 0 & -\frac{1}{2} \end{array}\right]$$

which is the augmented matrix of

$$\begin{aligned} x - \tfrac{1}{3}y + \tfrac{1}{3}z &= \tfrac{1}{3} \\ y - \quad z &= \tfrac{11}{10} \\ 0 &= -\tfrac{1}{2} \end{aligned} \tag{4}$$

System 4 clearly has no solution, for the last equation cannot hold for any choice of x, y, and z.

DISCUSSION The procedure for solving nonhomogeneous systems is thus the following: we form the augmented matrix of the system and proceed to reduce this matrix to a reduced matrix. Suppose during this reduction we obtain a matrix in which

5 *There is a row in which the first nonzero entry appears in the last column.*

If this occurs we *stop*; for such a matrix is the augmented matrix of a system with *no solutions.*

If property 5 does *not* occur, we finally obtain a reduced matrix with the property that

6 *No row has its first nonzero entry in the last column.*

In this case the system has *one or more* solutions, and we can easily determine the solution or solutions from the reduced form.

Of course, it is possible for a nonhomogeneous system to have more than one solution, as the next example illustrates.

EXAMPLE 2 The augmented matrix of

$$\begin{aligned} x - y + 2z &= 1 \\ 3x + y - \quad z &= 2 \end{aligned} \qquad \text{is} \qquad \left[\begin{array}{ccc:c} 1 & -1 & 2 & 1 \\ 3 & 1 & -1 & 2 \end{array}\right] \tag{7}$$

This matrix can be reduced to (the student should work this out)

$$\left[\begin{array}{ccc:c} 1 & 0 & \tfrac{1}{4} & \tfrac{3}{4} \\ 0 & 1 & -\tfrac{7}{4} & -\tfrac{1}{4} \end{array}\right]$$

which is the augmented matrix of

$$\begin{aligned} x + \tfrac{1}{4}z &= \tfrac{3}{4} \\ y - \tfrac{7}{4}z &= -\tfrac{1}{4} \end{aligned}$$

We can assign to z any arbitrary value, then compute x and y from this to obtain a solution to system 7. For example, if we put $z = 0$, we obtain the solution $x = \frac{3}{4}$, $y = -\frac{1}{4}$, $z = 0$; and if we put $z = 1$, we have the solution $x = \frac{1}{2}$, $y = \frac{3}{2}$, $z = 1$.

We can express the dependence of these solutions upon z by rewriting to obtain

8
$$\begin{aligned} x &= -\tfrac{1}{4}z + \tfrac{3}{4} \\ y &= \tfrac{7}{4}z - \tfrac{1}{4} \end{aligned}$$

DISCUSSION We see that three cases can occur for nonhomogeneous systems: no solutions, exactly one solution, and more than one solution. This first case *cannot* occur for a homogeneous system because such a system always has at least one solution.

A complete discussion of the relation between homogeneous systems and nonhomogeneous systems will be given in later sections. The next example indicates one of the possibilities.

EXAMPLE 3 Consider the systems

9
$$\begin{aligned} 2x - y + z &= 1 \\ 3x \quad + 2z &= -1 \\ 4x + y + 2z &= 2 \end{aligned} \qquad \text{and} \qquad \begin{aligned} 2x - y + z &= 0 \\ 3x \quad + 2z &= 0 \\ 4x + y + 2z &= 0 \end{aligned}$$

Form the matrix

10
$$\begin{bmatrix} 2 & -1 & 1 \\ 3 & 0 & 2 \\ 4 & 1 & 2 \end{bmatrix}$$

and reduce it with the following sequence of operations:

1 Multiply row two by $\frac{1}{3}$.
2 Add to row one -2 times row two; then add to row three -4 times row two.
3 Interchange rows one and two.
4 Add to row two 1 times row three; then interchange rows two and three.
5 Add to row one $\frac{2}{3}$ times row three; then add to row two $-\frac{2}{3}$ times row three.
6 Multiply row three by -1.

This procedure results in the matrix (the student should check this)

11
$$\begin{bmatrix} 1 & 0 & 0 \\ 0 & 1 & 0 \\ 0 & 0 & 1 \end{bmatrix}$$

so that the second system of the systems **9** has the unique solution

$$x = y = z = 0$$

Now apply the same operations, in the same order, to the augmented matrix of the first system of the systems **9**.

12
$$\left[\begin{array}{ccc|c} 2 & -1 & 1 & 1 \\ 3 & 0 & 2 & -1 \\ 4 & 1 & 2 & 2 \end{array}\right]$$

The resulting matrix (which should be checked by the student) is

13
$$\left[\begin{array}{ccc|c} 1 & 0 & 0 & 3 \\ 0 & 1 & 0 & 0 \\ 0 & 0 & 1 & -5 \end{array}\right]$$

so that the unique solution to the first system of the systems **9** is $x = 3$, $y = 0$, and $z = -5$.

Notice that the homogeneous system has a *unique* solution and that the reduction of matrix **10** and matrix **12** resulted in matrices **11** and **13**, in which the first three columns are identical. The form of matrix **13** showed us that the nonhomogeneous system also has a *unique* solution. In this case no matter what the constant terms in the first system of the systems **9** are, there will be a *unique* solution.

EXERCISES

1 For each of the following systems find the augmented matrix; then, by reducing, determine whether the system has a solution. If the system has a solution, reduce the augmented matrix to a reduced matrix and determine the form of the solutions.

a
$$\begin{aligned} x - 3y &= 1 \\ 2x - y &= 4 \end{aligned}$$

b
$$\begin{aligned} 3x + y + 6z &= 6 \\ x + y + 2z &= 2 \\ 2x + y + 4z &= 3 \end{aligned}$$

c
$$\begin{aligned} 2x_1 + x_2 \qquad\qquad + x_4 &= 2 \\ 3x_1 + 3x_2 + 3x_3 + 5x_4 &= 4 \\ 3x_1 \qquad - 3x_3 - 2x_4 &= 3 \end{aligned}$$

d
$$\begin{aligned} 2x + y \qquad\quad + w &= 2 \\ 3x + 3y + 3z + 5w &= 3 \\ 3x \qquad - 3z - 2w &= 3 \end{aligned}$$

e
$$\begin{aligned} 2x + y + z &= 1 \\ 4x + 2y + 3z &= 1 \\ -2x - y + z &= 2 \end{aligned}$$

f
$$\begin{aligned} 2x_1 + x_2 + 2x_3 + 3x_4 + x_5 + 4x_6 &= 1 \\ x_2 + x_3 + 2x_4 + 2x_5 &= -1 \\ 2x_1 + x_2 + 3x_3 + x_4 + 5x_6 &= 1 \\ 4x_1 + 3x_2 + 6x_3 + 6x_4 + 3x_5 + 10x_6 &= -1 \\ 3x_4 + x_5 + x_6 &= 1 \\ x_2 + x_3 + 2x_4 + 4x_5 &= 0 \end{aligned}$$

g
$$\begin{aligned} 2x_1 + x_2 + 2x_3 + 3x_4 + x_5 + 4x_6 &= 1 \\ x_2 + x_3 + 2x_4 + 2x_5 &= -1 \\ 2x_1 + x_2 + 3x_3 + x_4 + 5x_6 &= 1 \end{aligned}$$

2 Form the matrix of coefficients of

$$\begin{aligned} 3x + y - z &= 0 \\ 6x + 2y - z &= 0 \end{aligned}$$

and reduce to determine the solutions. Then apply the same row operations to the augmented matrix of

$$\begin{aligned} 3x + y - z &= 2 \\ 6x + 2y - z &= -1 \end{aligned}$$

and determine whether a solution exists and is unique. Compare the first three columns of the reduced form of each of these matrices.

3 Show that if

$$\begin{aligned} ax + by &= 0 \\ cx + dy &= 0 \end{aligned}$$

has a unique solution, then for any choice of c_1 and c_2, the system

$$\begin{aligned} ax + by &= c_1 \\ cx + dy &= c_2 \end{aligned}$$

has a unique solution. (Hint: Show that the coefficient matrix must reduce to

$$\begin{bmatrix} 1 & 0 \\ 0 & 1 \end{bmatrix}$$

and proceed as in Example 3.)

4 Show that there are no numbers c_0, c_1, c_2 such that the equation $x^3 = c_0 + c_1x + c_2x^2$ holds for all values of x. (Hint: Put $x = 0, 1, 2, 3$ to find four equations in the three unknowns, c_0, c_1, c_2. An alternative system of three equations in the three unknowns can be found by differentiating twice and setting $x = 0$ in each of the equations obtained.)

5 **a** Show that there are no numbers c_1 and c_2 such that $\sin 3x = c_1 \sin x + c_2 \sin 2x$ holds for all x.

b Show that there are no numbers c_1, c_2, c_3 such that $e^{4x} = c_1e^x + c_2e^{2x} + c_3e^{3x}$ holds for all x. (Hint: Use the second method given in Exercise 4.)

6 Assume that each of the following matrices is the matrix of the coefficients of a homogeneous system and decide whether the system has a solution

and, if so, whether the solution is unique.

a $\begin{bmatrix} 1 & 0 & 0 \\ 0 & 1 & 1 \\ 0 & 0 & 1 \end{bmatrix}$ **b** $\begin{bmatrix} 1 & 2 & 1 \\ 0 & 1 & 1 \\ 0 & 0 & 0 \end{bmatrix}$

c $\begin{bmatrix} 1 & 2 & 0 & 0 \\ 0 & 0 & 1 & 1 \\ 0 & 0 & 0 & 1 \end{bmatrix}$ **d** $\begin{bmatrix} 1 & 3 & 2 \\ 0 & 1 & 1 \\ 0 & 0 & 2 \\ 0 & 0 & 0 \end{bmatrix}$

7 Assume that each of the matrices of Exercise 6 is the augmented matrix of a nonhomogeneous system and decide whether the system has a solution and, if so, whether the solution is unique.

8 Assume that each of the matrices of Exercise 6 is the matrix of coefficients of a nonhomogeneous system and decide whether the system can always be solved (no matter what the constant terms may be). If the system can be solved (sometimes or always), must the solutions be unique?

□ **9** The technique of forming the augmented matrix and reducing also works for systems with complex coefficients and constants. For each of the following systems find the augmented matrix and determine whether a solution exists. If a solution exists, reduce to a reduced matrix and determine the solutions.

a
$$\begin{aligned} ix + 2y &= 1 + i \\ (1 + 3i)x - iy &= 0 \end{aligned}$$

b
$$\begin{aligned} (1 + i)x + iy &= 0 \\ 2x + (1 + i)y &= 1 \end{aligned}$$

c
$$\begin{aligned} ix + (1 + i)y + 2iz &= 3 \\ (1 - 2i)x - y &= 1 \\ (2 - i)x + y + (2 + 2i)z &= 4 - 3i \end{aligned}$$

SECTION 3 Existence and Uniqueness Theorems

A homogeneous system of linear equations in the unknowns $x_1, x_2, \ldots, x_n$ always has at least one solution, namely,

1
$$x_1 = x_2 = \cdots = x_n = 0$$

If the system has *more* unknowns than equations, then other solutions can also be found. We state this result as a theorem.

THEOREM 1 Any homogeneous linear system in the unknowns $x_1, x_2, \ldots, x_n$ that has fewer equations than unknowns always has a solution $x_1, x_2, \ldots, x_n$ in which at least one of the x_i's is *not* zero.

In Appendix 2 a proof of this result that does not involve the method of reduction is given. At this point we merely show how this theorem can be established from the reduction method.

Suppose A is the matrix of coefficients of the system, so that A has m rows and n columns, where m is the number of equations and n the number of unknowns of the system. We apply row operations to A until we obtain a reduced matrix R which also has m rows and n columns.

The matrix R is the matrix of coefficients of a homogeneous system which has the *same* solutions as the original system. This system also has a particularly simple form, because of the reduced nature of R. (*See* statement **15**, page 6.)

By assumption, the matrix R has fewer rows than columns, so it must have *one or more* columns with the property that *no* entry of the column is the first nonzero entry of its row. In the corresponding system of equations this means that there are one or more variables which never appear as the first variable in any equation. These variables can be given arbitrary values, and the system can still be solved. Hence there must be a solution $x_1, x_2, \ldots, x_n$ in which at least one of the x_i's is not zero. (*See* Example 1, below.)

EXAMPLE 1 We exhibit the above argument for

2

$$\begin{aligned} 2x - y + z &= 0 \\ x + 4y - z &= 0 \end{aligned}$$

We form the matrix of coefficients

$$A = \begin{bmatrix} 2 & -1 & 1 \\ 1 & 4 & -1 \end{bmatrix}$$

By applying row operations we finally obtain the reduced matrix

$$R = \begin{bmatrix} 1 & 0 & \frac{1}{3} \\ 0 & 1 & -\frac{1}{3} \end{bmatrix}$$

which gives

3

$$\begin{aligned} x \quad + \tfrac{1}{3}z &= 0 \\ y - \tfrac{1}{3}z &= 0 \end{aligned}$$

System **3** has the same solutions as system **2**. The fact that the variable z does not appear as the first variable in either equation of system **3** corresponds to the fact that no entry of the third column of R is the first nonzero entry of its row. We can give z any value and compute x and y from equations **3**, thereby obtaining a solution to the system **2**. In particular, if we put $z = 1$, then equations **3** give $x = -\frac{1}{3}$, $y = \frac{1}{3}$, which, in turn, give us a solution to system **2**

$$x = -\tfrac{1}{3},\ y = \tfrac{1}{3},\ z = 1$$

in which at least one of x, y, and z is not zero.

DISCUSSION Now consider a homogeneous system that has at least as many equations as unknowns. We can proceed to eliminate by forming the matrix of coefficients A and reducing it to a reduced matrix R. The system determined by R will have the same solutions as the system determined by A. Suppose we discard those superfluous equations corresponding to the zero rows of R, which are of the form

$$0 \cdot x_1 + 0 \cdot x_2 + \cdots + 0 \cdot x_n = 0$$

If we finally obtain in this manner a system with fewer equations than unknowns then we can apply Theorem 1 to conclude that there must be a solution in which *not all* the variables are zero. (*See* Example 2 below.)

It always happens that

4 *The reduced form never has more equations than unknowns.*

A discussion of this is given in Example 3, below.

We may obtain a reduced system with exactly the same number of equations as unknowns. In this case R must have a particularly simple form, and the system has *only* the obvious solution **1**, as demonstrated in Example 4.

EXAMPLE 2 Consider the system (*see* equations **1**, page 1)

5
$$\begin{aligned} x - y + 2z &= 0 \\ 3x + y - z &= 0 \\ 2x + 2y - 3z &= 0 \end{aligned}$$

The matrix of coefficients

$$A = \begin{bmatrix} 1 & -1 & 2 \\ 3 & 1 & -1 \\ 2 & 2 & -3 \end{bmatrix} \quad \text{reduces to} \quad R = \begin{bmatrix} 1 & 0 & \frac{1}{4} \\ 0 & 1 & -\frac{7}{4} \\ 0 & 0 & 0 \end{bmatrix}$$

The latter is the matrix of coefficients of the system

$$\begin{aligned} x + 0 \cdot y + \tfrac{1}{4}z &= 0 \\ 0 \cdot x + \quad y - \tfrac{7}{4}z &= 0 \\ 0 \cdot x + 0 \cdot y + 0 \cdot z &= 0 \end{aligned}$$

which must have the same solutions as system **5**. We can discard the bottom equation and obtain

$$\begin{aligned} x \quad + \tfrac{1}{4}z &= 0 \\ y - \tfrac{7}{4}z &= 0 \end{aligned}$$

which has the same solutions as system **5**. We know (from Theorem 1) that this system must have a solution in which not all of the variables are zero. Such a solution is easily found. For example, putting $z = 1$, we obtain the solution $x = -\frac{1}{4}$, $y = \frac{7}{4}$, and $z = 1$, in which at least one of the variables is not zero.

EXAMPLE 3 Consider the system

$$\begin{aligned} 3x - \quad y &= 0 \\ 2x + \quad y &= 0 \\ x - 3y &= 0 \end{aligned}$$

We can form the matrix of coefficients A and reduce to a reduced matrix R which gives a system with the same solutions as this system. Without explicitly doing this we can obtain some information about R using description **15**, page 6.

The matrix R must have three rows and two columns. Each column can contain at most one entry which is the first nonzero entry of its row. (*See* property **15a**, page 6.) Since each row that does not consist of zeros must have a first nonzero entry we conclude that R can have at most two rows with nonzero entries. In other words, the bottom row of R must consist of zeros, so that discarding this superfluous equation gives a reduced system of *at most* two equations in two unknowns. We conclude that statement **4** must be true in this case.

The student can show that

$$R = \begin{bmatrix} 1 & 0 \\ 0 & 1 \\ 0 & 0 \end{bmatrix} \quad \text{so that the reduced form is} \quad \begin{aligned} x \quad &= 0 \\ y &= 0 \end{aligned}$$

EXAMPLE 4 Consider the system

6
$$\begin{aligned} 2x - 7y &= 0 \\ 3x + 5y &= 0 \end{aligned}$$

The reduced form of this is

7
$$\begin{aligned} x \quad &= 0 \\ y &= 0 \end{aligned}$$

(The student should always check assertions of this type by carrying out the reduction.) This system has the same solutions as system **6**. Since system **7** has only the obvious solution

$$x = 0, \quad y = 0$$

we conclude that system **6** has exactly one solution, namely

$$x = 0, \quad y = 0$$

Once we know that the reduced matrix R obtained from the matrix of coefficients of a system has two columns and exactly two rows with nonzero entries, we can argue directly from the properties **15** of Section 1 that the reduced system must look like system **7**.

Suppose, for example, that R is a reduced matrix with two nonzero rows and two columns. Each nonzero row of R must have a first nonzero entry, and, from property **15a**, page 6, these must appear in different columns. Since the first nonzero entry of the second row must be to the right of the first nonzero entry of the first row (property **15b**, page 6), we conclude that the first two rows of R must be

$$\begin{bmatrix} 1 & 0 \\ 0 & 1 \end{bmatrix}$$

while the remaining rows (if any) must consist of zeros.

DISCUSSION The arguments used in Example 4 can be extended to the general case to obtain

THEOREM 2 A system of homogeneous equations in the n unknowns $x_1, x_2, \ldots, x_n$ has a *unique* solution if the corresponding reduced matrix R has *exactly n* rows with nonzero entries. This solution must be

$$x_1 = x_2 = \cdots = x_n = 0$$

Conversely, if the system has this as its *only* solution, then the corresponding reduced matrix has exactly n rows with nonzero entries. Furthermore, the first n rows of R must then have the form:

$$\begin{bmatrix} 1 & 0 & 0 & \cdots & 0 \\ 0 & 1 & 0 & \cdots & 0 \\ 0 & 0 & 1 & \cdots & 0 \\ \vdots & \vdots & \vdots & \vdots\vdots\vdots & \vdots \\ 0 & 0 & 0 & \cdots & 1 \end{bmatrix} \tag{8}$$

Matrix **8** is called the n by n **identity matrix** and will be denoted by I_n. In particular this theorem tells us that a homogeneous system of n equations in n unknowns has a unique solution when and *only* when the coefficient matrix can be reduced to the n by n identity matrix I_n.

We could now deduce theorems similar to the above for nonhomogeneous examples. (*See* Example 3, page 18, which indicates one possible theorem.) We shall delay such a discussion until later, for the results will be trivial consequences of much more useful considerations.

EXAMPLE 5 In using the theorems of this section it is generally unnecessary to completely reduce the coefficient matrix, but only necessary to reduce far enough so that the theorems can be applied. For example, the matrix

$$A = \begin{bmatrix} 2 & 1 & 4 \\ 3 & 0 & 1 \\ 2 & -1 & 1 \end{bmatrix}$$

can be reduced as follows: Add to row two $-\frac{3}{2}$ times row one; then add to row three -1 times row one; and then add to row three $-\frac{4}{3}$ times row two.

We now have

$$\begin{bmatrix} 2 & 1 & 4 \\ 0 & -\frac{3}{2} & -5 \\ 0 & 0 & \frac{11}{3} \end{bmatrix}$$

from which we can see that further reduction will give

$$\begin{bmatrix} 1 & 0 & 0 \\ 0 & 1 & 0 \\ 0 & 0 & 1 \end{bmatrix}$$

Therefore, if A is the coefficient matrix of a homogeneous system in x, y, and z, Theorem 2 tells us that the only solution is $x = y = z = 0$.

Now suppose

$$B = \begin{bmatrix} 1 & 1 & 1 \\ 2 & -1 & 1 \\ 4 & 1 & 3 \\ 7 & 1 & 5 \end{bmatrix}$$

Using the first row to eliminate in the first column we obtain

$$\begin{bmatrix} 1 & 1 & 1 \\ 0 & -3 & -1 \\ 0 & -3 & -1 \\ 0 & -6 & -2 \end{bmatrix}$$

which reduces further to

$$\begin{bmatrix} 1 & 1 & 1 \\ 0 & -3 & -1 \\ 0 & 0 & 0 \\ 0 & 0 & 0 \end{bmatrix}$$

Thus if B is the matrix of coefficients of a homogeneous system in x, y, and z, the system can be reduced to a system with two equations in three unknowns. Theorem 1 then guarantees that there is at least one solution in which x, y, and z are not all zero.

EXERCISES

1 By using Theorem 1 directly, or by reducing the coefficient matrix and then using Theorem 1, show that each of the following systems has a solution in which not all of the variables are zero. (Generally, it is unnecessary to obtain the final reduced form, for it is enough to reduce to a system with fewer equations than unknowns, as in Example 5.)

a $2x - y = 0$

b
$$\begin{aligned} 2x - y &= 0 \\ 4x - 2y &= 0 \\ -x + \tfrac{1}{2}y &= 0 \end{aligned}$$

c
$$\begin{aligned} 3x - 2y + z + w &= 0 \\ 4x + 2y + z - w &= 0 \\ y - 3z + 2w &= 0 \end{aligned}$$

d
$$\begin{aligned} x + y + z &= 0 \\ x + 2y + z &= 0 \\ x + 4y + z &= 0 \\ -x + y - z &= 0 \end{aligned}$$

e
$$\begin{aligned} x_1 + x_2 - x_3 + x_4 &= 0 \\ x_3 + x_4 + x_5 &= 0 \\ 2x_1 + 2x_2 - x_3 + x_5 &= 0 \\ x_1 + x_2 - 2x_3 - x_5 &= 0 \\ 2x_3 - 4x_4 + 2x_5 &= 0 \\ x_1 - x_2 + 2x_3 - 3x_4 + x_5 &= 0 \end{aligned}$$

2 For each of the systems of Exercise 1, find at least one solution in which not all of the variables are zero.

3 Use Theorem 2 to show that each of the following systems has a unique solution. What is this solution? (It is necessary to reduce only far enough to see that the final reduced form has the right number of nonzero rows, as in Example 5.)

a
$$\begin{aligned} 2x - y &= 0 \\ x + 3y &= 0 \end{aligned}$$

b
$$\begin{aligned} 3x - 2y + z &= 0 \\ 2x - 4y + 2z &= 0 \\ -x - y + 3z &= 0 \end{aligned}$$

c
$$\begin{aligned} 4x + 3y &= 0 \\ 7x - y &= 0 \\ x + 2y &= 0 \end{aligned}$$

d
$$\begin{aligned} 2x - y + z - w &= 0 \\ 3x + y + w &= 0 \\ 2x + 2z + w &= 0 \\ 4x - 2y - z - w &= 0 \\ 5x - y - 2z &= 0 \end{aligned}$$

e
$$\begin{aligned} x_1 + x_2 + x_3 + x_4 + x_5 &= 0 \\ x_1 - x_2 + x_3 + x_4 - x_5 &= 0 \\ -x_1 + x_2 - x_3 + x_4 - x_5 &= 0 \\ x_1 + x_2 - x_3 + x_4 + x_5 &= 0 \\ x_1 + x_2 + x_3 - x_4 + x_5 &= 0 \end{aligned}$$

4 Show that

$$\begin{aligned} ax + by &= 0 \\ cx + dy &= 0 \end{aligned}$$

has more than one solution if and only if $ad - bc = 0$.

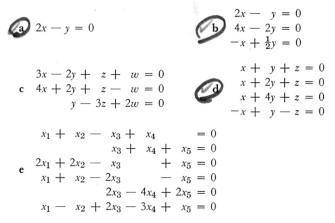

5 Show that

$$\begin{aligned} a_1x + a_2y &= 0 \\ b_1x + b_2y &= 0 \\ c_1x + c_2y &= 0 \end{aligned}$$

has more than one solution if and only if

$$a_1b_2 - a_2b_1 = a_1c_2 - a_2c_1 = b_1c_2 - b_2c_1 = 0$$

6 Without reducing determine the form of the reduced matrix and use Theorems 1 and 2 to decide which of the following systems have a unique solution.

a $$\begin{aligned} x + 2y &= 0 \\ 3y &= 0 \end{aligned}$$

b $$\begin{aligned} x_1 + 2x_2 + x_3 + x_4 &= 0 \\ x_3 - x_4 &= 0 \\ x_3 + x_4 &= 0 \\ 2x_4 &= 0 \end{aligned}$$

c $$\begin{aligned} x_1 + x_2 + x_3 + x_4 &= 0 \\ 2x_2 - x_3 + x_4 &= 0 \\ 3x_3 - x_4 &= 0 \\ 4x_4 &= 0 \end{aligned}$$

7 **a** Show that there are numbers c_1, c_2, and c_3, *not* all zero, such that

$$c_1(1,2) + c_2(1,-2) + c_3(-1,1) = (0,0)$$

(Hint: Express the left-hand side as a single pair; obtain a system of equations in the unknowns c_1, c_2, and c_3; and then apply Theorem 1.)

b Show that there are numbers c_1, c_2, c_3, and c_4, *not* all zero, such that $c_1(1,2,1) + c_2(-1,0,1) + c_3(2,1,0) + c_4(3,1,3) = (0,0,0)$.

c Show that if $c_1(1,2) + c_2(2,1) = (0,0)$, then $c_1 = c_2 = 0$.

d Show that if $c_1(1,1,1) + c_2(1,-1,1) + c_3(1,1,-1) = (0,0,0)$, then $c_1 = c_2 = c_3 = 0$.

8 We often use equivalent formulations of the conclusion of Theorem 1. Which of the following statements are the same as the conclusion of Theorem 1?

a There is a solution $x_1, x_2, \ldots, x_n$ such that for each i, $x_i \neq 0$.

b There is a solution $x_1, x_2, \ldots, x_n$ such that for some i, $x_i \neq 0$.

c The system has a unique solution.

d The system has more than one solution.

e Any two solutions of the system are identical.

f There is a solution $x_1, x_2, \ldots, x_n$ such that $x_1^2 + x_2^2 + \cdots + x_n^2 > 0$.

g There is a solution $x_1, x_2, \ldots, x_n$ such that the product $x_1x_2 \ldots x_n \neq 0$.

h There is a solution $x_1, x_2, \ldots, x_n$ such that $1/x_i$ exists for some i.

9 Can you find a solution to

$$\begin{aligned} x + 2y + z &= 0 \\ -x - 2y + 3z &= 0 \end{aligned}$$

in which $z \neq 0$? Why does this not contradict Theorem 1?

10 A linear equation in two unknowns is the equation of a line in the two-dimensional plane. Each of the following questions refers to equations or systems of equations in two unknowns. Graphing some examples may be helpful.

a What is true about the line of a homogeneous equation?

b What can be said about the intersection of the lines of a homogeneous system of equations if the solution is unique? If there is more than one solution?

c What can be said about the intersection of the lines of a nonhomogeneous system if the system has no solution? Exactly one solution? More than one solution?

d Deduce from the above by geometric arguments that if a system of equations has more than one solution it must have at least three solutions.

e Deduce from the above by geometric arguments that if a homogeneous system of two equations in two unknowns has a unique solution, any nonhomogeneous system with the same coefficients has a unique solution.

11 A linear equation in three unknowns is the equation of a plane in space. Each of the following questions refers to equations or systems of equations in three unknowns.

a What is true about the plane of a homogeneous system?

b What can be said about the intersection of the planes of a homogeneous system of equations if the solution is unique? If there is more than one solution?

c What does Theorem 1 say about the intersection of two planes through the origin?

d What can be said about the intersection of the planes of a nonhomogeneous system if the system has no solution? Exactly one solution? More than one solution?

e State and prove results for planes similar to parts **d** and **e** of Exercise 10.

□ **12** The theorems of this section can be extended to the case of complex systems.

a Does the following system have a unique solution?

$$\begin{aligned} ix + (1 + i)y &= 0 \\ 2x - (3i + 1)y &= 0 \end{aligned}$$

If so, what must this solution be?

b Does the following system have a unique solution?

$$\begin{aligned} x - iy + 2iz &= 0 \\ 3x + (1 - i)y - iz &= 0 \end{aligned}$$

SECTION 4 Vectors and Vector Spaces

Homogeneous systems have the property that sums and multiples of solutions are also solutions. For example, if x_1, y_1, z_1 and x_2, y_2, z_2 are each solutions to the system

$$\begin{aligned} x - y + 2z &= 0 \\ 3x + y - z &= 0 \\ 2x + 2y - 3z &= 0 \end{aligned}$$

then so are $x_1 + x_2$, $y_1 + y_2$, $z_1 + z_2$, and tx_1, ty_1, tz_1. Thus we can "add" two solutions to obtain another solution, and we can "multiply" a solution by a number to obtain another solution.

These same properties hold for the solutions to the homogeneous linear differential equation

$$f''' - 2f'' + 3f' + 5f = 0$$

that is, if f_1 and f_2 are solutions to this equation, then so are the sum $f_1 + f_2$ and the multiple tf_1.

In each of these situations we have conceived of a complicated object, such as a triple of numbers or a function, as a single entity. Furthermore, we could then add these entities together, or multiply them by numbers, in each case obtaining another entity with the same properties. Also, many of the rules of ordinary arithmetic hold for these operations. For example, our addition of triples is commutative, the triple $x_1 + x_2$, $y_1 + y_2$, $z_1 + z_2$ clearly being the same as the triple $x_2 + x_1$, $y_2 + y_1$, $z_2 + z_1$.

These observations have become central to the study of modern mathematics. In this section we shall introduce some of the terminology which is now commonly used in discussing the above conceptions and operations. The first of these is the word *vector*. In physics a vector is defined as a quantity having both magnitude and direction, which is usually represented by an arrow. In current usage, however, **vector** is the general name given to any object, such as a triple of numbers, or functions, polynomials, and so on, which can be added together and multiplied by numbers, subject to some of the laws of ordinary arithmetic. A **vector space** is a collection of objects for which such an addition and multiplication can be defined. To be more precise we list the addition and multiplication rules below for a vector space, V.

Addition Rules

A1 *If* $\bar{u}$ *and* $\bar{v}$ *are in* V, *then* $\bar{u} + \bar{v}$ *is defined and is in* V.

A2 $\bar{u} + \bar{v} = \bar{v} + \bar{u}$.

A3 $\bar{u} + (\bar{v} + \bar{w}) = (\bar{u} + \bar{v}) + \bar{w}$.

A4 *There is a unique member of* V, *usually denoted by* $\bar{0}$, *such that* $\bar{u} + \bar{0} = \bar{u}$ *for all* $\bar{u}$ *in* V.

A5 *If* $\bar{u}$ *is in* V, *there is a unique member of* V, *usually denoted by* $-\bar{u}$, *such that* $\bar{u} + (-\bar{u}) = \bar{0}$.

1

Multiplication Rules

M1 *If* a *is a real number and* $\bar{u}$ *is in* V, *then* $a\bar{u}$ *is defined and is in* V.

M2 $a(\bar{u} + \bar{v}) = a\bar{u} + a\bar{v}$.

M3 $(a + b)\bar{u} = a\bar{u} + b\bar{u}$.

M4 $(ab)\bar{u} = a(b\bar{u})$.

M5 $1\bar{u} = \bar{u}$.

M6 $0\bar{u} = \bar{0}$.

M7 $(-1)\bar{u} = -\bar{u}$.

Such a collection V is commonly called a **real vector space**. The members of V are called **vectors** or **points**. In this context we often refer to numbers as **scalars**.

REMARK The above names are somewhat unfortunate, for a given collection V may have little or no relationship to the student's previous acquaintance with "vectors," "space," or "points." The use of geometric terminology for fairly general algebraic systems can, however, be quite helpful in guiding our intuition. This requires, at first, considerable effort on the part of the student to expand his perception and also requires a willingness to learn algebraic definitions.

We stress the fact that a vector space is merely a collection of objects for which an addition and a multiplication are so defined that the rules **1** hold. If we can also multiply by complex numbers, we call V a **complex vector space**. Our discussion will be confined to real vector spaces; the complex discussion will be treated in the exercises.

We usually denote $\bar{u} + (-1)\bar{v}$ by $\bar{u} - \bar{v}$, thinking of $\bar{u} - \bar{v}$ as subtraction. Equations involving vectors and scalars can be solved in much the same manner as are equations involving numbers. For example, to solve

$$2\bar{u} - 3\bar{w} = \bar{v} \qquad \text{for} \quad \bar{w}$$

we add $-2\bar{u}$ to both sides and then multiply both sides by $-\frac{1}{3}$ to obtain

$$\bar{w} = \tfrac{2}{3}\bar{u} - \tfrac{1}{3}\bar{v}$$

A number of examples of vector spaces are given below. In the next section it will be seen that systems of equations can be expressed as vector equations. We will then be able to describe the solutions to these equations in terms of subsets of vector spaces. These subsets are called subspaces.

A **subspace** M of a vector space V is a subset of V which contains $\bar{0}$ and is closed under addition and multiplication by scalars. In other words, a subset M of a vector space V is a subspace if

2
- **a** *$\bar{0}$ is in M.*
- **b** *If $\bar{u}$ and $\bar{v}$ are in M, then $\bar{u} + \bar{v}$ is in M.*
- **c** *If $\bar{u}$ is in M and a is a scalar, then $a\bar{u}$ is in M.*

A subspace M is also a vector space, for statement **2** guarantees that rules **A1**, **A4**, and **M1** are true for vectors in M. Since the remaining rules are true for V, they are automatically true for M.

We now give a number of examples of vector spaces, that is, collections of objects for which addition and scalar multiplication are defined so that rules **1** are true, and subspaces, that is, subsets, of vector spaces for which properties **2** are true.

EXAMPLE 1 *The Space R^2.*

We denote the collection of all ordered pairs (x,y) of real numbers by R^2. Addition and multiplication by real numbers are defined for pairs by

$$(x_1,y_1) + (x_2,y_2) = (x_1 + x_2, y_1 + y_2)$$
$$a(x,y) = (ax,ay)$$

It is a fairly simple but somewhat dull task to show that the vector space rules **1** are satisfied for these objects. For example, since $(x,y) + (0,0) = (x,y)$, and $(0,0)$ is the only pair with this property, we see that rule **A4** holds for R^2 with $\bar{u} = (x,y)$ and $\bar{0} = (0,0)$.

Therefore R^2 is a vector space. In other words, R^2 is a collection of objects for which an addition and a multiplication by numbers are so defined that the rules **1** are satisfied.

The space R^2 does have a convenient geometric representation. For the usual selection of coordinate axes in a plane, a pair (x,y) can be represented in the usual manner as the point whose coordinates are (x,y). In this representation, the sum and multiple of a pair have simple geometric interpretations, as shown in Figure 1a and b.

In physics, a vector is a physical quantity that possesses both magnitude and direction. If such quantities act in a plane, they can be represented by arrows in a plane, the length of the arrow being the magnitude of the quantity and the direction of the arrow being the direction in which the quantity acts.

We usually say that two such arrows represent the same quantity if they have the same length and the same direction. Hence, each such quantity can be uniquely represented by an arrow issuing from (0,0). In this case, such an arrow is completely described by giving the coordinates of its terminal point. Therefore, we can also represent pairs (x,y) in R^2 as arrows; namely, the pair (x,y) corresponds to the arrow from (0,0) to (x,y). This is the origin of the word "vector" in our setting.

If (x_1,y_1) is represented as the arrow from (0,0) to (x_1,y_1), and (x_2,y_2) is represented as the arrow from (0,0) to (x_2,y_2), then $(x_1 + x_2, y_1 + y_2)$ is represented as the arrow from (0,0) to $(x_1 + x_2, y_1 + y_2)$. (*See* Figure 1a.)

Figure 1a *The parallelogram law for the sum in* R^2.

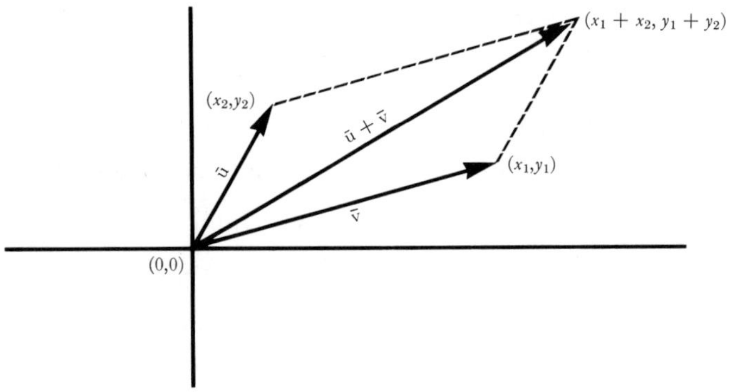

Figure 1b *A multiple of a vector.*

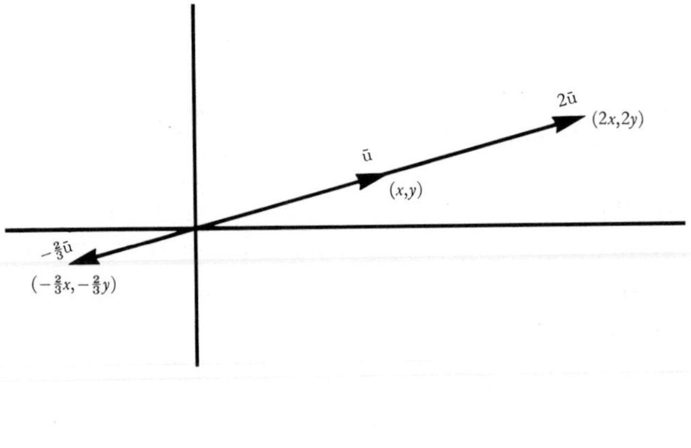

A quite useful fact about this representation is the following:

3 *The arrow from* $(0,0)$ *to* $(x_2 - x_1, y_2 - y_1)$ *points in the same direction as and has the same length as the arrow from* (x_1,y_1) *to* (x_2,y_2).

This is shown in Figure 2. Thus we often find it useful to represent $(x_2 - x_1, y_2 - y_1)$ as the arrow from (x_1,y_1) to (x_2,y_2).

One kind of subspace of R^2 has a convenient geometric interpretation: if M consists of all multiples of a single point (x_0,y_0), M is then a subspace of R^2. Certainly M will contain $(0,0)$ because $(0,0) = 0(x_0,y_0)$, and M is closed under addition and multiplication by numbers.

The set of all multiples of (x_0,y_0) is just the line through $(0,0)$ and (x_0,y_0), as Figure 1b indicates. Thus, the subspace M can be represented as a line through the origin. In summary:

4 *If* M *consists of all multiples of* (x_0,y_0), M *is a subspace of* R^2 *which can be represented as the line through* $(0,0)$ *and* (x_0,y_0).

It is also common practice to denote the vector from $(0,0)$ to $(1,0)$ as $\vec{i}$ and the vector from $(0,0)$ to $(0,1)$ as $\vec{j}$. The vector from $(0,0)$ to (x,y) is thus denoted by $x\vec{i} + y\vec{j}$.

Figure 2

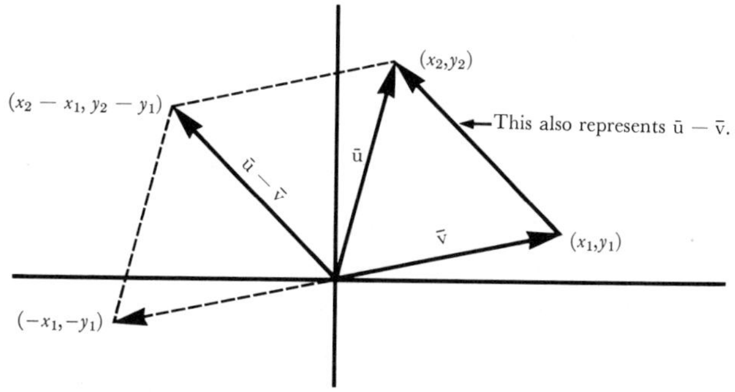

EXAMPLE 2 *The Space R^3.*

We denote the collection of all ordered triples (x,y,z) of real numbers by R^3. Addition and multiplication by real numbers for triples are defined by

$$(x_1,y_1,z_1) + (x_2,y_2,z_2) = (x_1 + x_2, y_1 + y_2, z_1 + z_2)$$
$$a(x,y,z) = (ax,ay,az)$$

Again it is fairly simple to see that the vector space rules **1** are satisfied. For example, the triple (0,0,0) certainly satisfies rule **A4**, while $-(x,y,z)$ is given by $(-x,-y,-z)$.

We conclude that R^3 is a vector space, which again is just a name for the fact that addition and multiplication are so defined for triples that the basic rules **1** hold. This space also has a convenient representation as points in three-dimensional space. (This is the origin of the word "space" in the phrase "vector space.") In fact, by selecting suitable coordinate axes in space, we can represent a triple (x,y,z) in the usual manner as the point whose coordinates are (x,y,z).

In a manner similar to that given for R^2 we can also represent (x,y,z) as the arrow from (0,0,0) to (x,y,z) or as any arrow with the same direction and length. In this way R^3 can be used as a representation of physical vectors which act in space.

It is common practice to denote the vector from (0,0,0) to (1,0,0) by $\bar{i}$, the vector from (0,0,0) to (0,1,0) by $\bar{j}$, and the vector from (0,0,0) to (0,0,1) by $\bar{k}$, so that $x\bar{i} + y\bar{j} + z\bar{k}$ represents the vector from (0,0,0) to (x,y,z).

In this situation rule **3** can be given as

$$(x_2 - x_1)\bar{i} + (y_2 - y_1)\bar{j} + (z_2 - z_1)\bar{k}$$

which represents the arrow from (x_1,y_1,z_1) to (x_2,y_2,z_2).

If M is the subset of R^3 consisting of all multiples of a single vector (x_0,y_0,z_0) then, as in result **4**, M is a subspace of R^3 and can be represented as the line through (0,0,0) and (x_0,y_0,z_0).

If the points (0,0,0), (x_1,y_1,z_1), and (x_2,y_2,z_2) are not collinear, and if M is the set of all vectors of the form

$$a(x_1,y_1,z_1) + b(x_2,y_2,z_2)$$

M is a subspace of R^3. This subspace can be represented as the plane determined by (x_1,y_1,z_1), (x_2,y_2,z_2), and (0,0,0).

In Appendix 1 a number of applications to geometry that use these interpretations of R^2 and R^3 as collections of arrows are given.

EXAMPLE 3 *The Space R^n.*

The first two examples have a natural generalization that serves as a useful model for many vector spaces. We denote by R^n, the collection of all ordered n-tuples $(x_1,x_2,\ldots,x_n)$ of real numbers. The sum and multiple are defined by

$$(x_1,x_2,\ldots,x_n) + (y_1,y_2,\ldots,y_n) = (x_1 + y_1, x_2 + y_2,\ldots,x_n + y_n)$$
$$a(x_1,x_2,\ldots,x_n) = (ax_1,ax_2,\ldots,ax_n)$$

We usually call the numbers $x_1, x_2, \ldots, x_n$ the **coordinates** of $(x_1,x_2,\ldots,x_n)$.

Clearly the rules **1** are satisfied for these definitions, and R^n is therefore a vector space. For example, if $\bar{0} = (0,0,\ldots,0)$ then for $\bar{x} = (x_1,x_2,\ldots,x_n)$ we certainly have $\bar{x} + \bar{0} = \bar{x}$.

We note that:

> *If n is larger than three, R^n can not be represented in a useful geometric way, so that we must use the algebraic properties in our study of R^n.*

If M is the set of all multiples of a single n-tuple $\bar{x}$, then as in Example 1, M is a subspace of R^n. By analogy with result **4** we often say that M is the line through $(0,0,\ldots,0)$ and $\bar{x} = (x_1,x_2,\ldots,x_n)$. It can be shown, in fact, that such an M and a line in R^2 do have quite similar algebraic properties. Of course, two n-tuples $(x_1,x_2,\ldots,x_n)$ and $(y_1,y_2,\ldots,y_n)$ are equal if and only if their corresponding coordinates are equal; that is,

$$(x_1,x_2,\ldots,x_n) = (y_1,y_2,\ldots,y_n)$$

if and only if $x_i = y_i$, $i = 1, 2, \ldots, n$.

EXAMPLE 4 *Function Spaces.*

Since sums and multiples of continuous functions are also continuous we should expect that various collections of continuous functions are vector spaces. For example, denote by $C[0,1]$ the collection of all functions that are defined and continuous for $0 \leq x \leq 1$. The sum and multiple are defined by

5
$$(f + g)(x) = f(x) + g(x) \qquad 0 \leq x \leq 1$$
$$(af)(x) = af(x) \qquad 0 \leq x \leq 1$$

In other words, $f + g$ is that function whose value at x is $f(x) + g(x)$, and af is that function whose value at x is $af(x)$. Figure 3 illustrates this addition and scalar multiplication.

In calculus it is shown that if f and g are continuous at x, then $f + g$ and af are also continuous at x. In particular, if f and g belong to $C[0,1]$, then $f + g$ and af also belong to $C[0,1]$, so that this collection is closed under the operations **5**. The student can verify that the vector space rules **1** do indeed hold for these operations. Therefore $C[0,1]$ is a vector space. The realization that collections of continuous functions have an *algebraic structure* similar to R^2 and R^3 has made it possible to study many questions about continuous functions by methods originally geometric in form.

Among the subspaces of $C[0,1]$ that are of interest are the following two: the set M of all functions f that belong to $C[0,1]$ and are such that the derivative f' also belongs to $C[0,1]$ and the set M_1 of all polynomial functions that belong to $C[0,1]$. Certainly the zero function belongs to each of these. Furthermore, it is shown in calculus that

$$(f + g)' = f' + g' \qquad \text{and} \qquad (af)' = af'$$

Therefore M is closed under addition and scalar multiplication. Since sums and multiples of polynomials are again polynomials we see that M_1 is also a subspace of $C[0,1]$.

Figure 3

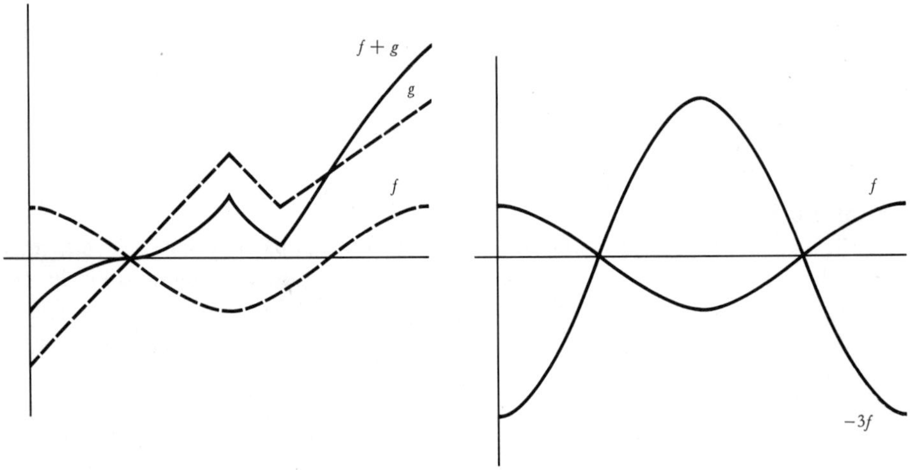

EXERCISES

1 Let $\bar{u} = (1,1,0)$, $\bar{v} = (-\frac{1}{2},0,\frac{2}{3})$, $\bar{w} = (0,\frac{1}{4},2)$.

a Find $\bar{u} + (2\bar{v} + \bar{w})$ and $(\bar{u} + 2\bar{v}) + \bar{w}$.

b Find $3(\bar{u} + \bar{v}) - 3(\bar{u} - \bar{w})$.

c Find $\bar{x}$ so that $\bar{u} + \bar{x} = \bar{w}$.

2 Let $\bar{u} = (1,-1,2,1,0)$, $\bar{v} = (3,1,2,0,0)$, $\bar{w} = (0,0,1,2,-1)$.

a Find $\bar{u} - (2\bar{v} + \bar{w})$.

b Find $3(\bar{u} + 2\bar{v}) + 3(\bar{w} - 2\bar{v})$.

c Find $\bar{x}$ so that $2\bar{u} + \bar{x} = 2\bar{w}$.

3 If $\bar{x} = (x_1, x_2, \ldots, x_n)$ in R^n, what is $-\bar{x}$?

4 Let $\bar{u} = 1 - 2x + x^3$, $\bar{v} = 3x - x^2$, $\bar{w} = 2x - 1$ be vectors in $C[0,1]$.

a Find $\bar{u} - 2\bar{v} + 3\bar{w}$.

b Find $3(\bar{u} + \bar{v}) - 3(\bar{u} - \bar{v})$.

c Find $\bar{z}$ so that $\bar{u} + \bar{z} = \bar{w} + \bar{v}$.

d Graph $\bar{v}$, $\bar{w}$, and $2\bar{v} - \bar{w}$ on the same axes.

5 Is the set of all real numbers a vector space?

6 Suppose $\bar{u} = (1,2)$ and $\bar{v} = (3,-1)$. Represent $\bar{u}$, $\bar{v}$, $\bar{u} - \bar{v}$, $\bar{u} + \bar{v}$, $2\bar{u}$, and $-3\bar{v}$ as points in a plane relative to the usual choice of coordinate axes.

7 Represent each of the points of Exercise 6 as sums of multiples of $\bar{i}$ and $\bar{j}$ and draw the arrows that represent these vectors.

8 a Express $(x - y,\ 2x + y,\ x - y,\ 2y)$ as a sum of multiples of $(1,2,1,0)$ and $(-1,1,-1,2)$.

b Express $(-\frac{5}{3}x_3 + 0 \cdot x_4 + \frac{1}{5}x_5,\ -\frac{1}{3}x_3 + 0 \cdot x_4 - \frac{3}{5}x_5, x_3, x_4, x_5)$ as a sum of multiples of $(-\frac{5}{3},-\frac{1}{3},1,0,0)$, $(0,0,0,1,0)$, and $(\frac{1}{5},-\frac{3}{5},0,0,1)$.

9 a Express the line whose equation is $x + 2y = 0$ as the subspace of R^2 which consists of multiples of a single vector.

b Suppose M consists of all multiples of $(3,1)$. Find an equation of the line which represents M.

c Express the plane whose equation is $x - 2y + z = 0$ as the subspace of R^3 which consists of sums of multiples of two vectors.

d Can the line $x + 2y = 1$ be represented as a subspace of R^2?

10 Express $2(x_1,x_2,x_3,x_4) - 3(y_1,y_2,y_3,y_4) + (z_1,0,1,z_4)$ as a single 4-tuple.

11 Show that $(0,0,0)$ is a sum of vectors of the form $a(1,0,1) + b(1,-1,1)$. Show that sums and multiples of vectors of the form $a(1,0,1) + b(1,-1,1)$ are also of this form, and consequently the set of vectors of this form is a subspace of R^3.

12 Show that the set of all vectors of the form $a(1,1,-1,1) + b(1,2,0,1) + c(1,2,1,1)$ is a subspace of R^4. (Hint: Proceed as in Exercise 11.)

13 Show that (0,0,0) is a solution to $2x - y + z = 0$ and that sums and multiples of solutions to this equation are also solutions to this equation and hence form a subspace of R^3.

14 Show that the set of all functions f such that $2f'' - 3f' + f = 0$ is a subspace of C[0,1]. (Hint: Proceed as in Exercise 13.)

□ **15** A set of objects V for which an addition is defined and a multiplication by *complex* numbers is defined so that the rules **1** hold, where the multiplication rules are assumed to hold for complex numbers, is called a **complex vector space.** The set C^n of all n-tuples of complex numbers is a complex vector space. For $\bar{u} = (i,2+i,0)$, $\bar{v} = (-1,i,2i)$, $\bar{w} = (i,0,1)$, find $\bar{u} - 2i\bar{v} + (1+i)\bar{w}$. Also find an $\bar{x}$ in C^3 such that $\bar{u} + (1+i)\bar{x} = \bar{w}$.

SECTION 5 Matrix Equations

We now introduce a formal way to interpret a system of equations as a matrix equation involving vectors in R^n. This will result in a considerable simplification of notation, which often enables us to give simple proofs of fairly complicated results.

For convenience vectors in R^n will be written as column matrices. For example, the form

$$\begin{bmatrix} x \\ y \end{bmatrix}$$

will be used, rather than (x,y). Of course, then the sum and multiple become

$$\begin{bmatrix} x_1 \\ y_1 \end{bmatrix} + \begin{bmatrix} x_2 \\ y_2 \end{bmatrix} = \begin{bmatrix} x_1 + x_2 \\ y_1 + y_2 \end{bmatrix} \quad \text{and} \quad a\begin{bmatrix} x \\ y \end{bmatrix} = \begin{bmatrix} ax \\ ay \end{bmatrix}$$

We can express the system

1
$$\begin{aligned} ax + by &= 0 \\ cx + dy &= 0 \end{aligned}$$

as a matrix equation by suitably defining a matrix product. For

$$A = \begin{bmatrix} a & b \\ c & d \end{bmatrix} \quad \text{and} \quad \bar{u} = \begin{bmatrix} x \\ y \end{bmatrix}$$

the **product** $A\bar{u}$ is defined by

2 $$A\bar{u} = \begin{bmatrix} ax + by \\ cx + dy \end{bmatrix}$$

The system **1** can then be expressed as the vector equation

3 $$A\bar{u} = \bar{0}$$

In other words, once we agree that $A\bar{u}$ is defined by equation **2**, we can rewrite system **1** in the shorter form, **3**. This shorter vector form is particularly useful for treating large systems. The general definition of the product $A\bar{u}$ is as follows:

For
$$A = \begin{bmatrix} A_{11} & A_{12} & \cdots & A_{1n} \\ A_{21} & A_{22} & \cdots & A_{2n} \\ \vdots & & & \\ A_{m1} & A_{m2} & \cdots & A_{mn} \end{bmatrix} \quad \text{and} \quad \bar{u} = \begin{bmatrix} x_1 \\ x_2 \\ \vdots \\ x_n \end{bmatrix}$$

the **product** $A\bar{u}$ is defined by

4 $$A\bar{u} = \begin{bmatrix} A_{11}x_1 + A_{12}x_2 + \cdots + A_{1n}x_n \\ A_{21}x_1 + A_{22}x_2 + \cdots + A_{2n}x_n \\ \vdots \\ A_{m1}x_1 + A_{m2}x_2 + \cdots + A_{mn}x_n \end{bmatrix}$$

Notice that the right-hand side has m entries (the number of rows of A) so that $A\bar{u}$ is a vector in R^m. The ith coordinate of $A\bar{u}$ is obtained by adding together the products of the ith row of A with the corresponding entries of $\bar{u}$. We observe that the product is defined only when the number of entries of $\bar{u}$ *equals* the number of columns of A. The student should learn to calculate products quickly and accurately.

EXAMPLE 1 Formula **4** gives

$$\begin{bmatrix} 3 & 1 & 2 \\ 0 & 1 & 1 \end{bmatrix} \begin{bmatrix} x_1 \\ x_2 \\ x_3 \end{bmatrix} = \begin{bmatrix} 3x_1 + x_2 + 2x_3 \\ x_2 + x_3 \end{bmatrix}$$

We can therefore express

5 $$\begin{aligned} 3x_1 + x_2 + 2x_3 &= 6 \\ x_2 + x_3 &= 8 \end{aligned}$$

as the equation

$$\textbf{6} \quad A\bar{u} = \bar{c}, \qquad \text{where } A = \begin{bmatrix} 3 & 1 & 2 \\ 0 & 1 & 1 \end{bmatrix}, \qquad \bar{u} = \begin{bmatrix} x_1 \\ x_2 \\ x_3 \end{bmatrix}, \qquad \bar{c} = \begin{bmatrix} 6 \\ 8 \end{bmatrix}$$

We use much the same terminology for vector equations as we do for systems. We say that A is the *matrix of coefficients* of equation **6**. We also say that this equation is *nonhomogeneous* because $\bar{c} \neq \bar{0}$.

The vector

$$\bar{u} = \begin{bmatrix} -1 \\ 7 \\ 1 \end{bmatrix}$$

is a *solution* to equation **6** since

$$\begin{bmatrix} 3 & 1 & 2 \\ 0 & 1 & 1 \end{bmatrix} \begin{bmatrix} -1 \\ 7 \\ 1 \end{bmatrix} = \begin{bmatrix} 3(-1) + 1 \cdot 7 + 2 \cdot 1 \\ 0(-1) + 1 \cdot 7 + 1 \cdot 1 \end{bmatrix} = \begin{bmatrix} 6 \\ 8 \end{bmatrix}$$

The vector

$$\bar{u} = \begin{bmatrix} \frac{1}{2} \\ -\frac{3}{2} \\ 0 \end{bmatrix}$$

is *not* a solution to equation **6**, for we have

$$\begin{bmatrix} 3 & 1 & 2 \\ 0 & 1 & 1 \end{bmatrix} \begin{bmatrix} \frac{1}{2} \\ -\frac{3}{2} \\ 0 \end{bmatrix} = \begin{bmatrix} 3(\frac{1}{2}) + 1(-\frac{3}{2}) + 2 \cdot 0 \\ 0(\frac{1}{2}) + 1(-\frac{3}{2}) + 1 \cdot 0 \end{bmatrix} = \begin{bmatrix} 0 \\ -\frac{3}{2} \end{bmatrix}$$

and this last vector is not the same as $\bar{c}$.

EXAMPLE 2

a $$\begin{bmatrix} -1 & 0 \\ 1 & 2 \\ 6 & 1 \end{bmatrix} \begin{bmatrix} 0 \\ -3 \end{bmatrix} = \begin{bmatrix} 0 \\ -6 \\ -3 \end{bmatrix}$$

b $$\begin{bmatrix} 2 & 1 & -3 & 5 \end{bmatrix} \begin{bmatrix} 1 \\ 2 \\ -1 \\ 0 \end{bmatrix} = 7$$

c $\begin{bmatrix} -1 & \frac{1}{2} \\ \frac{1}{3} & -4 \end{bmatrix} \begin{bmatrix} \frac{2}{3} \\ \frac{1}{4} \end{bmatrix} = \begin{bmatrix} -\frac{13}{24} \\ -\frac{7}{9} \end{bmatrix}$ **d** $\begin{bmatrix} -1 & 0 \\ 1 & 2 \end{bmatrix} \begin{bmatrix} 1 \\ 3 \\ 1 \end{bmatrix}$ is not defined

EXAMPLE 3

$$\begin{bmatrix} 7 & 0 & 1 & 1 & 2 & 1 \\ 3 & 1 & 0 & 1 & -1 & 0 \\ 4 & 0 & 1 & 1 & 6 & 0 \\ 1 & 1 & 2 & 1 & 0 & 3 \\ 0 & 0 & 0 & 1 & 0 & 0 \\ 0 & 0 & 0 & 0 & 0 & 0 \\ 1 & 0 & 0 & 0 & 0 & 0 \end{bmatrix} \begin{bmatrix} x_1 \\ x_2 \\ x_3 \\ x_4 \\ x_5 \\ x_6 \end{bmatrix} = \begin{bmatrix} 7x_1 + x_3 + x_4 + 2x_5 + x_6 \\ 3x_1 + x_2 + x_4 - x_5 \\ 4x_1 + x_3 + x_4 + 6x_5 \\ x_1 + x_2 + 2x_3 + x_4 + 3x_6 \\ x_4 \\ 0 \\ x_1 \end{bmatrix}$$

Note that the sixth row of the coefficient matrix consists of zeros, resulting in the zero in the sixth row of the right-hand matrix. Using an example with numbers rather than letters we have

$$\begin{bmatrix} 7 & 0 & 1 & 1 & 2 & 1 \\ 3 & 1 & 0 & 1 & -1 & 0 \\ 4 & 0 & 1 & 1 & 6 & 0 \\ 1 & 1 & 2 & 1 & 0 & 3 \\ 0 & 0 & 0 & 1 & 0 & 0 \\ 0 & 0 & 0 & 0 & 0 & 0 \\ 1 & 0 & 0 & 0 & 0 & 0 \end{bmatrix} \begin{bmatrix} -1 \\ 1 \\ 2 \\ 0 \\ 1 \\ 0 \end{bmatrix} = \begin{bmatrix} -3 \\ -3 \\ 4 \\ 4 \\ 0 \\ 0 \\ -1 \end{bmatrix}$$

DISCUSSION The following theorem summarizes two useful properties of this multiplication.

THEOREM 3 If A is a matrix with m rows and n columns, $\bar{u}$ and $\bar{v}$ are in R^n, and a is a number, then

7 $A(\bar{u} + \bar{v}) = A\bar{u} + A\bar{v}$

8 $A(a\bar{u}) = a(A\bar{u})$

We give the proof only for the case when A has 2 rows and 2 columns:

$$\begin{bmatrix} A_{11} & A_{12} \\ A_{21} & A_{22} \end{bmatrix} \left\{ \begin{bmatrix} u_1 \\ u_2 \end{bmatrix} + \begin{bmatrix} v_1 \\ v_2 \end{bmatrix} \right\} = \begin{bmatrix} A_{11} & A_{12} \\ A_{21} & A_{22} \end{bmatrix} \begin{bmatrix} u_1 + v_1 \\ u_2 + v_2 \end{bmatrix}$$

$$= \begin{bmatrix} A_{11}(u_1 + v_1) + A_{12}(u_2 + v_2) \\ A_{21}(u_1 + v_1) + A_{22}(u_2 + v_2) \end{bmatrix}$$

$$= \begin{bmatrix} (A_{11}u_1 + A_{12}u_2) + (A_{11}v_1 + A_{12}v_2) \\ (A_{21}u_1 + A_{22}u_2) + (A_{21}v_1 + A_{22}v_2) \end{bmatrix}$$

$$= \begin{bmatrix} A_{11}u_1 + A_{12}u_2 \\ A_{21}u_1 + A_{22}u_2 \end{bmatrix} + \begin{bmatrix} A_{11}v_1 + A_{12}v_2 \\ A_{21}v_1 + A_{22}v_2 \end{bmatrix}$$

$$= \begin{bmatrix} A_{11} & A_{12} \\ A_{21} & A_{22} \end{bmatrix} \begin{bmatrix} u_1 \\ u_2 \end{bmatrix} + \begin{bmatrix} A_{11} & A_{12} \\ A_{21} & A_{22} \end{bmatrix} \begin{bmatrix} v_1 \\ v_2 \end{bmatrix}$$

This proves part **7** for this case. The proof is just a consequence of the definition and the usual laws of arithmetic. The proof of part **8** is even easier and will be omitted.

In the next section we shall show how the rules of Theorem 3 allow us to deduce a number of results about matrix equations which would otherwise involve quite complicated notation. In Chapter 2 we give a general discussion of operations on vectors that satisfy rules such as those of Theorem 3.

EXAMPLE 4 Suppose

$$A = \begin{bmatrix} 1 & -1 & 2 \\ 3 & 1 & -1 \end{bmatrix}, \quad \bar{u}_1 = \begin{bmatrix} 3 \\ -1 \\ 0 \end{bmatrix}, \quad \bar{v} = \begin{bmatrix} -1 \\ 7 \\ 4 \end{bmatrix}$$

We then have

$$A\bar{u}_1 = \begin{bmatrix} 1 & -1 & 2 \\ 3 & 1 & -1 \end{bmatrix} \begin{bmatrix} 3 \\ -1 \\ 0 \end{bmatrix} = \begin{bmatrix} 4 \\ 8 \end{bmatrix}$$

so that $\bar{u}_1$ is a solution to the equation

9 $$A\bar{u} = \bar{c}, \quad \text{where } \bar{c} = \begin{bmatrix} 4 \\ 8 \end{bmatrix}$$

We also have

$$A\bar{v} = \begin{bmatrix} 1 & -1 & 2 \\ 3 & 1 & -1 \end{bmatrix} \begin{bmatrix} -1 \\ 7 \\ 4 \end{bmatrix} = \begin{bmatrix} 0 \\ 0 \end{bmatrix}$$

so that $\bar{v}$ is a solution to the equation $A\bar{u} = \bar{0}$.

Now calculate $A(\bar{u}_1 + \bar{v})$ by using Theorem 3. The result is

$$A(\bar{u}_1 + \bar{v}) = A\bar{u}_1 + A\bar{v} = \begin{bmatrix} 4 \\ 8 \end{bmatrix} + \begin{bmatrix} 0 \\ 0 \end{bmatrix} = \begin{bmatrix} 4 \\ 8 \end{bmatrix}$$

Thus

$$\bar{u}_1 + \bar{v} = \begin{bmatrix} 3 \\ -1 \\ 0 \end{bmatrix} + \begin{bmatrix} -1 \\ 7 \\ 4 \end{bmatrix} = \begin{bmatrix} 2 \\ 6 \\ 4 \end{bmatrix}$$

is *also* a solution to equation **9**.

Furthermore, Theorem 3 also gives

$$\begin{aligned} A(\bar{u}_1 + 2\bar{v}) &= A\bar{u}_1 + A(2\bar{v}) = A\bar{u}_1 + 2A\bar{v} \\ &= \begin{bmatrix} 4 \\ 8 \end{bmatrix} + 2\begin{bmatrix} 0 \\ 0 \end{bmatrix} = \begin{bmatrix} 4 \\ 8 \end{bmatrix} \end{aligned}$$

so that

$$\bar{u}_1 + 2\bar{v} = \begin{bmatrix} 3 \\ -1 \\ 0 \end{bmatrix} + 2\begin{bmatrix} -1 \\ 7 \\ 4 \end{bmatrix} = \begin{bmatrix} 1 \\ 13 \\ 8 \end{bmatrix}$$

is *also* a solution to equation **9**. In fact, for *any* real number a, the vector $\bar{u}_1 + a\bar{v}$ is a solution to equation **9**. To see this we merely apply Theorem 3 to calculate $A(\bar{u}_1 + a\bar{v})$. We have

$$\begin{aligned} A(\bar{u}_1 + a\bar{v}) &= A\bar{u}_1 + A(a\bar{v}) = A\bar{u}_1 + a(A\bar{v}) \\ &= \begin{bmatrix} 4 \\ 8 \end{bmatrix} + a\begin{bmatrix} 0 \\ 0 \end{bmatrix} = \begin{bmatrix} 4 \\ 8 \end{bmatrix} \end{aligned}$$

We will now show that the solutions to equation **9** are *precisely* the vectors of the form $\bar{u}_1 + a\bar{v}$.

The augmented matrix of equation **9** is

$$\left[\begin{array}{ccc:c} 1 & -1 & 2 & 4 \\ 3 & 1 & -1 & 8 \end{array}\right] \quad \text{which reduces to} \quad \left[\begin{array}{ccc:c} 1 & 0 & \frac{1}{4} & 3 \\ 0 & 1 & -\frac{7}{4} & -1 \end{array}\right]$$

This is the augmented matrix of

10
$$\begin{aligned} x \quad + \tfrac{1}{4}z &= 3 \\ y - \tfrac{7}{4}z &= -1 \end{aligned}$$

Suppose $\bar{u} = \begin{bmatrix} x \\ y \\ z \end{bmatrix}$

is a solution to equation **9**. The coordinates of $\bar{u}$ must therefore be a solution to system **10**. Since this is so, we can write $\bar{u} = \bar{u}_1 + (z/4)\bar{v}$, for this is the same as the equation

$$\begin{bmatrix} x \\ y \\ z \end{bmatrix} = \begin{bmatrix} 3 \\ -1 \\ 0 \end{bmatrix} + \frac{z}{4}\begin{bmatrix} -1 \\ 7 \\ 4 \end{bmatrix} = \begin{bmatrix} 3 - z/4 \\ -1 + \tfrac{7}{4}z \\ z \end{bmatrix}$$

which is just a rewritten version of equations **10**.

EXERCISES

1 Suppose $\bar{u} = \begin{bmatrix} 1 \\ 0 \\ 1 \end{bmatrix}, \quad \bar{v} = \begin{bmatrix} 3 \\ 2 \\ -1 \end{bmatrix}, \quad \bar{w} = \begin{bmatrix} 0 \\ 1 \\ 1 \end{bmatrix}$

Find

a $\bar{u} - 2\bar{v} + \bar{w}$

b $3\bar{v} - 2\bar{w}$

c a vector $\bar{x}$ such that $\bar{u} + \bar{x} = 2\bar{w}$

2 For $\bar{u} = (1,0,1)$, $\bar{v} = (3,2,-1)$ and $\bar{w} = (0,1,1)$ find

a $\bar{u} - 2\bar{v} + \bar{w}$

b $3\bar{v} - 2\bar{w}$

c a vector $\bar{x}$ such that $\bar{u} + \bar{x} = 2\bar{w}$

How do your answers compare with those of Exercise 1?

3 Find each of the following products.

a $\begin{bmatrix} 3 & 1 & 2 \\ -1 & 1 & 1 \end{bmatrix}\begin{bmatrix} 1 \\ 2 \\ 1 \end{bmatrix}$ **b** $\begin{bmatrix} 2 & -1 & 0 & 1 \\ 1 & 0 & 1 & 1 \end{bmatrix}\begin{bmatrix} 1 \\ 2 \\ 1 \\ 4 \end{bmatrix}$

c $\begin{bmatrix} 2 & 1 & 0 \\ 1 & 1 & 1 \\ 0 & 1 & 1 \end{bmatrix} \begin{bmatrix} 1 \\ 0 \\ 1 \end{bmatrix}$ **d** $\begin{bmatrix} 0 & 0 & 0 \\ 0 & 0 & 0 \\ 0 & 0 & 0 \end{bmatrix} \begin{bmatrix} 1 \\ 2 \\ 1 \end{bmatrix}$

e $\begin{bmatrix} 1 & 0 & 0 \\ 0 & 1 & 0 \\ 0 & 0 & 1 \end{bmatrix} \begin{bmatrix} 1 \\ 3 \\ 1 \end{bmatrix}$ **f** $\begin{bmatrix} 0 & 0 & 0 & 0 & 0 \\ 1 & 1 & 1 & 1 & 1 \\ 2 & 2 & 2 & 2 & 2 \end{bmatrix} \left\{ \begin{bmatrix} 1 \\ 2 \\ 3 \\ 4 \\ 5 \end{bmatrix} + \begin{bmatrix} -1 \\ 0 \\ 1 \\ 1 \\ 1 \end{bmatrix} \right\}$

g $\begin{bmatrix} 2 & 1 & 0 & 1 & 1 \\ 1 & 0 & 1 & 0 & 2 \\ 0 & 0 & 3 & 0 & 0 \\ 4 & 1 & 2 & 1 & 0 \\ 0 & 0 & 0 & 0 & 0 \end{bmatrix} \left\{ \begin{bmatrix} 1 \\ 1 \\ 1 \\ -1 \\ 2 \end{bmatrix} + 3 \begin{bmatrix} 4 \\ 1 \\ 0 \\ 1 \\ 1 \end{bmatrix} \right\}$

4 Express each of the following systems as a matrix equation.

a
$$\begin{aligned} 2x - y + z &= 1 \\ x - 3y + z &= 2 \\ x + y - z &= 0 \\ 4x - y + 2z &= 1 \end{aligned}$$

b $x - y = 0$

c
$$\begin{aligned} 0 \cdot x + 0 \cdot y + 0 \cdot z &= 0 \\ 0 \cdot x + 0 \cdot y + 0 \cdot z &= 0 \\ 0 \cdot x + 0 \cdot y + 0 \cdot z &= 0 \end{aligned}$$

5 Suppose $A = \begin{bmatrix} 2 & 1 & 0 \\ 1 & 1 & 1 \end{bmatrix}$ and $\bar{c} = \begin{bmatrix} 3 \\ 1 \end{bmatrix}$

Which of the following vectors are solutions to the equation $A\bar{x} = \bar{c}$?

a $\begin{bmatrix} 3 \\ 1 \\ 2 \end{bmatrix}$ **b** $\begin{bmatrix} 2 \\ -1 \\ 0 \end{bmatrix} + 4 \begin{bmatrix} 1 \\ -2 \\ 1 \end{bmatrix}$ **c** $\begin{bmatrix} 2 \\ -1 \\ 0 \end{bmatrix}$ **d** $3 \begin{bmatrix} 2 \\ -1 \\ 0 \end{bmatrix}$

6 Suppose $\bar{x} = \begin{bmatrix} x_1 \\ x_2 \end{bmatrix}$ is *not* a solution to $\begin{bmatrix} 1 & 3 \\ 1 & 2 \end{bmatrix} \bar{x} = \begin{bmatrix} 0 \\ 0 \end{bmatrix}$

Is $2\bar{x}$ a solution to this equation?

7 Show that if $\bar{x}$ is the zero vector in R^3 and A has two rows and three columns, then $A\bar{x}$ is the zero vector in R^2. Generalize this result.

8 For $A = \begin{bmatrix} 2 & 1 \\ 1 & 3 \end{bmatrix}, \quad \bar{u} = \begin{bmatrix} 1 \\ -1 \end{bmatrix}, \quad \bar{v} = \begin{bmatrix} 2 \\ 1 \end{bmatrix}$

calculate $A(\bar{u} + \bar{v})$ and $A(3\bar{u})$ in two ways, using Theorem 3.

9 Suppose $A\bar{u} = \bar{0}$ and $A\bar{v} = \bar{0}$. Show that $A(\bar{u} + \bar{v}) = \bar{0}$ and that $A(a\bar{u}) = \bar{0}$ for any scalar a.

10 Suppose A has three rows and four columns. Does the equation $A\bar{u} = \bar{0}$ have a solution $\bar{u} \neq \bar{0}$?

11 Suppose A can be reduced to $\begin{bmatrix} 1 & 0 & 0 \\ 0 & 1 & 0 \\ 0 & 0 & 1 \end{bmatrix}$

Does the equation $A\bar{u} = \bar{0}$ have a solution $\bar{u} \neq \bar{0}$?

12 Express the equation $c_1(1,2) + c_2(-1,3) = (4,2)$ as a matrix equation. (Hint: First write the vectors as column matrices.)

13 Suppose the second row of A consists of zeros. What can you say about the second coordinate of $A\bar{u}$?

14 Suppose $A = \begin{bmatrix} 1 & 1 & 2 \\ 3 & -1 & 1 \end{bmatrix}$ and $\bar{c} = \begin{bmatrix} 2 \\ 1 \end{bmatrix}$

Write the solutions to $A\bar{x} = \bar{c}$ in the form $\bar{u} + a\bar{v}$, where $A\bar{u} = \bar{c}$ and $A\bar{v} = \bar{0}$. (*See* Example 4.)

15 Suppose $A = \begin{bmatrix} 1 & 4 & 1 & 2 \\ 2 & 8 & -1 & 1 \end{bmatrix}, \quad \bar{u}_1 = \begin{bmatrix} -4 \\ 1 \\ 0 \\ 0 \end{bmatrix}, \quad \bar{u}_2 = \begin{bmatrix} -1 \\ 0 \\ -1 \\ 1 \end{bmatrix}$

Show that $\bar{u}_1$ and $\bar{u}_2$ are both solutions to $A\bar{x} = \bar{0}$.

Are $\bar{u}_1 + \bar{u}_2$ and $3\bar{u}_1 - 7\bar{u}_2$ also solutions to $A\bar{x} = \bar{0}$?

☐ **16** The definitions and results of this section extend immediately to the complex case. Find

a $\begin{bmatrix} i & 1-i \\ 2 & 3+i \end{bmatrix} \begin{bmatrix} 1+i \\ 0 \end{bmatrix}$ **b** $\begin{bmatrix} 2-i & 0 \\ 1 & i \end{bmatrix} \left\{ i \begin{bmatrix} 1 \\ -i \end{bmatrix} + (1+i) \begin{bmatrix} i \\ 0 \end{bmatrix} \right\}$

c The matrix form of the system

$$\begin{aligned} ix - 2iy &= i \\ (3-i)x + (i-1)y &= i/2 \end{aligned}$$

SECTION 6 The Theory of Matrix Equations

We have shown how to express a system of equations as a matrix equation. We can now easily establish a number of results about homogeneous systems and the relationship between homogeneous and nonhomogeneous systems. These results are all consequences of Theorem 3.

Suppose A has n columns. The solutions to the equation $A\bar{u} = \bar{0}$ are a subset of R^n, known as the **null space** of A. Theorem 4 establishes that this set is in fact a subspace of R^n. After proving this theorem, we will give an alternative means of describing this subspace. Exercises 9, 10, and 11 provide a geometric discussion of the results.

THEOREM 4 If A has n columns, then the null space of A is a subspace of R^n.

PROOF: To say that the null space of A is a subspace of R^n is just a shorter way of saying that (*see* statement **2**, page 33):

a $\bar{0}$ belongs to the null space of A.

b If $\bar{u}_1$ and $\bar{u}_2$ belong to the null space of A, then $\bar{u}_1 + \bar{u}_2$
1 belongs to the null space of A.

c If $\bar{u}$ belongs to the null space of A, then for any scalar a, $a\bar{u}$ belongs to the null space of A.

Certainly we have $A\bar{0} = \bar{0}$; therefore, the first of these statements is true. If $\bar{u}_1$ and $\bar{u}_2$ belong to the null space of A, the definition of null space tells us that $A\bar{u}_1 = \bar{0}$ and $A\bar{u}_2 = \bar{0}$. We apply Theorem 3 to see that

$$A(\bar{u}_1 + \bar{u}_2) = A\bar{u}_1 + A\bar{u}_2 = \bar{0} + \bar{0} = \bar{0}$$

so that $\bar{u}_1 + \bar{u}_2$ also belongs to the null space of A. This proves that statement **1b** is true. The proof of statement **1c** follows from the fact that $A(a\bar{u}) = a(A\bar{u})$.

We have shown in the examples of Section 1 how we can describe the form of solutions to a homogeneous system. To convert this description to vector form we use the following definition: A vector $\bar{u}$ is a **linear combination** of the vectors $\bar{u}_1, \bar{u}_2, \ldots, \bar{u}_k$ if there are scalars $c_1, c_2, \ldots, c_k$ such that $\bar{u} = c_1\bar{u}_1 + c_2\bar{u}_2 + \cdots + c_k\bar{u}_k$.

We shall show in the examples below how to find a set of vectors $\bar{u}_1, \bar{u}_2, \ldots, \bar{u}_k$ in the null space of A such that *every* vector in the null space of A is a linear combination of $\bar{u}_1, \bar{u}_2, \ldots, \bar{u}_k$. We then say that the expression

$$c_1\bar{u}_1 + c_2\bar{u}_2 + \ldots + c_k\bar{u}_k$$

is a **general solution** to the equation $A\bar{u} = \bar{0}$.

EXAMPLE 1 The matrix

$$A = \begin{bmatrix} 1 & 2 & 1 & 1 \\ 2 & 4 & -1 & 0 \end{bmatrix} \quad \text{reduces to} \quad \begin{bmatrix} 1 & 2 & 0 & \frac{1}{3} \\ 0 & 0 & 1 & \frac{2}{3} \end{bmatrix}$$

(The student should always verify such assertions.) Therefore the solutions to $A\bar{u} = \bar{0}$ are the same as the solutions to the reduced system

2 $$\begin{aligned} x_1 + 2x_2 \quad\quad + \tfrac{1}{3}x_4 &= 0 \\ x_3 + \tfrac{2}{3}x_4 &= 0 \end{aligned}$$

This system has two leading variables (namely, x_1 and x_3) and can be solved to express these in terms of the remaining variables:

3 $$\begin{aligned} x_1 &= -2x_2 - \tfrac{1}{3}x_4 \\ x_3 &= 0x_2 - \tfrac{2}{3}x_4 \end{aligned}$$

We can find two particular solutions to this as follows: first set $x_2 = 1$ and $x_4 = 0$; calculate to find $x_1 = -2$ and $x_3 = 0$; then set $x_2 = 0$, $x_4 = 1$; and calculate to find $x_1 = -\frac{1}{3}$ and $x_3 = -\frac{2}{3}$. Thus

$$\bar{u}_1 = \begin{bmatrix} -2 \\ 1 \\ 0 \\ 0 \end{bmatrix} \quad \text{and} \quad \bar{u}_2 = \begin{bmatrix} -\frac{1}{3} \\ 0 \\ -\frac{2}{3} \\ 1 \end{bmatrix}$$

are solutions to $A\bar{u} = \bar{0}$.

We now show that the general solution to the equation $A\bar{u} = \bar{0}$ is

4 $$c_1\bar{u}_1 + c_2\bar{u}_2$$

In other words, the null space of A consists *precisely* of the linear combination of $\bar{u}_1$ and $\bar{u}_2$.

We certainly know that any vector of form **4** lies in the null space of A; for if $\bar{v} = c_1\bar{u}_1 + c_2\bar{u}_2$ we can use Theorem 3 to obtain

$$\begin{aligned} A\bar{v} &= A(c_1\bar{u}_1 + c_2\bar{u}_2) = A(c_1\bar{u}_1) + A(c_2\bar{u}_2) \\ &= c_1A\bar{u}_1 + c_2A\bar{u}_2 = c_1\bar{0} + c_2\bar{0} = \bar{0} \end{aligned}$$

Therefore $\bar{v}$ must be in the null space of A.

Equations 3 can be rewritten in vector form as

$$\begin{bmatrix} x_1 \\ x_2 \\ x_3 \\ x_4 \end{bmatrix} = \begin{bmatrix} -2x_2 - \frac{1}{3}x_4 \\ x_2 \\ 0 \cdot x_2 - \frac{2}{3}x_4 \\ x_4 \end{bmatrix} = x_2 \begin{bmatrix} -2 \\ 1 \\ 0 \\ 0 \end{bmatrix} + x_4 \begin{bmatrix} -\frac{1}{3} \\ 0 \\ -\frac{2}{3} \\ 1 \end{bmatrix}$$

so that any vector in the null space of A is indeed a linear combination of $\bar{u}_1$ and $\bar{u}_2$. This completes the proof of the fact that $c_1\bar{u}_1 + c_2\bar{u}_2$ is a general solution to $A\bar{u} = \bar{0}$.

DISCUSSION The combination of Theorem 4 with Theorems 1 and 2 gives the following result.

THEOREM 5

a If A has more columns than rows, then the null space of A contains nonzero vectors.

b If A has n columns, then the null space of A consists only of the zero vector if and only if A can be reduced to a matrix whose first n rows are the identity matrix.

For the number of columns of A corresponds to the number of unknowns, and the number of rows of A corresponds to the number of equations in the related homogeneous system.

The general solution to a nonhomogeneous system can be expressed in terms of a particular solution plus the general solution to the related homogeneous system. This is also a simple consequence of Theorem 3 and is expressed by the following result.

THEOREM 6 Suppose $A\bar{v} = \bar{c}$. The set of solutions to $A\bar{u} = \bar{c}$ is then precisely the set of vectors of the form $\bar{v} + \bar{w}$, where $\bar{w}$ is in the null space of A.

PROOF: Suppose $A\bar{u}_1 = \bar{c}$. Then, applying Theorem 3, we have

$$A(\bar{u}_1 - \bar{v}) = A\bar{u}_1 - A\bar{v} = \bar{c} - \bar{c} = \bar{0}$$

so that $\bar{u}_1 - \bar{v}$ is in the null space of A. Setting

$$\bar{w} = \bar{u}_1 - \bar{v}$$

we have $\bar{u}_1 = \bar{v} + \bar{w}$. Thus each solution to $A\bar{u} = \bar{0}$ is of the form $\bar{v} + \bar{w}$ where $\bar{w}$ is in the null space of A. Not only is this true, but the converse is also true; for suppose $\bar{u}_1 = \bar{v} + \bar{w}$, where $\bar{w}$ is in the null space of A. Then

$$A\bar{u}_1 = A(\bar{v} + \bar{w}) = A\bar{v} + A\bar{w} = \bar{c} + \bar{0} = \bar{c}$$

so that $\bar{u}_1$ is a solution to $A\bar{u} = \bar{c}$. This completes the proof of Theorem 6.

Suppose $\bar{v}$ is a particular solution to $A\bar{u} = \bar{c}$ and that

$$c_1\bar{u}_1 + c_2\bar{u}_2 + \cdots + c_k\bar{u}_k$$

is a general solution to $A\bar{u} = \bar{0}$. We then say that

5 $$\bar{v} + c_1\bar{u}_1 + c_2\bar{u}_2 + \cdots + c_k\bar{u}_k$$

is a **general solution** to $A\bar{u} = \bar{c}$. Theorem 6 states that indeed the vectors of this form are precisely the solutions to $A\bar{u} = \bar{c}$.

Before turning to further examples we note one more important consequence of Theorem 3:

THEOREM 7 Suppose $A\bar{u} = \bar{0}$ has only one solution (which must, of course, be $\bar{u} = \bar{0}$). Then for any $\bar{c}$, the equation $A\bar{u} = \bar{c}$ cannot have more than one solution.

PROOF: This statement can be proved by showing that if there are two solutions we will have a contradiction. Suppose

$$A\bar{u}_1 = \bar{c}, \qquad A\bar{u}_2 = \bar{c}, \qquad \bar{u}_1 \neq \bar{u}_2$$

Then $\bar{u}_1 - \bar{u}_2 \neq \bar{0}$ and

$$A(\bar{u}_1 - \bar{u}_2) = A\bar{u}_1 - A\bar{u}_2 = \bar{c} - \bar{c} = \bar{0}$$

Thus $\bar{u}_1 - \bar{u}_2$ is a nonzero solution to $A\bar{u} = \bar{0}$, and the assumption that this equation has only the zero solution has been contradicted. This establishes Theorem 7.

After we have developed more results about vectors we shall be able to show that uniqueness of solutions to $A\bar{u} = \bar{0}$ will actually, in certain cases, *imply the existence* (and from Theorem 7, uniqueness) of solutions to $A\bar{u} = \bar{c}$. (*See* Section 9; *see also* Example 3, page 18.)

EXAMPLE 2 The matrix $A = \begin{bmatrix} 2 & 1 \\ -1 & 3 \end{bmatrix}$ reduces to $\begin{bmatrix} 1 & 0 \\ 0 & 1 \end{bmatrix}$

so that Theorem 5 tells us that the null space of A is the *zero* subspace; that is, it consists of the zero vector only.

We have

$$A\begin{bmatrix}-5\\6\end{bmatrix}=\begin{bmatrix}-4\\23\end{bmatrix}$$

Thus, Theorem 7 guarantees that

$$A\bar{u}=\begin{bmatrix}-4\\23\end{bmatrix} \quad \text{has the unique solution} \quad \bar{u}=\begin{bmatrix}-5\\6\end{bmatrix}$$

EXAMPLE 3 For

$$A=\begin{bmatrix}1&2&1&0&1\\3&1&2&0&0\end{bmatrix}, \quad \bar{v}=\begin{bmatrix}2\\1\\-3\\1\\0\end{bmatrix}, \quad \bar{c}=\begin{bmatrix}1\\1\end{bmatrix}$$

we have $A\bar{v}=\bar{c}$; therefore, $\bar{v}$ is a particular solution to $A\bar{u}=\bar{c}$. To find the general solution to this equation we first find the general solution to $A\bar{u}=\bar{0}$. The matrix A reduces to

$$\begin{bmatrix}1&0&\frac{3}{5}&0&-\frac{1}{5}\\0&1&\frac{1}{5}&0&\frac{3}{5}\end{bmatrix}$$

so the null space of A consists of the solutions to the reduced system

6
$$\begin{aligned}x_1&=-\tfrac{3}{5}x_3+0\cdot x_4+\tfrac{1}{5}x_5\\x_2&=-\tfrac{1}{5}x_3+0\cdot x_4-\tfrac{3}{5}x_5\end{aligned}$$

Three solutions to this can be found by setting $x_3=1$, $x_4=0$, $x_5=0$, computing to obtain $x_1=-\frac{3}{5}$, $x_2=-\frac{1}{5}$; setting $x_3=0$, $x_4=1$, $x_5=0$, computing to obtain $x_1=0$, $x_2=0$; and finally setting $x_3=0$, $x_4=0$, $x_5=1$ to find that $x_1=\frac{1}{5}$, $x_2=-\frac{3}{5}$. Thus

$$\bar{u}_1=\begin{bmatrix}-\frac{3}{5}\\-\frac{1}{5}\\1\\0\\0\end{bmatrix} \quad \bar{u}_2=\begin{bmatrix}0\\0\\0\\1\\0\end{bmatrix} \quad \bar{u}_3=\begin{bmatrix}\frac{1}{5}\\-\frac{3}{5}\\0\\0\\1\end{bmatrix}$$

are solutions to $A\bar{u} = \bar{0}$. We can rewrite equations **6** as the vector equation

$$\begin{bmatrix} x_1 \\ x_2 \\ x_3 \\ x_4 \\ x_5 \end{bmatrix} = \begin{bmatrix} -\frac{3}{5}x_3 + 0 \cdot x_4 + \frac{1}{5}x_5 \\ -\frac{1}{5}x_3 + 0 \cdot x_4 - \frac{3}{5}x_5 \\ x_3 \\ x_4 \\ x_5 \end{bmatrix} = x_3\bar{u}_1 + x_4\bar{u}_2 + x_5\bar{u}_3$$

so that a general solution to $A\bar{u} = \bar{0}$ is $c_1\bar{u}_1 + c_2\bar{u}_2 + c_3\bar{u}_3$. We see from definition **5** that $\bar{v} + c_1\bar{u}_1 + c_2\bar{u}_2 + c_3\bar{u}_3$ is a general solution to $A\bar{u} = \bar{c}$.

EXAMPLE 4 It is of course possible that $A\bar{v} = \bar{0}$ has a unique solution, and that for certain $\bar{c}$ the equation $A\bar{x} = \bar{c}$ has no solution. For example, if

$$A = \begin{bmatrix} 1 & 0 \\ 0 & 1 \\ 0 & 0 \end{bmatrix}$$

then $A\begin{bmatrix} x \\ y \end{bmatrix} = \bar{0}$ necessarily implies that $x = y = 0$. The equation

$$A\begin{bmatrix} x \\ y \end{bmatrix} = \begin{bmatrix} 0 \\ 0 \\ 1 \end{bmatrix}$$

however, has no solution.

It was no accident that the above example has more rows than columns; for, in order that $A\bar{x} = \bar{0}$ have a unique solution, we know that A has at least as many rows as columns (from Theorem 5). Furthermore, it will be shown later that if A has the same number of rows as columns, and if $A\bar{x} = \bar{0}$ has a unique solution, then for any $\bar{c}$ the equation $A\bar{x} = \bar{c}$ has a solution.

EXERCISES

1 Which of the following vectors are in the null space of $A = \begin{bmatrix} 1 & 1 & 1 \\ 1 & -1 & 1 \end{bmatrix}$?

a $\begin{bmatrix} 1 \\ 1 \\ -2 \end{bmatrix}$ **b** $\begin{bmatrix} 1 \\ 0 \\ 1 \end{bmatrix}$ **c** $100\begin{bmatrix} 1 \\ 0 \\ -1 \end{bmatrix}$ **d** $\begin{bmatrix} 1 \\ 1 \\ -2 \end{bmatrix} + \begin{bmatrix} 1 \\ 0 \\ -1 \end{bmatrix}$ **e** $\begin{bmatrix} 0 \\ 0 \\ 0 \end{bmatrix}$

2 Which of the following vectors are solutions to

$$\begin{bmatrix} 1 & 1 & 1 \\ 1 & -1 & 1 \end{bmatrix} \begin{bmatrix} x \\ y \\ z \end{bmatrix} = \begin{bmatrix} 0 \\ -2 \end{bmatrix}$$

a $\begin{bmatrix} 1 \\ 1 \\ -2 \end{bmatrix}$ **b** $\begin{bmatrix} 1 \\ 0 \\ -1 \end{bmatrix}$ **c** $\begin{bmatrix} 1 \\ 1 \\ -2 \end{bmatrix} + 100 \begin{bmatrix} 1 \\ 0 \\ -1 \end{bmatrix}$

d $\begin{bmatrix} 1 \\ 1 \\ -2 \end{bmatrix} - \begin{bmatrix} 1 \\ 0 \\ -1 \end{bmatrix}$ **e** $\begin{bmatrix} 0 \\ 0 \\ 0 \end{bmatrix}$

3 Describe the null space of each of the following matrices as in Example 1.

a $A = \begin{bmatrix} 1 & 0 & 3 \\ 2 & 1 & 1 \end{bmatrix}$ **b** $A = \begin{bmatrix} 3 & 1 & 1 & 0 \\ 6 & 2 & 2 & 1 \end{bmatrix}$

c $A = \begin{bmatrix} 1 & 1 \\ 1 & -1 \end{bmatrix}$ **d** $A = \begin{bmatrix} 2 & 1 & 0 & 6 & 1 & 1 & 2 \\ 4 & 1 & 0 & 6 & 2 & 2 & 1 \end{bmatrix}$

4 For each of the matrices A of Exercise 3 describe the general solution to

$$A\bar{x} = \begin{bmatrix} 1 \\ 1 \end{bmatrix} \quad \text{as in Example 3.}$$

5 Suppose $A = \begin{bmatrix} 1 & -1 \\ 2 & 1 \end{bmatrix}$

a Show that $A \begin{bmatrix} -3 \\ 1 \end{bmatrix} = \begin{bmatrix} -4 \\ -5 \end{bmatrix}$

b Does the equation $A\bar{u} = \bar{0}$ have a unique solution?

c Use part **b** and Theorem 7 to decide whether

$$A\bar{u} = \begin{bmatrix} -4 \\ -5 \end{bmatrix} \quad \text{has a unique solution.}$$

6 Suppose
$$A = \begin{bmatrix} 1 & -1 & 2 \\ 3 & 1 & -1 \\ 2 & 2 & -3 \end{bmatrix}$$

a Show that
$$A \begin{bmatrix} 1 \\ 3 \\ -1 \end{bmatrix} = \begin{bmatrix} -4 \\ 7 \\ 11 \end{bmatrix}$$

b Does $A\bar{u} = \bar{0}$ have a unique solution?

c Does
$$A\bar{u} = \begin{bmatrix} -4 \\ 7 \\ 11 \end{bmatrix}$$
have a unique solution? Why does this not contradict Theorem 7? (*See also* Exercise 13.)

7 Suppose $\bar{v} \neq \bar{0}$. Are the solutions to $A\bar{u} = \bar{v}$ a subspace?

8 Without reducing decide whether the equation
$$\begin{bmatrix} 2 & 1 & 3 \\ 1 & 0 & 2 \end{bmatrix} \begin{bmatrix} x \\ y \\ z \end{bmatrix} = \begin{bmatrix} 1 \\ 1 \end{bmatrix}$$
has a unique solution.

9 Suppose A has one row and three columns, and $A \neq 0$.
a Describe geometrically the null space of A.
b Describe geometrically the solutions to $A\bar{u} = \bar{v}$.

10 Suppose A has two rows and three columns, and $A \neq 0$.
a Describe geometrically the null space of A.
b What does it mean geometrically when $A\bar{u} = \bar{v}$ has no solutions? Describe the possibilities when $A\bar{u} = \bar{v}$ has at least one solution.

11 Suppose A has three rows and three columns.
a Describe geometrically the null space of A.
b What does it mean geometrically when $A\bar{u} = \bar{v}$ has no solution?
c Suppose $A\bar{u} = \bar{v}$ has a unique solution. Describe geometrically the null space of A.
d Suppose the general solution to $A\bar{u} = \bar{v}$ is $\bar{u}_1 + a\bar{u}_2$, where $A\bar{u}_1 = \bar{v}$, $\bar{u}_2 \neq 0$, and $A\bar{u}_2 = \bar{0}$. Describe geometrically the set of solutions to $A\bar{u} = \bar{v}$.

12 Show that $2(2,1,0) - 3(1,-1,2) + (1,2,1) = (2,7,-5)$
a How many solutions does $c_1(2,1,0) + c_2(1,-1,2) + c_3(1,2,1) = (0,0,0)$ have? (Hint: Express as a homogeneous system in c_1, c_2, c_3.)
b How many solutions does $c_1(2,1,0) + c_2(1,-1,2) + c_3(1,2,1) = (2,7,-5)$ have?

13 Use Theorem 3 to prove that if $A\bar{u} = \bar{c}$ has a unique solution, $A\bar{u} = \bar{0}$ also has a unique solution.

□ 14 The results of this section also extend to the complex case. Describe the null space of A as in Example 1,

where $$A = \begin{bmatrix} 1+i & i & 0 \\ 1-i & 1 & i \end{bmatrix}$$

Describe the solutions to $$A\bar{x} = \begin{bmatrix} 1 \\ i \end{bmatrix}$$ as in Example 3.

15 The results of this section can be applied to other situations in which properties analogous to Theorem 3 hold, in particular to linear differential operators. Consider the operator L, defined for twice differentiable functions by

$$Lf = f'' - f' - 2f$$

a Show that $L(f + g) = Lf + Lg$.
b Show that $L(af) = aLf$.
c Show that the solutions to $Lf = 0$ are a subspace of $C[0,1]$. (*See* Example 4, page 37.)
d Show that e^{-x} and e^{2x} are solutions to $Lf = 0$. Must $3e^{-x} + 4e^{2x}$ also be a solution?
e Show that if f_1 is a solution to $Lf = g$, and f_2 is a solution to $Lf = 0$, then $f_1 + f_2$ is a solution to $Lf = g$.
f Show that if f_1 and f_2 are solutions to $Lf = g$, then $f_1 - f_2$ is a solution to $Lf = 0$.
g Show that if f_1 is a solution to $Lf = g$, then all solutions to this equation are of the form $f_1 + f_2$, where f_2 is a solution to $Lf = 0$.
h In Chapter 4 it will be shown that the solutions to $Lf = 0$ are precisely those functions of the form $ae^{-x} + be^{2x}$. Show that $Lx = -1 - 2x$ and deduce that the solutions to $Lf = -1 - 2x$ are the functions of the form $x + ae^{-x} + be^{2x}$.

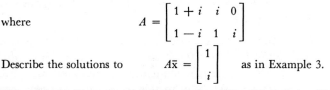

SECTION 7 Independence

A plane in R^3 through the origin can be expressed as the collection of sums of multiples of two vectors, which are not collinear, as shown, for example, in Figure 4.

Such a plane is a subspace of R^3, for it certainly contains $\bar{0}$, which is the sum of $0 \cdot \bar{u}$ and $0 \cdot \bar{v}$, and it is closed under addition and scalar multiplication. The statement that $\bar{u}$ and $\bar{v}$ are not collinear is a geometric statement. We shall in this section give an algebraic formulation of the concept of noncollinearity which is also very useful in studying those vector spaces which have no convenient geometric representation. It will be seen that the simplest way to do this is to discuss the properties of equations of the form

1 $$c_1\bar{u}_1 + c_2\bar{u}_2 + \cdots + c_n\bar{u}_n = \bar{0}$$

where $\bar{u}_1, \bar{u}_2, \ldots, \bar{u}_n$ are vectors in a vector space V and $c_1, c_2, \ldots, c_n$ are numbers.

If we are given the vectors $\bar{u}_1, \bar{u}_2, \ldots, \bar{u}_n$ we can consider the $c_1, c_2, \ldots, c_n$ as variables and ask whether we can find solutions to equation **1**. Since

$$0\bar{u}_1 + 0\bar{u}_2 + \cdots + 0\bar{u}_n = \bar{0}$$

is always true, we know that

$$c_1 = c_2 = \cdots = c_n = 0$$

is always a solution to equation **1**. Thus the relevant question to ask is whether this is the *only* solution to equation **1**.

We give the following two definitions:

> *A given set of vectors* $\bar{u}_1, \bar{u}_2, \ldots, \bar{u}_n$ *is* **independent** *if the only solution to* $c_1\bar{u}_1 + c_2\bar{u}_2 + \cdots + c_n\bar{u}_n = \bar{0}$ *is* $c_1 = c_2 = \cdots = c_n = 0$.

Figure 4 *The vectors $\bar{w}_1$, $\bar{w}_2$, and $\bar{w}_3$ are sums of multiples of $\bar{u}$ and $\bar{v}$ and lie in the plane of $\bar{u}$ and $\bar{v}$. Any vector in the plane of $\bar{u}$ and $\bar{v}$ is a sum of multiples of $\bar{u}$ and $\bar{v}$.*

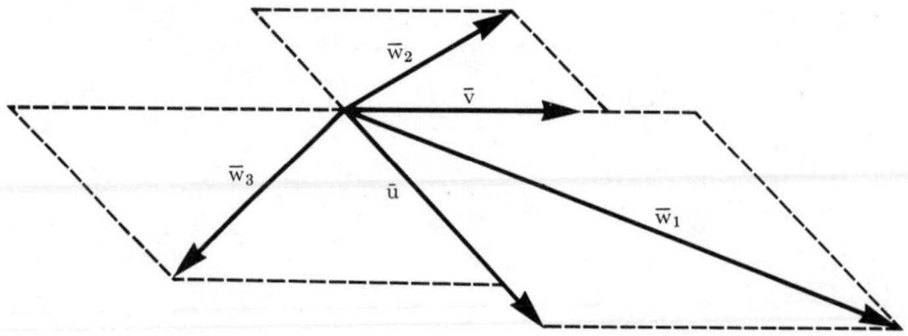

A set which is not independent is said to be **dependent**. A useful formulation of this is:

> *A given set of vectors* $\bar{u}_1, \bar{u}_2, \ldots, \bar{u}_n$ *is* dependent *if there are numbers* $c_1, c_2, \ldots, c_n$, not *all zero such that* $c_1\bar{u}_1 + c_2\bar{u}_2 + \cdots + c_n\bar{u}_n = \bar{0}$.

In many vector spaces, rather simple methods can be applied to determine independence or dependence of a set of vectors. The following examples indicate some of these methods.

EXAMPLE 1 We shall again find it convenient to express vectors in R^n as column matrices, just as we did in the two previous sections. We shall show that $\begin{bmatrix} 1 \\ 0 \end{bmatrix}$ and $\begin{bmatrix} 0 \\ 1 \end{bmatrix}$ are independent in R^2. In this case, equation 1 has the form

2 $$c_1\begin{bmatrix} 1 \\ 0 \end{bmatrix} + c_2\begin{bmatrix} 0 \\ 1 \end{bmatrix} = \begin{bmatrix} 0 \\ 0 \end{bmatrix}$$

The left-hand side can be rewritten as

$$\begin{bmatrix} c_1 \\ 0 \end{bmatrix} + \begin{bmatrix} 0 \\ c_2 \end{bmatrix} = \begin{bmatrix} c_1 \\ c_2 \end{bmatrix} \quad \text{so that} \quad \begin{bmatrix} c_1 \\ c_2 \end{bmatrix} = \begin{bmatrix} 0 \\ 0 \end{bmatrix}$$

Thus the only solution to equation 2 is $c_1 = c_2 = 0$ and, from the definition of independence,

$$\begin{bmatrix} 1 \\ 0 \end{bmatrix} \quad \text{and} \quad \begin{bmatrix} 0 \\ 1 \end{bmatrix}$$

are independent.

EXAMPLE 2 We shall show that

$$\begin{bmatrix} 1 \\ 2 \end{bmatrix} \quad \text{and} \quad \begin{bmatrix} -1 \\ 1 \end{bmatrix} \quad \text{are independent in } R^2.$$

In this case, equation 1 is

3 $$c_1\begin{bmatrix} 1 \\ 2 \end{bmatrix} + c_2\begin{bmatrix} -1 \\ 1 \end{bmatrix} = \begin{bmatrix} 0 \\ 0 \end{bmatrix}$$

The left-hand side can be rewritten as

$$c_1\begin{bmatrix} 1 \\ 2 \end{bmatrix} + c_2\begin{bmatrix} -1 \\ 1 \end{bmatrix} = \begin{bmatrix} c_1 - c_2 \\ 2c_1 + c_2 \end{bmatrix}$$

Note that this is just the same as

$$\begin{bmatrix} 1 & -1 \\ 2 & 1 \end{bmatrix} \begin{bmatrix} c_1 \\ c_2 \end{bmatrix}$$

Equation **3** therefore takes the form

4 $$\begin{bmatrix} 1 & -1 \\ 2 & 1 \end{bmatrix} \begin{bmatrix} c_1 \\ c_2 \end{bmatrix} = \begin{bmatrix} 0 \\ 0 \end{bmatrix}$$

We now apply our previous methods to this equation, to determine whether it has a unique solution. We can reduce

$$\begin{bmatrix} 1 & -1 \\ 2 & 1 \end{bmatrix} \quad \text{to} \quad \begin{bmatrix} 1 & 0 \\ 0 & 1 \end{bmatrix}$$

and thus conclude from Theorem 5 that equation **4** and hence equation **3** has the unique solution $c_1 = c_2 = 0$.

EXAMPLE 3 The statement that $\bar{u}$ and $\bar{v}$, in R^2 or R^3, are dependent is equivalent to saying that their arrow representations are collinear. For suppose $\bar{u}$ and $\bar{v}$ are dependent; we can then apply the definition of dependence and conclude that there must be numbers c_1 and c_2 *not both zero* such that $c_1\bar{u} + c_2\bar{v} = \bar{0}$.

Suppose $c_1 \neq 0$; we can then solve for $\bar{u}$:

$$\bar{u} = -(c_2/c_1)\bar{v}$$

If $c_2 \neq 0$, we can solve for $\bar{v}$:

$$\bar{v} = -(c_1/c_2)\bar{u}$$

One of these two equations must hold if $\bar{u}$ and $\bar{v}$ are dependent. Either equation expresses the fact that the arrow representations of $\bar{u}$ and $\bar{v}$ are *parallel* and hence collinear. This shows that

5 *If* $\bar{u}$ *and* $\bar{v}$ *are dependent, their arrow representations are collinear.*

Conversely, suppose the arrow representations of $\bar{u}$ and $\bar{v}$ are collinear; $\bar{u}$ and $\bar{v}$ must then be parallel. Thus

$$\bar{u} = a\bar{v} \qquad \text{or} \qquad \bar{v} = b\bar{u} \qquad \text{(or both)}$$

These two equations can be rewritten as

$$1 \cdot \bar{u} + (-a)\bar{v} = \bar{0} \qquad \text{or} \qquad b\bar{u} + (-1)\bar{v} = \bar{0}$$

We conclude that

$$c_1\bar{u} + c_2\bar{v} = \bar{0}$$

must have a solution in which either $c_1 \neq 0$ or $c_2 \neq 0$, for it must have at least one of the two solutions

$$c_1 = 1 \quad \text{and} \quad c_2 = -a, \quad \text{or} \quad c_1 = b \quad \text{and} \quad c_2 = -1$$

From the definition of dependence we must therefore have:

6 *If the arrow representations of* $\bar{u}$ *and* $\bar{v}$ *are collinear,* $\bar{u}$ *and* $\bar{v}$ *are dependent.*

We can restate facts **5** and **6** in terms of independence and noncollinearity as follows:

Two vectors $\bar{u}$ *and* $\bar{v}$ *in* R^2 *or* R^3 *are independent if and only if their arrow representations are noncollinear.*

We conclude that a plane in R^3 through the origin can be described as the collection of sums of multiples of two *independent* vectors.

DISCUSSION These examples indicate a method for determining independence in coordinate spaces as well as an alternative description of independence. We first discuss the method for determining independence indicated in Example 2. In order not to confuse the subscripts with the notation for our vector space we shall write R^m rather than R^n.

Suppose $\bar{u}_1, \bar{u}_2, \ldots, \bar{u}_n$ are vectors in R^m, written as column matrices as in previous sections. Then equation **1**, that is,

$$c_1\bar{u}_1 + c_2\bar{u}_2 + \cdots + c_n\bar{u}_n = \bar{0}$$

can be rewritten as the matrix equation

7 $A\bar{c} = \bar{0}$, *where* $$\bar{c} = \begin{bmatrix} c_1 \\ c_2 \\ \vdots \\ c_n \end{bmatrix}$$

and the columns of A *are the vectors* $\bar{u}_1, \bar{u}_2, \ldots, \bar{u}_n$.

Equation **1** therefore has a unique solution (which must be $c_1 = c_2 = \cdots = c_n = 0$) if and only if the equation $A\bar{c} = \bar{0}$ has the unique solution $\bar{c} = \bar{0}$. The condition that equation **1** have a unique solution is just the statement that the vectors $\bar{u}_1, \bar{u}_2, \ldots, \bar{u}_n$ are independent. In summary, we have

THEOREM 8 The equation $A\bar{c} = \bar{0}$ has a unique solution if and only if the *columns* of A are independent vectors.

Equivalent formulations of the fact that the columns of A are independent are:

8 *If A has m rows and n columns, then A can be reduced to a matrix whose first n rows are the identity matrix.*

9 *The null space of A is the zero subspace.*

The above are consequences of Theorem 5, as is the fact that

10 *Any set $\bar{u}_1, \bar{u}_2, \ldots, \bar{u}_n$ of vectors in R^m with $m < n$ must be dependent.*

For the matrix A, whose columns are $\bar{u}_1, \bar{u}_2, \ldots, \bar{u}_n$, must then have fewer rows than columns.

EXAMPLE 4

a The vectors (1,2,0), (1,−1,1), (2,1,1), and (3,1,2) must be dependent (from statement **10**).

b The matrix $\begin{bmatrix} 2 & 1 \\ 1 & 2 \\ 3 & 0 \end{bmatrix}$ reduces to $\begin{bmatrix} 1 & 0 \\ 0 & 1 \\ 0 & 0 \end{bmatrix}$

therefore the vectors (2,1,3) and (1,2,0) must be independent.

c The matrix $\begin{bmatrix} 1 & 3 & 15 \\ 2 & 1 & 10 \\ 1 & 0 & 3 \end{bmatrix}$

reduces to a matrix with a row of zeros; therefore the columns of this matrix are dependent.

DISCUSSION In Example 3 it was noted that a plane in R^3 is the set of all linear combinations of two independent vectors. We showed in that example that if two vectors are dependent, one is a multiple of the other. (*See* statement **5**.) We then established the converse, that if one vector is a multiple of the other, the vectors are dependent. (*See* statement **6**.) This pair of results is a special case of the following (the general proof is omitted):

11 *If one of the vectors $\bar{u}_1, \bar{u}_2, \ldots, \bar{u}_n$ is a linear combination of the others, these vectors are dependent. Conversely, if the vectors are dependent, one of them is a linear combination of the others.*

The next two examples give some methods for using the idea of linear combination, while the final example gives a method for showing independence in function space.

EXAMPLE 5 The vectors $(1,-2)$, $(3,1)$, and $(6,4)$ must be dependent because any set of three vectors in R^2 must be dependent, from statement **10**. We shall show how to express one of them as a combination of the other two. First we find c_1, c_2, and c_3, not all zero, such that $c_1(1,-2) + c_2(3,1) + c_3(6,4) = (0,0)$. Equation **7** in this case is

$$\begin{bmatrix} 1 & 3 & 6 \\ -2 & 1 & 4 \end{bmatrix} \begin{bmatrix} c_1 \\ c_2 \\ c_3 \end{bmatrix} = \begin{bmatrix} 0 \\ 0 \end{bmatrix}$$

By reducing the coefficient matrix we see that one solution is $c_1 = 6$, $c_2 = -16$, and $c_3 = 7$, and, therefore, $6(1,-2) - 16(3,1) + 7(6,4) = (0,0)$.

Since the coefficient of $(1,-2)$ is not zero, we can solve for $(1,-2)$. We have

$$(1,-2) = \frac{16}{6}(3,1) - \frac{7}{6}(6,4)$$

which expresses $(1,-2)$ as a linear combination of $(3,1)$ and $(6,4)$.

EXAMPLE 6 In order to express a vector $\bar{u}$ as a linear combination of $\bar{u}_1, \bar{u}_2, \ldots, \bar{u}_n$ we must find a solution $c_1, c_2, \ldots, c_n$ to $\bar{u} = c_1\bar{u}_1 + c_2\bar{u}_2 + \cdots + c_n\bar{u}_n$. If the vectors are in R^m and are written as columns, the equation is just $A\bar{c} = \bar{u}$, where the columns of A are $\bar{u}_1, \bar{u}_2, \ldots, \bar{u}_n$, and

$$\bar{c} = \begin{bmatrix} c_1 \\ c_2 \\ \vdots \\ c_n \end{bmatrix}$$

For example, suppose we wish to know whether $(15,10,3)$ is a linear combination of $(1,2,1)$ and $(3,1,0)$. Writing these as columns we seek to solve the equation

$$\begin{bmatrix} 15 \\ 10 \\ 3 \end{bmatrix} = c_1 \begin{bmatrix} 1 \\ 2 \\ 1 \end{bmatrix} + c_2 \begin{bmatrix} 3 \\ 1 \\ 0 \end{bmatrix}$$

which can be rewritten as

$$\begin{bmatrix} 1 & 3 \\ 2 & 1 \\ 1 & 0 \end{bmatrix} \begin{bmatrix} c_1 \\ c_2 \end{bmatrix} = \begin{bmatrix} 15 \\ 10 \\ 3 \end{bmatrix}$$

We apply reduction to find a solution $c_1 = 3$, $c_2 = 4$ so that $(15,10,3) = 3(1,2,1) + 4(3,1,0)$.

We conclude also that the vectors (1,2,1), (3,1,0), and (15,10,3) are dependent. In fact we have $3(1,2,1) + 4(3,1,0) - (15,10,3) = (0,0,0)$.

EXAMPLE 7 Suppose we wish to know whether the functions 1, x, and x^2 are independent in $C[0,1]$. (*See* Example 4, page 37.)

Equation **1** in this case is

12 $$0 = c_1 + c_2x + c_3x^2, \qquad 0 \le x \le 1$$

We could set $x = 0, \frac{1}{2}$, and 1 and obtain three equations for the unknowns c_1, c_2, and c_3 and then show that this system has the unique solution $c_1 = c_2 = c_3 = 0$. Instead we apply the following useful trick: Set $x = 0$ in equation **12**. The result is $c_1 = 0$. Then differentiate equation **12** to obtain

$$0 = c_2 + 2c_3x.$$

Put $x = 0$ to obtain $c_2 = 0$. Differentiating again, we have $0 = 2c_3$. We conclude that the only solution to equation **12** is $c_1 = c_2 = c_3 = 0$, and therefore the functions 1, x, and x^2 are independent.

EXERCISES

1 Is a single nonzero vector independent?

2 Use the methods of Example 4 to determine which of the following sets are independent and which are dependent.
 a (1,2), (2,1), (3,0) **b** (4,1,0), (2,−1,1) **c** (3,6,1), (2,1,1), (−1,0,1)
 d (1,1,0,1), (1,2,1,1), (2,1,1,1), (0,1,0,1), (1,0,1,1)
 e (1,1,1,1), (0,1,1,1), (0,0,1,1), (0,0,0,1)

3 Show that each of the following sets are dependent. Express one of the vectors as a linear combination of the others using the methods of Example 5.
 a (−4,3,−5), (1,3,−1), (2,1,1) **b** (1,3), (1,−1), (4,1)
 c (1,2,1,1,0), (1,3,−1,0,−1), (1,0,5,3,2)

4 Use the method of Example 6 to determine whether (1,2,1) is a linear combination of (3,1,0) and (−1,1,1).

5 Show that $\bar{u}_1 = (1, -1, 0)$, $\bar{u}_2 = (2,1,3)$, and $\bar{u}_3 = (4,2,6)$ are dependent.

Can you express $\bar{u}_1$ as a linear combination of $\bar{u}_2$ and $\bar{u}_3$? Why does this not contradict statement **11**?

6 Determine whether (1,0,3) is a linear combination of (2,1,1), (1,−1,1), and (0,0,1) and find one such combination.

7 Show that $(x - 1)^2$ is a linear combination of 1, x, and x^2.

8 Show that the vectors (a,b) and (c,d) are dependent if and only if they are collinear with (0,0).

9 Show that three vectors in R^3 are dependent if and only if they are coplanar or collinear with (0,0,0).

10 Show that $\sin x$ and $\sin 2x$ are independent.

11 Show that e^x and e^{2x} are independent.

12 Suppose f_1 and f_2 are solutions to the differential equation $f'' + f = 0$ and that $f_1(0) = 1$, $f_1'(0) = 0$, $f_2(0) = 0$, $f_2'(0) = 1$. Show that f_1 and f_2 are independent. Deduce from this that $\sin x$ and $\cos x$ are independent.

13 **a** Can an independent set of vectors contain the zero vector?
b Suppose $\bar{u}_1, \bar{u}_2, \bar{u}_3, \ldots, \bar{u}_n$ are independent. Are $\bar{u}_2, \bar{u}_3, \ldots, \bar{u}_n$ independent?
c Suppose $\bar{u}_1, \bar{u}_2, \ldots, \bar{u}_n$ are dependent. Are $\bar{u}_1, \bar{u}_2, \ldots, \bar{u}_n, \bar{v}_1, \bar{v}_2, \ldots, \bar{v}_k$ dependent?

14 Suppose $\bar{u}_1$, $\bar{u}_2$, and $\bar{u}_3$ are independent.
a Show that if $a \neq 0$, then $a\bar{u}_1$, $\bar{u}_2$, and $\bar{u}_3$ are independent.
b Show that $\bar{u}_1 + a\bar{u}_2, \bar{u}_2, \bar{u}_3$ are independent.

□ **15** The definitions and results of this section extend to the complex case.
a Show that $(1 + i, 2i)$ and $(i, 1 - i)$ are independent.
b Show that $(1,i)$ and $(i,-1)$ are dependent.
c Express $(3 + i, i)$ as a linear combination of $(1 + i, 2i)$ and $(i, 1 - i)$.

SECTION 8 Bases and Coordinates

In the previous section we discussed the question of a unique solution to

$$c_1\bar{u}_1 + c_2\bar{u}_2 + \cdots + c_n\bar{u}_n = \bar{0}$$

We said that the vectors $\bar{u}_1, \bar{u}_2, \ldots, \bar{u}_n$ are independent if this equation has a unique solution (which must be $c_1 = c_2 = \cdots = c_n = 0$); otherwise they are dependent.

Suppose $\bar{u}_1, \bar{u}_2, \ldots, \bar{u}_n$ are vectors contained in a vector space V. Consider the equation

1 $$\bar{u} = c_1\bar{u}_1 + c_2\bar{u}_2 + \cdots + c_n\bar{u}_n$$

We say that $\bar{u}_1, \bar{u}_2, \ldots, \bar{u}_n$ **span** the vector space V if for *each* $\bar{u}$ in V

there is *at least one* solution to equation **1**, that is, if each vector in V is a linear combination of $\bar{u}_1, \bar{u}_2, \ldots, \bar{u}_n$.

We say that $\bar{u}_1, \bar{u}_2, \ldots, \bar{u}_n$ are a **basis** for V if for *each* $\bar{u}$ in V equation **1** has a *unique* solution. We will show that:

2 *A basis is an independent set that spans V.*

A basis is certainly independent. For, if for each $\bar{u}$ in V equation **1** has a unique solution, then, *in particular*, it has a unique solution when $\bar{u} = \bar{0}$. A basis also spans V, for, if for each $\bar{u}$ in V equation **1** has a unique solution, then such a solution certainly expresses $\bar{u}$ as a linear combination of the basis vectors.

Suppose $\bar{u}_1, \bar{u}_2, \ldots, \bar{u}_n$ are an independent set that spans V. We shall show that this set is a basis for V. For simplicity we assume $n = 2$, so that $\bar{u}_1$ and $\bar{u}_2$ are independent and span V. Suppose $\bar{u}$ is in V. Then, since $\bar{u}_1$ and $\bar{u}_2$ span V, there must be scalars c_1 and c_2 so that

3
$$\bar{u} = c_1\bar{u}_1 + c_2\bar{u}_2$$

We shall show that there is *only one pair* c_1, c_2 such that this statement holds. Suppose that, if possible, we also have

$$\bar{u} = d_1\bar{u}_1 + d_2\bar{u}_2$$

Subtract this from equation **3** and regroup as follows:

$$\begin{aligned} \bar{0} &= \bar{u} - \bar{u} \\ &= (d_1\bar{u}_1 + d_2\bar{u}_2) - (c_1\bar{u}_1 + c_2\bar{u}_2) \\ &= (d_1 - c_1)\bar{u}_1 + (d_2 - c_2)\bar{u}_2 \end{aligned}$$

By assumption $\bar{u}_1$ and $\bar{u}_2$ are independent, so we must have

$$d_1 - c_1 = 0 \quad \text{and} \quad d_2 - c_2 = 0$$

We are thus forced to conclude that $d_1 = c_1$, $d_2 = c_2$.

We have shown that if $\bar{u}_1$ and $\bar{u}_2$ are independent and span V, then for each $\bar{u}$ in V, equation **3** has a unique solution. This completes the proof of statement **2** for $n = 2$.

In the next section we shall discuss some useful properties of bases. Since, for a given basis $\bar{u}_1, \bar{u}_2, \ldots, \bar{u}_n$ and a given $\bar{u}$ equation **1** has a unique solution, it is appropriate to give a name to this solution. We say that the numbers $c_1, c_2, \ldots, c_n$ are the **coordinates** of $\bar{u}$ **relative to the basis** $\bar{u}_1, \bar{u}_2, \ldots, \bar{u}_n$ if

$$\bar{u} = c_1\bar{u}_1 + c_2\bar{u}_2 + \cdots + c_n\bar{u}_n$$

EXAMPLE 1 The vectors (1,0) and (0,1) are a basis for R^2. In this case equation **1** is, for a given (x,y),

$$(x,y) = c_1(1,0) + c_2(0,1)$$

Since $c_1(1,0) + c_2(0,1) = (c_1,c_2)$, this equation can be rewritten as

$$(x,y) = (c_1, c_2)$$

which clearly has the unique solution

$$c_1 = x, c_2 = y$$

Therefore $(x,y) = x(1,0) + y(0,1)$.

In other words, x and y are the coordinates of (x,y) relative to the basis (1,0) and (0,1). Thus the concept of coordinates relative to a basis is an extension of the usual definition of the coordinates of a point.

A similar argument shows that (1,0,0), (0,1,0), and (0,0,1) are a basis for R^3; that (1,0,0,0), (0,1,0,0), (0,0,1,0), and (0,0,0,1) are a basis for R^4, and so forth. In summary

4 *The rows of the n-rowed identity matrix are a basis for* R^n.

DISCUSSION The coordinates of (x,y,z) relative to (1,0,0), (0,1,0), and (0,0,1) are just x, y, and z, for we have

$$(x,y,z) = x(1,0,0) + y(0,1,0) + z(0,0,1)$$

Note that the ordering chosen to denote the basis affects the coordinates. For example the coordinates of (x,y), relative to the basis (0,1) and (1,0), are y and x, for $(x,y) = y(0,1) + x(1,0)$.

The basis given by the identity matrix is called the **standard basis** of R^n. When it is written in the usual order (the first row of I first, the second row second, and so on), the coordinates of a vector $(x_1, x_2, \ldots, x_n)$ relative to the standard basis are $x_1, x_2, \ldots, x_n$.

When we use the word "coordinates" without reference to a basis *we shall always mean the coordinates relative to the standard basis in its usual order.*

EXAMPLE 2 We shall show that (1,2,1), (1,−1,3), and (1,1,4) are a basis for R^3, and in the process we shall exhibit a general method for finding bases in R^n.

Suppose (x,y,z) is a vector in R^3. Then, if we write vectors as column matrices, equation **1** becomes

5
$$\begin{bmatrix} x \\ y \\ z \end{bmatrix} = c_1 \begin{bmatrix} 1 \\ 2 \\ 1 \end{bmatrix} + c_2 \begin{bmatrix} 1 \\ -1 \\ 3 \end{bmatrix} + c_3 \begin{bmatrix} 1 \\ 1 \\ 4 \end{bmatrix}$$

Since the right-hand side is

$$\begin{bmatrix} c_1 \\ 2c_1 \\ c_1 \end{bmatrix} + \begin{bmatrix} c_2 \\ -c_2 \\ 3c_2 \end{bmatrix} + \begin{bmatrix} c_3 \\ c_3 \\ 4c_3 \end{bmatrix} = \begin{bmatrix} c_1 + c_2 + c_3 \\ 2c_1 - c_2 + c_3 \\ c_1 + 3c_2 + 4c_3 \end{bmatrix}$$

which can be rewritten as

$$\begin{bmatrix} 1 & 1 & 1 \\ 2 & -1 & 1 \\ 1 & 3 & 4 \end{bmatrix} \begin{bmatrix} c_1 \\ c_2 \\ c_3 \end{bmatrix}$$

we see that equation **5** can be expressed as

$$\begin{bmatrix} 1 & 1 & 1 \\ 2 & -1 & 1 \\ 1 & 3 & 4 \end{bmatrix} \begin{bmatrix} c_1 \\ c_2 \\ c_3 \end{bmatrix} = \begin{bmatrix} x \\ y \\ z \end{bmatrix}$$

The augmented matrix is

$$\left[\begin{array}{ccc:c} 1 & 1 & 1 & x \\ 2 & -1 & 1 & y \\ 1 & 3 & 4 & z \end{array}\right]$$

which reduces to

$$\left[\begin{array}{ccc:c} 1 & 0 & 0 & x + \frac{1}{7}y - \frac{2}{7}z \\ 0 & 1 & 0 & x - \frac{3}{7}y - \frac{1}{7}z \\ 0 & 0 & 1 & -x + \frac{2}{7}y + \frac{3}{7}z \end{array}\right]$$

Thus, for each (x,y,z) equation **5** has the unique solution

6
$$\begin{aligned} c_1 &= x + \tfrac{1}{7}y - \tfrac{2}{7}z \\ c_2 &= x - \tfrac{3}{7}y - \tfrac{1}{7}z \\ c_3 &= -x + \tfrac{2}{7}y + \tfrac{3}{7}z \end{aligned}$$

We conclude that (1,2,1), (1,−1,3), and (1,1,4) are a basis for R^3. Formulas **6** give the coordinates c_1, c_2, c_3 of (x,y,z) relative to this basis. After further discussion of the theory of bases, we shall obtain in the next section a somewhat shorter method for determining whether a given set of vectors is a basis. We shall also later simplify the process of finding coordinates relative to a basis. (*See* Section 7, Chapter 2.)

EXAMPLE 3 The construction of the general solution to $A\bar{u} = \bar{0}$ given in Example 1, page 50, actually involves the construction of a basis for the null space of A. For example, consider the matrix of Example 1.

$$A = \begin{bmatrix} 1 & 2 & 1 & 1 \\ 2 & 4 & -1 & 0 \end{bmatrix}$$

We showed in that example that the null space of A consisted of all vectors of the form

$$a \begin{bmatrix} -2 \\ 1 \\ 0 \\ 0 \end{bmatrix} + b \begin{bmatrix} -\frac{1}{3} \\ 0 \\ -\frac{2}{3} \\ 1 \end{bmatrix}$$

In other words, the null space of A consists of all linear combinations of the vectors

$$\bar{u}_1 = \begin{bmatrix} -2 \\ 1 \\ 0 \\ 0 \end{bmatrix} \quad \text{and} \quad \bar{u}_2 = \begin{bmatrix} -\frac{1}{3} \\ 0 \\ -\frac{2}{3} \\ 1 \end{bmatrix}$$

These vectors are independent, for the second coordinate of the sum $c_1\bar{u}_1 + c_2\bar{u}_2$ must be c_1, and the fourth coordinate must be c_2 (the vectors were chosen so as to achieve this). Therefore, if the sum were the zero vector, we must have $c_1 = c_2 = 0$.

We conclude that the vectors $\bar{u}_1$ and $\bar{u}_2$ are independent. We already knew that every vector in the null space of A must be a linear combination of $\bar{u}_1$ and $\bar{u}_2$. Our final conclusion, using result **2**, is that

$\bar{u}_1$ *and* $\bar{u}_2$ *are a basis for the null space of* A.

EXAMPLE 4 Suppose V is the set of polynomial functions of degree not exceeding 3. Since 0 is such a polynomial, and sums and multiples of such polynomials must again be polynomials of degree ≤ 3, we see that V is a subspace of the space $C[0,1]$ of Example 4 on page 37.

The polynomials 1, x, x^2, and x^3 can be shown to be independent using the differentiation trick of Example 7, page 64. Since, by definition, a polynomial of degree ≤ 3 is a linear combination of 1, x, x^2, and x^3, this shows that

1, x, x^2, *and* x^3 *form a basis for* V.

The coordinates of the polynomial $a_0 + a_1x + a_2x^2 + a_3x^3$ relative to $1, x, x^2$, and x^3 are just the coefficients a_0, a_1, a_2, and a_3.

EXERCISES

1 Show that each of the following sets of vectors is a basis for R^3 by using the methods of Example 2.

a (3,6,1), (2,1,1), (−1,0,1)

b (1,1,1), (0,1,1), (0,0,1)

c (3,7,0), (0,2,4), (5,0,−5)

2 Show that each of the following sets of vectors is not a basis for R^3.

a (−4,3,−5), (1,3,−1), (2,1,1)

b (2,1,0), (1,2,−1), (6,7,12), (300,703,427)

3 Show that each of the following sets of vectors is a basis for R^4.

a (1,1,1,−1), (1,1,−1,1), (1,−1,1,1), (−1,1,1,1)

b (1,2,3,4), (0,1,2,3), (0,0,1,2), (0,0,0,1)

4 Using the methods of Example 3 find a basis for the null space of each of the following matrices.

a $\begin{bmatrix} 1 & 0 & 3 \\ 2 & 1 & 1 \end{bmatrix}$ **b** $\begin{bmatrix} 3 & 1 & 1 & 0 \\ 6 & 2 & 2 & 1 \end{bmatrix}$ **c** $\begin{bmatrix} 2 & 1 & 0 & 6 & 1 & 1 & 2 \\ 4 & 1 & 0 & 6 & 2 & 2 & 1 \end{bmatrix}$

5 Find the coordinates of (x,y,z) relative to each of the bases of Exercise 1.

6 Find the coordinates of (x,y,z,w) relative to each of the bases of Exercise 3.

7 Find a basis for the set of vectors of the form $(0,y,z)$.

8 Show that (a,b) and (c,d) form a basis for R^2 if and only if $ad - bc \neq 0$.

9 Suppose V is the vector space of polynomials of degree ≤ 1.

a Show that $1 + x$ and $1 - x$ are a basis for V.

b Calculate the coordinates of $a + bx$ relative to the basis $1 + x$, $1 - x$.

10 **a** Show that the polynomials $1, x, x^2, \ldots, x^n$ are independent. (Hint: Use the differentiation process of Example 7, page 64.)

b Show that no matter how large n is, the set $1, x, x^2, \ldots, x^n$ is *not* a basis for $C[0,1]$, the space defined in Example 4, page 37. (Hint: Show that x^{n+1} is not a linear combination of $1, x, x^2, \ldots, x^n$.)

11 **a** Show that if f_1 and f_2 are solutions to $f'' + af = 0$ such that $f_1(0)f_2'(0) - f_1'(0)f_2(0) \neq 0$, f_1 and f_2 are then independent.

b It can be shown that if f_1 and f_2 satisfy the conditions of part **a**, they form a basis for the space of solutions to $f'' + af = 0$. Deduce from this that every solution to $f'' + f = 0$ can be uniquely expressed as $c_1 \sin x + c_2 \cos x$.

c Show that every solution to $f'' - f = 0$ can be uniquely expressed as $c_1e^x + c_2e^{-x}$.

□ **12** The results of this section extend immediately to the complex case. Show that each of the following sets of vectors is a basis for C^2.

a $(1,0)$, $(0,1)$.

b $(i,1)$, $(-1, -i)$.

c $(2 + i,3)$, $(1 - i, 1 - 2i)$.

SECTION 9 Dimension

We present two theorems about bases in this section. The proofs of these results are somewhat technical and can be found in Appendix 2. With the aid of these theorems we shall be able to complete our existence and uniqueness theory for matrix equations which was begun in Section 6.

Theorem 9 tells us that any two bases for a finite-dimensional vector space must contain the same number of vectors.

THEOREM 9 Suppose $\bar{u}_1, \bar{u}_2, \ldots, \bar{u}_n$ are a basis for V. Any other basis for V must contain exactly n vectors.

A vector space V that has a basis consisting of a finite number of vectors is said to be **finite-dimensional.** The number of vectors in such a basis is called the **dimension** of V.

EXAMPLE 1 Since the rows of the n-rowed identity matrix are a basis for R^n, we see that R^n has dimension n. (*See* Example 1 of the previous section.)

A line through the origin in R^2 or R^3 consists of all multiples of a single nonzero vector; therefore, such a line has dimension *one*. A plane in R^3 through $(0,0,0)$ consists of all linear combinations of two independent vectors and hence is *two*-dimensional. Thus, our algebraic concept of dimension coincides with our geometric intuition (as it should).

EXAMPLE 2 One consequence of Theorem 9 is that if the dimension of V is n, then no set containing either *more* or *less* than n vectors can be a basis for V. We have seen in statement **10**, page 62, that *no* set containing more than n vectors can be independent and hence such a set cannot be a basis for R^n. We now also know that *no* set containing less than n vectors can be a basis for R^n.

Consider the matrix

$$A = \begin{bmatrix} 2 & 1 \\ 1 & 1 \\ 0 & 1 \end{bmatrix}$$

The columns of A are independent. Since A has only two columns they cannot be a basis for R^3. We conclude that the columns of A *cannot* span R^3 (for, otherwise, they would be an independent set that spans R^3 and hence a basis for R^3). Since the columns of A do not span R^3, there must be a vector $\bar{u}$ in R^3 such that

$$\bar{u} = c_1 \begin{bmatrix} 2 \\ 1 \\ 0 \end{bmatrix} + c_2 \begin{bmatrix} 1 \\ 1 \\ 1 \end{bmatrix}$$

has *no* solution. In other words, there must be a vector $\bar{u}$ in R^3 such that

$$A \begin{bmatrix} c_1 \\ c_2 \end{bmatrix} = \bar{u}$$

has no solution.

A general statement of this result would be:

1 *If A has more rows than columns, there is a vector $\bar{u}$ such that $A\bar{c} = \bar{u}$ has no solution.*

A proof of this is outlined in the exercises.

DISCUSSION Our second result about bases will enable us to deduce spanning from independence or independence from spanning when the number of vectors equals the dimension.

THEOREM 10 Suppose V has dimension n.

a If $\bar{u}_1, \bar{u}_2, \ldots, \bar{u}_n$ are independent, they span V.
b If $\bar{u}_1, \bar{u}_2, \ldots, \bar{u}_n$ span V, they are independent.

The proof will be found in Appendix 2. A fundamental consequence of this result for matrix equations is given in

THEOREM 11 Suppose A has n rows and n columns.

a If the columns of A are independent, they span R^n.
b If the columns of A span R^n, they are independent.
In particular,
c If $A\bar{u} = \bar{0}$ has a unique solution, then *for any* $\bar{v}$ in R^n, $A\bar{u} = \bar{v}$ has a unique solution.

PROOF: Parts **a** and **b** are just restatements of Theorem 10**a** and **b**. We shall prove part **c**.

If $A\bar{u} = \bar{0}$ has a unique solution, Theorem 8 then tells us that the columns of A are independent. Part **a** of this theorem tells us that the columns of A must span R^n. Denote the columns of A by $\bar{u}_1, \bar{u}_2, \ldots, \bar{u}_n$. Since these span R^n and are independent we know that they are a basis for R^n. Hence, for *any* $\bar{v}$ in R^n, the equation

2 $$\bar{v} = c_1\bar{u}_1 + c_2\bar{u}_2 + \cdots + c_n\bar{u}_n$$

has a *unique* solution. This equation can be rewritten as

3 $$A\bar{u} = \bar{v} \qquad \text{where} \qquad \bar{u} = \begin{bmatrix} c_1 \\ c_2 \\ \vdots \\ c_n \end{bmatrix}$$

Since equation **2** has a unique solution we are forced to conclude that equation **3** has a unique solution. This proves part **c** and completes the proof of Theorem 11.

EXAMPLE 3 Consider the matrix

$$A = \begin{bmatrix} 1 & 1 & 1 \\ 2 & -1 & 1 \\ 1 & 3 & 4 \end{bmatrix}$$

It reduces to the identity; therefore, the columns of A are independent. Theorem 11 shows that (1,2,1), (1,−1,3), (1,1,4) are a basis for R^3. We know, therefore, that for any vector (x,y,z) the equation

4 $$A\begin{bmatrix} c_1 \\ c_2 \\ c_3 \end{bmatrix} = \begin{bmatrix} x \\ y \\ z \end{bmatrix}$$

has a unique solution. In Example 2 of the previous section we also deduced this by reducing the augmented matrix of equation **4**. As a result of Theorem 11 we are able to deduce *existence* and uniqueness for equation **4** merely by reducing the *coefficient* matrix.

EXAMPLE 4 Consider the vector space V of polynomials of degree not exceeding two. The polynomials 1, x, and x^2 are independent. (*See* Example 7, page 64.) They also span V, since, by definition, a polynomial of degree not exceeding 2 is a linear combination of 1, x, and x^2. We conclude that V is *three*-dimensional.

We shall construct another basis for V, which is of interest. Let

$$f_1 = \frac{(x-1)(x-2)}{2}, \qquad f_2 = \frac{x(x-2)}{-1}, \qquad f_3 = \frac{x(x-1)}{2}$$

We note that

5
$$\begin{aligned} f_1(1) &= f_1(2) = 0 \qquad & f_1(0) &= 1 \\ f_2(0) &= f_2(2) = 0 \qquad & f_2(1) &= 1 \\ f_3(0) &= f_3(1) = 0 \qquad & f_3(2) &= 1 \end{aligned}$$

The polynomials f_1, f_2, and f_3 each have degree 2 and thus belong to V. We shall use the relations **5** to show that they are independent.

Suppose that for all x

6
$$c_1f_1(x) + c_2f_2(x) + c_3f_3(x) = 0$$

Substitute $x = 0$ and use relations **5**. The result is

$$f_1(0) = 1 \qquad f_2(0) = 0 \qquad f_3(0) = 0$$

Thus we must have $c_1 = 0$. Substituting $x = 1$ and using relations **5** give $c_2 = 0$, and a similar argument with $x = 2$ shows that $c_3 = 0$. We conclude that identity **6** necessarily entails that $c_1 = c_2 = c_3 = 0$. Consequently, f_1, f_2, and f_3 are independent.

Since V has dimension 3, we apply Theorem 10 to conclude that f_1, f_2, and f_3 are a basis for V. In particular if f is a polynomial of degree not exceeding 2, then we can find c_1, c_2, and c_3 such that *for all* x

7
$$f(x) = c_1f_1(x) + c_2f_2(x) + c_3f_3(x)$$

Setting $x = 0$ and using relations **5** we have $c_1 = f(0)$. Repeating this process with $x = 1$ and $x = 2$ gives

$$c_2 = f(1) \qquad c_3 = f(2)$$

Equation **7** can then be rewritten as

$$f(x) = f(0)f_1(x) + f(1)f_2(x) + f(2)f_3(x)$$

This formula is known as the **Lagrange interpolation formula** and expresses a polynomial of degree 2 or less in terms of its values at 0, 1, and 2, relative to a basis consisting of polynomials of degree exactly 2.

EXAMPLE 5 *Subspaces of R^2 and R^3.*

Several other results will be established in Appendix 2. Among them are the following facts:

If V has a spanning set containing n vectors, then

a *V has a basis containing no more than n vectors.*

8 **b** *No independent set in V can contain more than n vectors.*

c *Any nonzero subspace of V has a basis containing no more than n vectors.*

We shall use this result to classify the subspaces of R^3. First, there is the subspace consisting of the zero vector only. This is called the *zero* subspace and is said to have dimension *zero*.

A subspace of R^3 which is not the zero subspace, must, because of statement **8c**, be of dimension 1, 2, or 3, since R^3 is spanned by (1,0,0), (0,1,0), and (0,0,1). A one-dimensional subspace has a basis consisting of one independent vector. A single vector is independent if and only if it is nonzero. Thus, a one-dimensional subspace must consist of all multiples of a single nonzero vector. In summary

The one-dimensional subspaces of R^3 are precisely the lines through the origin.

The two-dimensional subspaces have bases containing two vectors and hence must consist of all linear combinations of *two* independent vectors. In other words,

The two-dimensional subspaces of R^3 are precisely the planes through the origin.

A three-dimensional subspace has a basis consisting of three vectors. Since these vectors must be independent, they must (from Theorem 10) span R^3. Thus

R^3 has only one three-dimensional subspace, namely, R^3 itself.

In summary

The nonzero subspaces of R^3 which are not all *of R^3 are just the lines and planes through* (0,0,0).

EXERCISES Additional exercises concerning bases and independence can be found in Appendix 2.

1 Use the method of examples 2 and 3 to decide which of the following sets are bases for R^3.

a (3,6,1), (2,1,1), (−1,0,1)

b (1,1,1), (1,1,0)

c (−4,3,−5), (1,3,−1), (2,1,1)

d (3,7,0), (0,2,4), (5,0,−5)

2 Show that there are vectors $\bar{v}$ such that

$$\begin{bmatrix} 2 & 1 & 4 \\ 1 & 2 & 1 \\ 1 & 1 & 0 \\ 2 & 1 & 1 \end{bmatrix} \bar{u} = \bar{v}$$

has *no* solution. Show also that the columns of the coefficient matrix are independent.

3 Find the dimension of the null space of

$$A = \begin{bmatrix} 3 & 1 & 1 & 0 \\ 6 & 2 & 2 & 1 \end{bmatrix}$$

Note that this corresponds to the number of variables which are not leading variables in the reduced form.

4 Find the dimension of the null space of (*see* Exercise 3)

$$\begin{bmatrix} 2 & 1 & 0 & 6 & 1 & 1 & 2 \\ 4 & 1 & 0 & 6 & 2 & 2 & 1 \end{bmatrix}$$

5 Make a guess about the relationship between the dimension of the null space of A, the number of columns of A and the number of nonzero rows of the reduced form of A. (*See* Exercises 3 and 4.)

6 Show that the columns of $A = \begin{bmatrix} 3 & 1 & 2 \\ 2 & 6 & 4 \\ 2 & 1 & 3 \end{bmatrix}$ span R^3.

Do the rows of A also span R^3?

7 Show that if $ad - bc \neq 0$, then for any α and β the system

$$\begin{aligned} ax + by &= \alpha \\ cx + dy &= \beta \end{aligned}$$

has a unique solution.

8 What is the dimension of the subspace of vectors of the form $(0,y,z)$?

9 Classify the subspaces of R^2. The subspaces of R^4.

10 For which of the following matrices A can the equation $A\bar{u} = \bar{v}$ be solved, for any given $\bar{v}$ of appropriate size?

a $A = \begin{bmatrix} 2 & 1 \\ 1 & 2 \end{bmatrix}$ **b** $A = \begin{bmatrix} 2 & 1 & 1 \\ 1 & 2 & 1 \end{bmatrix}$

c $A = \begin{bmatrix} 2 & 1 \\ 1 & 2 \\ 1 & 1 \end{bmatrix}$ **d** $A = \begin{bmatrix} 2 & 1 & 3 \\ 1 & 2 & 3 \\ 1 & 1 & 2 \end{bmatrix}$ **e** $A = \begin{bmatrix} 2 & 1 & 3 & 4 \\ 1 & 2 & 3 & 1 \\ 1 & 1 & 2 & 0 \end{bmatrix}$

11 Suppose V is the space of polynomials of degree not exceeding 3. (*See* Example 4.)

a What is the dimension of V?

b Find a basis for V such that the coordinates of f relative to this basis are $f(0), f(1), f(2), f(3)$.

c Find a basis for V such that the coordinates of f relative to this basis are $f(-2), f(-1), f(1), f(2)$.

12 Show that $C[0,1]$ is not finite-dimensional. ($C[0,1]$ was defined in Example 4, page 37. First show that for any n, the set $1, x, x^2, \ldots, x^n$ is independent, then apply the result **8b**.)

13 Prove statement **1**. (Hint: Adjoin additional columns of zeros to obtain a square matrix B. Then apply Theorem 11**b**.)

□ 14 Suppose A has n rows and n columns and has the property that no matter what $\bar{v}$ is chosen in R^n, the equation $A\bar{u} = \bar{v}$ has a solution. Show that the equation $A\bar{u} = \bar{0}$ must have a unique solution. (Hint: Apply Theorem 11**b**.)

□ 15 The results of this section are also true for complex vector spaces. Decide which of the following are bases for C^2.

a $(i,1)$ **b** $(i,1), (1,-i)$

c $(i,1), (1,i)$ **d** $(2i + 1, 1), (1 - 3i, 0)$

SECTION 10 The Dot Product

We can often use geometric ideas to show independence of a set of vectors and to calculate coordinates with respect to a basis. For example, if two nonzero vectors are mutually perpendicular in the arrow representation of R^2, they are certainly independent and hence are a basis for R^2. The coordinates of a vector with respect to such a basis can be calculated by projecting onto the basis vectors.

In this section we show how the concepts of perpendicularity and projection can be given an algebraic formulation. We will then also be able to adapt these ideas to the study of vector spaces that have no convenient geometric description, such as R^4 and R^5, and to spaces of functions.

If $\bar{u} = (x_1, x_2, \ldots, x_n)$ and $\bar{v} = (y_1, y_2, \ldots, y_n)$, then the **dot product** is defined by

$$\bar{u} \cdot \bar{v} = x_1y_1 + x_2y_2 + \cdots + x_ny_n$$

The dot product has the following properties, all of which are simple consequences of the definition

1
a $\bar{u} \cdot \bar{v}$ *is a real number*
b $\bar{u} \cdot \bar{v} = \bar{v} \cdot \bar{u}$
c $\bar{u} \cdot (\bar{v} + \bar{w}) = \bar{u} \cdot \bar{v} + \bar{u} \cdot \bar{w}$
d $\bar{u} \cdot (a\bar{v}) = a(\bar{u} \cdot \bar{v})$ *for any real number a*
e $\bar{u} \cdot \bar{u} > 0$ *if* $\bar{u} \neq \bar{0}$

All these rules also hold for the ordinary product of real numbers. Hence, we can manipulate with the dot product just as though the vectors were numbers. [Of course, $\bar{u} \cdot (\bar{v} \cdot \bar{w})$ makes no sense in this situation since $\bar{v} \cdot \bar{w}$ would be a number, and the dot product of a number with a vector is not defined.]

For example, if a and b are numbers, then

$$(a - b)(a - b) = aa - 2ab + bb$$

This equation is simply a consequence of the distributive and commutative laws of ordinary multiplication. For the dot product, these laws are just properties **1b** and **c**. We therefore conclude that

2 $$(\bar{u} - \bar{v}) \cdot (\bar{u} - \bar{v}) = \bar{u} \cdot \bar{u} - 2\bar{u} \cdot \bar{v} + \bar{v} \cdot \bar{v}$$

must also be true.

We define the **length** (or **norm**) of $\bar{u}$, by

$$|\bar{u}| = \sqrt{\bar{u} \cdot \bar{u}}$$

Therefore, if $\bar{u} = (x_1, x_2, \ldots, x_n)$, the length of $\bar{u}$ is

$$|\bar{u}| = \sqrt{x_1^2 + x_2^2 + \cdots + x_n^2}$$

Figure 5 shows that when $n = 2$, this definition of length corresponds with the usual definition of length for the arrow used to represent $\bar{u}$.

We can show in this case that

3 $$\bar{u} \cdot \bar{v} = |\bar{u}|\,|\bar{v}| \cos \theta$$

where θ is the angle between the arrow representations of $\bar{u}$ and $\bar{v}$. For example, if $\bar{u} = (x_1,y_1)$ and $\bar{v} = (x_2,y_2)$, the law of cosines gives

4 $$|\bar{u} - \bar{v}|^2 = |\bar{u}|^2 + |\bar{v}|^2 - 2|\bar{u}|\,|\bar{v}| \cos \theta$$

as shown in Figure 6.

Figure 5 *The length of* $\bar{u}$ *is* $\sqrt{x^2 + y^2}$.

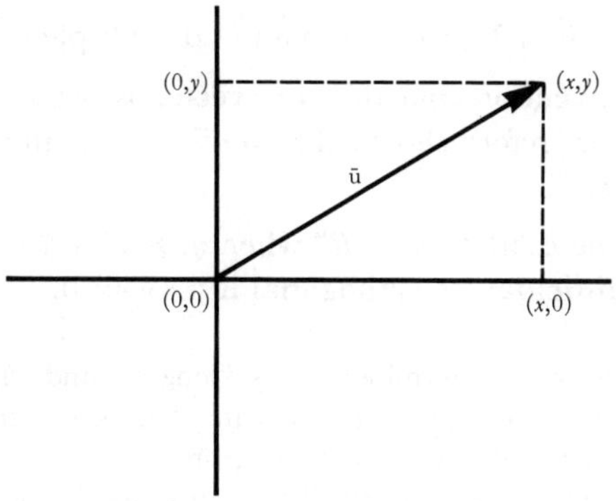

Figure 6 *The law of cosines gives* $|PQ|^2 = |OQ|^2 + |OP|^2 - 2|OQ|\,|OP| \cos \theta$.

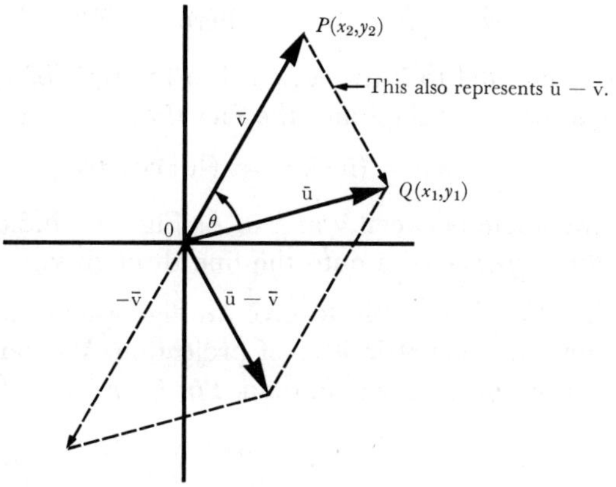

We can also compute $|\bar{u} - \bar{v}|^2$ using the definition of length and result **2** to obtain:

$$|\bar{u} - \bar{v}|^2 = (\bar{u} - \bar{v}) \cdot (\bar{u} - \bar{v}) = \bar{u} \cdot \bar{u} - 2\bar{u} \cdot \bar{v} + \bar{v} \cdot \bar{v}$$
$$= |\bar{u}|^2 - 2\bar{u} \cdot \bar{v} + |\bar{v}|^2$$

Comparing this with equation **4** we see that we must have

$$\bar{u} \cdot \bar{v} = |\bar{u}|\,|\bar{v}| \cos \theta$$

which establishes statement **3**.

It follows that for $\bar{u}$ and $\bar{v}$ in R^2 we must have

$$\bar{u} \cdot \bar{v} = 0$$

if and only if $\bar{u} = \bar{0}$ or $\bar{v} = \bar{0}$ or θ is an odd multiple of $\pi/2$.

We adopt the convention that the zero vector is perpendicular to every vector. We have therefore shown that $\bar{u} \cdot \bar{v} = 0$ if and only if $\bar{u}$ and $\bar{v}$ are perpendicular.

We take this as the definition in R^n when $n > 2$ and state that $\bar{u}$ and $\bar{v}$ in R^n are **perpendicular** or **orthogonal** if $\bar{u} \cdot \bar{v} = 0$.

REMARK This use of such geometric terminology as "length" and "perpendicular" for vectors in R^n is a good example of the way in which geometric names are used for vector spaces that have no convenient geometric description (which is the case for R^5, for example). In general, if we can show that a geometric concept can be given an algebraic formulation, then we can adopt the same terminology whenever the same algebraic formulation holds in a vector space. This enables us to borrow ideas and insight from geometry into more general situations.

For another application of formula **3**, consider the vector

5 $$\bar{w}_1 = (\bar{u} \cdot \bar{v})\bar{v} \qquad \text{where} \qquad |\bar{v}| = 1$$

This vector is parallel to $\bar{v}$ (because it is a multiple of $\bar{v}$). If $\bar{u}$ and $\bar{v}$ are in R^2, we can use formula **3** and the fact that $|\bar{v}| = 1$, to obtain

$$\bar{w}_1 = (\bar{u} \cdot \bar{v})\bar{v} = (|\bar{u}| \cos \theta)\bar{v}$$

where θ is the angle between $\bar{v}$ and $\bar{u}$. As Figure 7 indicates, this tells us that $\bar{w}_1$ is the *projection* of $\bar{u}$ onto the line through $\bar{v}$.

We have therefore been able to give an algebraic description (namely, formula **5**) for the geometric idea of projection. We can thus adopt this algebraic description as our definition. For $\bar{u}$ and $\bar{v}$ in R^n, with $|\bar{v}| = 1$, we say that

$$\bar{w}_1 = (\bar{u} \cdot \bar{v})\bar{v}$$

is the **projection** of $\bar{u}$ **onto** $\bar{v}$ (or in the direction of $\bar{v}$, or parallel to $\bar{v}$).

If we subtract $\bar{w}_1$ from $\bar{u}$, we then obtain, as Figure 8 shows, a vector $\bar{w}_2 = \bar{u} - \bar{w}_1$, which is *perpendicular* to $\bar{v}$. Furthermore, $\bar{u} = \bar{w}_1 + \bar{w}_2$.

For $\bar{u}$ and $\bar{v}$ in R^n and $|\bar{v}| = 1$, we say that

6 $$\bar{w}_2 = \bar{u} - \bar{w}_1 = \bar{u} - (\bar{u} \cdot \bar{v})\bar{v}$$

is the **projection** of $\bar{u}$ **orthogonal** to $\bar{v}$. We can use the dot product to show that indeed $\bar{w}_2$ is orthogonal to $\bar{v}$; for we have, using rules **1**:

$$\begin{aligned} \bar{w}_2 \cdot \bar{v} &= (\bar{u} - (\bar{u} \cdot \bar{v})\bar{v}) \cdot \bar{v} \\ &= \bar{u} \cdot \bar{v} - (\bar{u} \cdot \bar{v})(\bar{v} \cdot \bar{v}) \\ &= \bar{u} \cdot \bar{v} - \bar{u} \cdot \bar{v} = 0 \end{aligned}$$

Note that we also used the fact that $\bar{v} \cdot \bar{v} = 1$, which is a consequence of the assumption that $|\bar{v}| = 1$ and the fact that $|\bar{v}|^2 = \bar{v} \cdot \bar{v}$.

We see immediately from formula **6** that

$$\bar{u} = \bar{w}_1 + \bar{w}_2$$

so that $\bar{u}$ is the sum of its projections parallel to and orthogonal to $\bar{v}$.

Figure 7

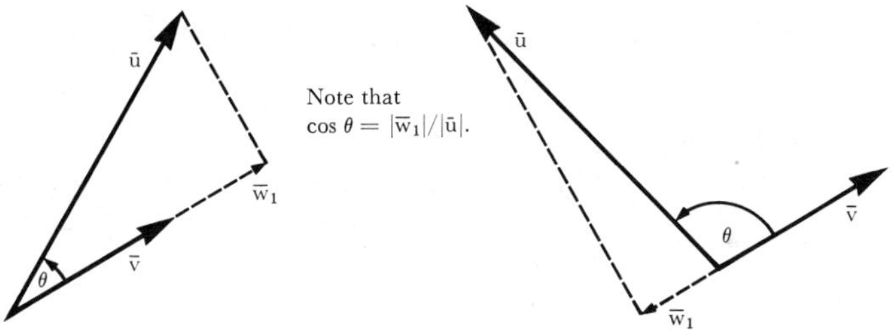

Figure 8 *In each case* $\bar{u} = \bar{w}_1 + \bar{w}_2$, $\bar{w}_1$ *is parallel to* $\bar{v}$, *and* $\bar{w}_2$ *is perpendicular to* $\bar{v}$.

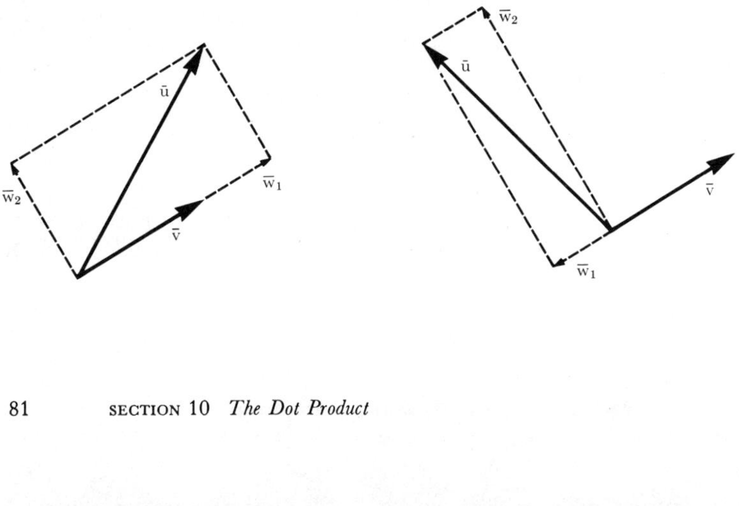

If $\bar{v}$ is not a unit vector and $\bar{v} \neq \bar{0}$, these projections can be defined by **normalizing** $\bar{v}$, that is, by replacing $\bar{v}$ by a unit vector parallel to $\bar{v}$. Such a vector is

$$\bar{w} = \frac{1}{|\bar{v}|}\bar{v}$$

Then the projection of $\bar{u}$ onto $\bar{v}$ is given by

7 $$\bar{w}_1 = (\bar{u}\cdot\bar{w})\bar{w} = \left(\bar{u}\cdot\frac{\bar{v}}{|\bar{v}|}\right)\frac{\bar{v}}{|\bar{v}|} = \frac{\bar{u}\cdot\bar{v}}{\bar{v}\,.\,\bar{v}}\bar{v}$$

and the projection of $\bar{u}$ orthogonal to $\bar{v}$ is given by

8 $$\bar{w}_2 = \bar{u} - (\bar{u}\cdot\bar{w})\bar{w} = \bar{u} - \frac{\bar{u}\cdot\bar{v}}{\bar{v}\cdot\bar{v}}\bar{v}$$

The student may find it easier to remember formulas **5** and **6** and use the normalizing process rather than memorizing formulas **7** and **8**. Some applications of projection methods to elementary analytic geometry are described in Appendix 1.

EXAMPLE 1 If $\bar{u} = (1,2,1)$ and $\bar{v} = (3,-1,0)$, then

$$\bar{u}\cdot\bar{v} = 1\cdot 3 + 2(-1) + 1\cdot 0 = 1$$

The lengths of $\bar{u}$ and $\bar{v}$ are $|\bar{u}| = \sqrt{1+4+1} = \sqrt{6}$ and $|\bar{v}| = \sqrt{9+1} = \sqrt{10}$.

The vector

$$\bar{w} = \frac{1}{|\bar{v}|}\bar{v} = \frac{1}{\sqrt{10}}(3,-1,0)$$

is a unit vector parallel to $\bar{v}$. Thus, the projection of $\bar{u}$ onto $\bar{v}$ is given by

$$\begin{aligned}(\bar{u}\cdot\bar{w})\bar{w} &= \left[(1,2,1)\cdot\frac{1}{\sqrt{10}}(3,-1,0)\right]\left[\frac{1}{\sqrt{10}}(3,-1,0)\right]\\ &= \frac{1}{10}[(1,2,1)\cdot(3,-1,0)](3,-1,0) = \frac{1}{10}(3,-1,0)\\ &= \left(\frac{3}{10},\frac{-1}{10},0\right)\end{aligned}$$

and the projection of $\bar{u}$ orthogonal to $\bar{v}$ is given by

$$\bar{u} - (\bar{u}\cdot\bar{w})\bar{w} = (1,2,1) - \left(\frac{3}{10},\frac{-1}{10},0\right) = \left(\frac{7}{10},\frac{21}{10},1\right)$$

Since

$$\left(\frac{3}{10}, \frac{-1}{10}, 0\right) \cdot \left(\frac{7}{10}, \frac{21}{10}, 1\right) = \frac{3}{10} \cdot \frac{7}{10} - \frac{1}{10} \cdot \frac{21}{10} + 0 \cdot 1 = 0$$

we have shown in this case that the two projections are perpendicular.

EXAMPLE 2 Suppose $\bar{u} = (4,0,1,2,0)$, $\bar{v} = (2,1,-1,1,1)$. Then

$$\bar{u} \cdot \bar{v} = 4 \cdot 2 + 0 \cdot 1 + 1 \cdot (-1) + 2 \cdot 1 + 0 \cdot 1 = 9$$

$$|\bar{u}| = \sqrt{16 + 1 + 4} = \sqrt{21}$$

$$|\bar{v}| = \sqrt{4 + 1 + 1 + 1 + 1} = \sqrt{8}$$

so that

$$\bar{w} = \frac{1}{|\bar{v}|}\bar{v} = \frac{1}{\sqrt{8}}(2,1,-1,1,1)$$

is a unit vector parallel to $\bar{v}$. The projection of $\bar{u}$ onto $\bar{v}$ is then given by

$$(\bar{u} \cdot \bar{w})\bar{w} = \left(\bar{u} \cdot \frac{\bar{v}}{|\bar{v}|}\right)\frac{\bar{v}}{|\bar{v}|} = \frac{\bar{u} \cdot \bar{v}}{|\bar{v}|^2}\bar{v} = \tfrac{9}{8}(2,1,-1,1,1)$$

$$= \left(\frac{18}{8}, \frac{9}{8}, \frac{-9}{8}, \frac{9}{8}, \frac{9}{8}\right)$$

and the projection of $\bar{u}$ orthogonal to $\bar{v}$ is given by

$$\bar{u} - (\bar{u} \cdot \bar{w})\bar{w} = (4,0,1,2,0) - \left(\frac{18}{8}, \frac{9}{8}, \frac{-9}{8}, \frac{9}{8}, \frac{9}{8}\right)$$

$$= \left(\frac{14}{8}, \frac{-9}{8}, \frac{17}{8}, \frac{7}{8}, \frac{-9}{8}\right)$$

$$= \tfrac{1}{8}(14,-9,17,7,-9)$$

Since these two projections are perpendicular, we must have

$$\tfrac{9}{8}(2,1,-1,1,1) \cdot \tfrac{1}{8}(14,-9,17,7,-9) = 0$$

which can, of course, be shown by direct calculation.

EXAMPLE 3 □ *An Inner Product.*

It is possible to define for functions a "product" that satisfies all the rules **1**. Since various geometric concepts, such as orthogonality and projection, can be described in terms of the algebraic properties of the dot product we should expect to be able to use the same terminology with this function product.

Suppose $C[0,1]$ is the vector space of functions that are defined and continuous for $0 \leq x \leq 1$. (*See* Example 4, page 37.) We shall define a product for this space with properties similar to those of the dot product. This product is usually called an **inner product** and denoted by (f,g). For f and g in $C[0,1]$ we define

$$(f,g) = \int_0^1 f(x)g(x)\,dx$$

The properties of continuous functions and the integral discussed in calculus enable us to conclude that

a (f,g) is a real number
b $(f,g) = (g,f)$
c $(f, (g + h)) = (f,g) + (f,h)$
d $(f, (ag)) = a(f,g)$ for any real number a
e $(f,f) > 0$ if f is not the zero function

Except for the use of different symbols, these properties are the same as those given in statement **1**. We can therefore adopt the language of dot products for this inner product. For example, we say that f and g are *orthogonal* if

$$(f,g) = 0$$

and we define the *length* of f to be

$$|f| = (f,f)^{1/2}$$

Suppose $f(x) = \sin \pi x$. Then

9 $$|f|^2 = \int_0^1 \sin^2 \pi x\,dx = \int_0^1 \frac{1 - \cos 2\pi x}{2}\,dx = \tfrac{1}{2}x - \frac{\sin 2\pi x}{4\pi}\Big|_0^1 = \tfrac{1}{2}$$

The functions $\sin \pi x$ and $\sin 2\pi x$ are orthogonal for

$$\sin \pi x \sin 2\pi x = \tfrac{1}{2}(\cos \pi x - \cos 3\pi x)$$

so that

$$\int_0^1 \sin \pi x \sin 2\pi x\,dx = \frac{1}{2\pi}\sin \pi x - \frac{1}{6\pi}\sin 3\pi x\Big|_0^1 = 0$$

To find the *projection* of x onto $\sin \pi x$ we first find a unit vector in the direction of $\sin \pi x$. Put

$$g(x) = \sqrt{2}\sin \pi x$$

Then formula **9** gives $|g| = 1$ so that the projection of x onto $\sin \pi x$ is given by (as in formula **5**)

$$(f,g)g, \quad \text{where } f(x) = x.$$

Integration by parts can be used to show that

$$\int_0^1 x \sin \pi x \, dx = -\frac{x \cos \pi x}{\pi} + \frac{\sin \pi x}{\pi^2}\Bigg|_0^1 = \frac{1}{\pi}$$

so that

$$(f,g) = \frac{\sqrt{2}}{\pi} \qquad \text{and} \qquad (f,g)g = \frac{2}{\pi} \sin \pi x$$

We note that the orthogonality of functions has an interesting geometric interpretation. For example, consider

$$f(x) = \sin \pi x \qquad \text{and} \qquad g(x) = \sin 2\pi x$$

As Figure 9 shows, the fact that the inner product $(f,g) = 0$ is just the fact that the area above the x-axis of $\sin \pi x \sin 2\pi x$ for $0 \leq x \leq 1$ equals the area below the x-axis of this function.

Figure 9

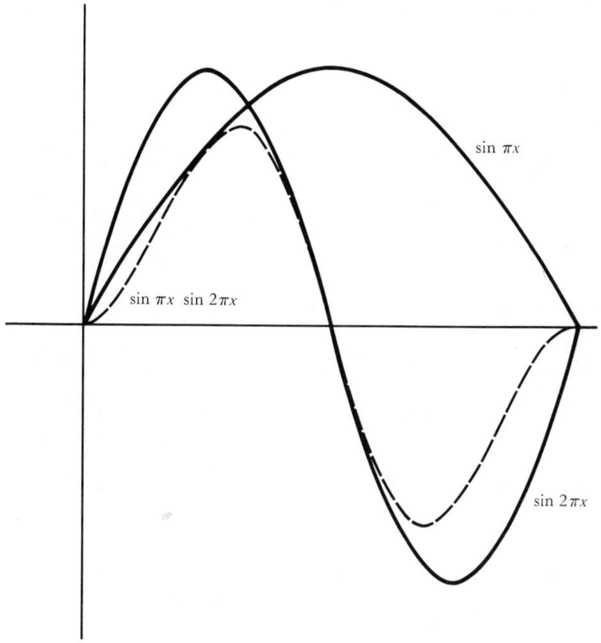

The projection of x onto $\sin \pi x$ is just *that* multiple of $\sin \pi x$ which gives the "best mean square approximation" in the sense that

10 $$\int_0^1 (x - a \sin \pi x)^2\, dx \quad \text{is } \textit{least} \text{ when} \quad a = \frac{2}{\pi}$$

For we have

$$\begin{aligned}\int_0^1 (x - a \sin \pi x)^2\, dx &= \int_0^1 \left[\left(x - \frac{2}{\pi} \sin \pi x\right) + \left(\frac{2}{\pi} - a\right) \sin \pi x\right]^2 dx \\ &= \int_0^1 \left(x - \frac{2}{\pi} \sin \pi x\right)^2 \\ &\quad + 2\left(\frac{2}{\pi} - a\right) \int_0^1 \left(x - \frac{2}{\pi} \sin \pi x\right) \sin \pi x\, dx \\ &\quad + \left(\frac{2}{\pi} - a\right)^2 \int_0^1 \sin^2 \pi x\, dx\end{aligned}$$

The first term does not depend upon a, and the third term is least when $a = \frac{2}{\pi}$; the second term is zero since $x - \frac{2}{\pi} \sin \pi x$ is orthogonal to $\sin \pi x$. Therefore, statement **10** is true.

EXAMPLE 4 □ *The Cross Product.*

Suppose

$$\bar{v}_1 = x_1\bar{i} + y_1\bar{j} + z_1\bar{k} \quad \text{and} \quad \bar{v}_2 = x_2\bar{i} + y_2\bar{j} + z_2\bar{k}$$

are vectors in R^3. These vectors are parallel if and only if they are dependent. (*See* Example 3, page 60.) They are dependent if and only if

11 $$c_1\bar{v}_1 + c_2\bar{v}_2 = \bar{0}$$

has a solution with at least one of the $c_i \neq 0$. We have

$$c_1\bar{v}_1 + c_2\bar{v}_2 = (c_1x_1 + c_2x_2)\bar{i} + (c_1y_1 + c_2y_2)\bar{j} + (c_1z_1 + c_2z_2)\bar{k}$$

so that equation **11** is the same as the system

$$\begin{aligned}c_1x_1 + c_2x_2 &= 0 \\ c_1y_1 + c_2y_2 &= 0 \\ c_1z_1 + c_2z_2 &= 0\end{aligned}$$

Using Exercise 5, page 29, we find that these equations have a nontrivial solution (c_1,c_2) if and only if

$$x_1y_2 - x_2y_1 = 0$$
$$y_1z_2 - y_2z_1 = 0$$
$$x_1z_2 - x_2z_1 = 0$$

In other words, the vectors $\bar{v}_1$ and $\bar{v}_2$ are parallel if and only if

$$x_1y_2 - x_2y_1 = y_1z_2 - y_2z_1 = x_1z_2 - x_2z_1 = 0.$$

This statement can be rewritten as

12 *The vectors* $\bar{v}_1$ *and* $\bar{v}_2$ *are nonparallel if and only if at least one of* $x_1y_2 - x_2y_1, y_1z_2 - y_2z_1, x_1z_2 - x_2z_1$ *is* not *zero.*

We shall show that if $\bar{v}_1$ and $\bar{v}_2$ are not parallel the vectors that are *perpendicular* to *both* $\bar{v}_1$ and $\bar{v}_2$ are precisely the multiples of

13 $$(y_1z_2 - y_2z_1)\bar{i} - (x_1z_2 - x_2z_1)\bar{j} + (x_1y_2 - x_2y_1)\bar{k}$$

This vector is called the **cross product** of $\bar{v}_1$ and $\bar{v}_2$ and is denoted by $\bar{v}_1 \times \bar{v}_2$.

Condition **12** shows that if $\bar{v}_1$ and $\bar{v}_2$ are not parallel, then $\bar{v}_1 \times \bar{v}_2 \neq \bar{0}$; formula **13** therefore gives us a means of finding a vector orthogonal to two given nonparallel vectors. A number of uses for this procedure are given in Appendix 1.

Suppose $\bar{u} = a\bar{i} + b\bar{j} + c\bar{k}$. Then $\bar{u}$ is orthogonal to $\bar{v}_1$ and $\bar{v}_2$ if and only if $\bar{v}_1 \cdot \bar{u} = 0$ and $\bar{v}_2 \cdot \bar{u} = 0$. In terms of coordinates these equations are

14 $$\begin{aligned} x_1a + y_1b + z_1c &= 0 \\ x_2a + y_2b + z_2c &= 0 \end{aligned}$$

Simple calculation shows that

$$a = y_1z_2 - y_2z_1$$
$$b = -(x_1z_2 - x_2z_1)$$
$$c = x_1y_2 - x_2y_1$$

is a solution to equations **14**. Thus $\bar{v}_1 \times \bar{v}_2$ is indeed orthogonal to $\bar{v}_1$ and $\bar{v}_2$.

The null space of system **14** has dimension 1, for conditions **12** guarantee that the matrix

$$\begin{bmatrix} x_1 & y_1 & z_1 \\ x_2 & y_2 & z_2 \end{bmatrix}$$

has a reduced form with two nonzero rows. (*See* Exercise 13, below.)

We have shown that if $\bar{v}_1$ and $\bar{v}_2$ are nonparallel the coordinates of $\bar{v}_1 \times \bar{v}_2$ give a nonzero solution to system **14**, and the null space of this system is one-dimensional. We conclude that indeed the vectors that are orthogonal to $\bar{v}_1$ and $\bar{v}_2$ are precisely the multiples of $\bar{v}_1 \times \bar{v}_2$.

EXERCISES

1 Given $\bar{u} = (1,1)$, $\bar{v} = (1,2)$, and $\bar{w} = (3,-1)$ find
a $\bar{u} \cdot (3\bar{v} + \bar{w})$ **b** $|\bar{u} - \bar{v}|^2$ **c** $(\bar{u} \cdot \bar{v})\bar{w}$

2 Given $\bar{u} = (1,-1,1)$, $\bar{v} = (1,1,2)$, and $\bar{w} = (1,3,-1)$ find
a $\bar{u} \cdot (3\bar{v} + \bar{w})$ **b** $|\bar{u} - \bar{v}|^2$ **c** $(\bar{u} \cdot \bar{v})\bar{w}$

3 Given $\bar{u} = (1,1,1,1)$, $\bar{v} = (1,1,-1,1)$, and $\bar{w} = (2,-1,1,3)$ find
a $\bar{u} \cdot (3\bar{v} + \bar{w})$ **b** $|\bar{u} - \bar{v}|^2$ **c** $(\bar{u} \cdot \bar{v})\bar{w}$

4 Find the lengths of each of the following.
a (1,1) **b** (−1,2,−2) **c** (3,1,0,1,−5)

5 Show that each of the following pairs of vectors are orthogonal.
a (1,1) and (1,−1) **b** (2,1,1) and (0,1,−1)
c (4,2,1,6,1) and (3,−1,0,−1,−4)

6 For each of the following vectors $\bar{u}$ find a unit vector parallel to $\bar{u}$.
a $\bar{u} = (1,2)$ **b** $\bar{u} = (1,-1,1)$
c $\bar{u} = (3,1,-1,0)$ **d** $\bar{u} = (1,1,1,1,1,1,1,1,1)$

7 For each of the following pairs $\bar{u}$ and $\bar{v}$ find the projection of $\bar{u}$ onto $\bar{v}$.
a $\bar{u} = (1,1)$, $\bar{v} = (1,2)$ **b** $\bar{u} = (1,1)$, $\bar{v} = (1,-1)$
c $\bar{u} = (1,2,1)$, $\bar{v} = (2,0,-1)$ **d** $\bar{u} = (2,1,0,0,6)$, $\bar{v} = (1,3,-1,1,0)$

8 For each of the pairs $\bar{u}$ and $\bar{v}$ of Exercise 7 find the projection of $\bar{u}$ orthogonal to $\bar{v}$.

b c

9 For each of the pairs $\bar{u}$ and $\bar{v}$ of Exercise 7, find vectors $\bar{w}_1$ and $\bar{w}_2$ such that $\bar{u} = \bar{w}_1 + \bar{w}_2$, $\bar{w}_1$ is parallel to $\bar{v}$, and $\bar{w}_2$ is orthogonal to $\bar{v}$.

b c

10 Suppose $\bar{u} \cdot \bar{v} = 0$ and $\bar{v} \neq \bar{0}$. Find the projections of $\bar{u}$ onto $\bar{v}$ and of $\bar{u}$ orthogonal to $\bar{v}$.

11 Establish the identities
a $|\bar{u} - \bar{v}|^2 + |\bar{u} + \bar{v}|^2 = 2|\bar{u}|^2 + 2|\bar{v}|^2$
b $\bar{u} \cdot \bar{v} = \frac{1}{4}|\bar{u} + \bar{v}|^2 - \frac{1}{4}|\bar{u} - \bar{v}|^2$

What does part **a** say about the diagonals of a parallelogram?

☐ **12** Use the inner product of Example 3 in each of the following.

a Find the length of $\cos \pi x$ in $C[0,1]$.

b Show that 1 and $\cos \pi x$ are orthogonal in $C[0,1]$.

c Find the projections of x onto 1 and $\cos \pi x$, and orthogonal to 1 and $\cos \pi x$ in $C[0,1]$.

d Show that $a + bx$ and $c + dx$ are orthogonal in $C[0,1]$ if and only if $ac + \frac{ad + bc}{2} + \frac{bd}{3} = 0$.

☐ **13** Show that if conditions **12** hold, the coefficient matrix of system **14** reduces to a reduced form with two nonzero rows.

☐ **14** Find a vector perpendicular to (3,1,0) and (−2,1,−1) by using the cross product.

☐ **15** Show that

$$|\bar{u} \times \bar{v}|^2 = |\bar{u}|^2|\bar{v}|^2 - (\bar{u} \cdot \bar{v})^2$$

and use this to deduce that

$$|\bar{u} \times \bar{v}| = |\bar{u}||\bar{v}| \sin \theta$$

where θ is the angle between $\bar{u}$ and $\bar{v}$.

☐ **16** **a** Show that $\bar{u} \times \bar{v} = -\bar{v} \times \bar{u}$.

b Show that $\bar{u} \times (\bar{v} \times \bar{w})$ lies in the plane of $\bar{v}$ and $\bar{w}$.

c Show that $(\bar{u} \times \bar{v}) \times \bar{w}$ lies in the plane of $\bar{u}$ and $\bar{v}$.

d Is it true that $\bar{u} \times (\bar{v} \times \bar{w}) = (\bar{u} \times \bar{v}) \times \bar{w}$?

☐ **17** The complex dot product is somewhat different. If $z = a + ib$, where a and b are real, then the *conjugate* z^* is defined by $z^* = a - ib$. Then $zz^* = a^2 + b^2$. The dot product of two vectors $\bar{u} = (x_1, x_2, \ldots, x_n)$ and $\bar{v} = (y_1, y_2, \ldots, y_n)$ in C^n is defined by $\bar{u} \cdot \bar{v} = x_1 y_1^* + x_2 y_2^* + \cdots + x_n y_n^*$

a Show that rules **1** all hold for this dot product, except that rules **1b** and **1d** are

$$\bar{u} \cdot \bar{v} = (\bar{v} \cdot \bar{u})^*$$
$$\bar{u} \cdot (a\bar{v}) = a^*(\bar{u} \cdot \bar{v})$$

b Find $\bar{u} \cdot \bar{v}$, $\bar{u} \cdot (i\bar{v})$ and $(3\bar{u} - i\bar{v}) \cdot (1 + i)\bar{u}$ for $\bar{u} = (1,i)$, $\bar{v} = (1 + i, 0)$.

c Show that $\bar{u} = (1,i)$ and $\bar{v} = (1,-i)$ are orthogonal. Find the length of $\bar{u}$ and $\bar{v}$.

d Find the projections of $\bar{u} = (i, 1 + i)$ onto and orthogonal to $\bar{v} = (1,i)$.

e If the conjugate were not used in the modified definition of $\bar{u} \cdot \bar{v}$, which of rules **1** would *not* be true?

SECTION 11 Orthogonal and Orthonormal Sets

In this section it will be seen that a set of nonzero mutually perpendicular vectors is automatically an independent set. A simple formula for calculating coordinates with respect to such a set will be given.

A collection of vectors is an **orthogonal** set if the vectors are mutually perpendicular. In other words, a set $\bar{u}_1, \bar{u}_2, \ldots, \bar{u}_k$ is orthogonal if

$$\bar{u}_i \cdot \bar{u}_j = 0, \text{ whenever } i \neq j.$$

We recall that the length of a vector $\bar{u}$ is given by $|\bar{u}| = (\bar{u} \cdot \bar{u})^{1/2}$ so that we have $|\bar{u}|^2 = \bar{u} \cdot \bar{u}$.

An orthogonal set may contain the zero vector. If an orthogonal set does not contain the zero vector, then we can normalize each vector in the set and obtain an orthogonal set in which the vectors all have length 1. For example, if $\bar{u}_1, \bar{u}_2, \ldots, \bar{u}_k$ is an orthogonal set, and none of the $\bar{u}_i$ are zero, we can then put

$$\bar{v}_1 = \frac{1}{|\bar{u}_1|}\bar{u}_1, \qquad \bar{v}_2 = \frac{1}{|\bar{u}_2|}\bar{u}_2, \ldots, \bar{v}_k = \frac{1}{|\bar{u}_k|}\bar{u}_k$$

The vectors $\bar{v}_1, \bar{v}_2, \ldots, \bar{v}_k$ are an orthogonal set, and furthermore each of the vectors $\bar{v}_i$ has length 1. Such a set is usually called an **orthonormal** set. In other words, a set $\bar{v}_1, \bar{v}_2, \ldots, \bar{v}_k$ is an orthonormal set if

$$\bar{v}_i \cdot \bar{v}_j = 0, \quad \text{if} \quad i \neq j, \quad \text{and} \quad \bar{v}_i \cdot \bar{v}_i = 1.$$

As we observed previously, formulas are easier to remember when given in terms of orthonormal, rather than orthogonal sets. Before discussing the basic formula of this section, we present some examples.

EXAMPLE 1 The vectors $\bar{u}_1 = (1,0)$ and $\bar{u}_2 = (0,1)$ are orthonormal, for, clearly, we have $\bar{u}_1 \cdot \bar{u}_2 = 0$ and $\bar{u}_1 \cdot \bar{u}_1 = \bar{u}_2 \cdot \bar{u}_2 = 1$.

In general, the vectors $\bar{u}_1 = (1,0,0, \ldots, 0)$, $\bar{u}_2 = (0,1,0, \ldots, 0), \ldots, \bar{u}_n = (0,0,0, \ldots, 0,1)$ are orthonormal in R^n.

EXAMPLE 2 The vectors $\bar{u}_1 = (1,1)$ and $\bar{u}_2 = (1,-1)$ are orthogonal since we have

$$\bar{u}_1 \cdot \bar{u}_2 = 1 \cdot 1 + 1 \cdot (-1) = 0$$

We have

$$|\bar{u}_1|^2 = \bar{u}_1 \cdot \bar{u}_1 = 2 \qquad |\bar{u}_2|^2 = \bar{u}_2 \cdot \bar{u}_2 = 2$$

so that if we put $\bar{v}_1 = (1/\sqrt{2})\bar{u}_1$, and $\bar{v}_2 = (1/\sqrt{2})\bar{u}_2$, $\bar{v}_1$ and $\bar{v}_2$ are then orthonormal.

EXAMPLE 3 The vectors $\bar{u}_1 = (1,1,1,1)$, $\bar{u}_2 = (1,-1,1,-1)$, and $\bar{u}_3 = (1,2,-1,-2)$ are orthogonal. The student should check that

$$\bar{u}_1 \cdot \bar{u}_2 = \bar{u}_1 \cdot \bar{u}_3 = \bar{u}_2 \cdot \bar{u}_3 = 0$$

We have

$$|\bar{u}_1|^2 = \bar{u}_1 \cdot \bar{u}_1 = 4$$
$$|\bar{u}_2|^2 = \bar{u}_2 \cdot \bar{u}_2 = 4$$
$$|\bar{u}_3|^2 = \bar{u}_3 \cdot \bar{u}_3 = 10$$

so that if we put

$$\bar{v}_1 = \tfrac{1}{2}\bar{u}_1 \qquad \bar{v}_2 = \tfrac{1}{2}\bar{u}_2 \qquad \bar{v}_3 = (1/\sqrt{10})\bar{u}_3$$

the vectors $\bar{v}_1$, $\bar{v}_2$, and $\bar{v}_3$ are orthonormal.

EXAMPLE 4 □ The definitions of orthogonal and orthonormal were formulated in terms of the dot product and thus can be given for functions in $C[0,1]$ relative to the inner product (f,g). (*See* Example 3, page 83.) We shall show that the functions 1, $\cos \pi x$, $\cos 2\pi x$, . . ., $\cos n\pi x$ are orthogonal relative to this inner product.

For any integer m

$$(1, \cos m\pi x) = \int_0^1 1 \cos m\pi t \, dt = \frac{1}{m\pi} \sin m\pi t \Big|_0^1 = 0$$

and 1 is therefore orthogonal to each of the functions $\cos \pi x$, $\cos 2\pi x$, . . ., $\cos n\pi x$. To show that these functions are orthogonal to each other we use the formula

1 $$\cos m\pi x \cos k\pi x = \tfrac{1}{2}[\cos (m+k)\pi x + \cos (m-k)\pi x]$$

It follows that if $m \neq k$

$$\begin{aligned}(\cos m\pi x, \cos k\pi x) &= \int_0^1 \cos m\pi t \cos k\pi t \, dt \\ &= \frac{1}{2}\int_0^1 (\cos (m+k)\pi t + \cos (m-k)\pi t) \, dt \\ &= \frac{1}{2}\left(\frac{\sin (m+k)\pi t}{(m+k)\pi} + \frac{\sin (m-k)\pi t}{(m-k)\pi}\right)\Bigg|_0^1 \\ &= 0\end{aligned}$$

In order to normalize this set we need to find the length of each of the functions, recalling that the length of f is $|f| = (f,f)^{1/2}$ or, in other words, $|f|^2 = (f,f)$.

Clearly, since

$$|1|^2 = \int_0^1 1\,dt = 1$$

the constant function 1 has length 1. For the function $\cos m\pi x$ we use formula **1** with $k = m$. We have

$$(\cos m\pi x, \cos m\pi x) = \int_0^1 \cos^2 m\pi t\,dt = \frac{1}{2}\int_0^1 (\cos 2m\pi t + 1)\,dt$$

$$= \frac{1}{2}\left(\frac{\sin 2m\pi t}{2m\pi} + t\right)\Bigg|_0^1 = \tfrac{1}{2}$$

so that the length of $\cos m\pi x$ is $1/\sqrt{2}$.

Thus, the functions $1,\ \sqrt{2}\cos \pi x,\ \sqrt{2}\cos 2\pi x, \ldots, \sqrt{2}\cos n\pi x$ are orthonormal.

DISCUSSION The next result shows that an orthonormal set is independent and provides a formula for calculation of coordinates with respect to an orthonormal basis. Formula **5** below gives the analogous result for orthogonal sets.

2 *If* $\bar{v}_1, \bar{v}_2, \ldots, \bar{v}_k$ *is an orthonormal set and* $\bar{u} = c_1\bar{v}_1 + c_2\bar{v}_2 + \cdots + c_k\bar{v}_k$ *then* $c_1 = \bar{u}\cdot\bar{v}_1,\ c_2 = \bar{u}\cdot\bar{v}_2, \ldots, c_k = \bar{u}\cdot\bar{v}_k$.

We shall give the proof of this statement only for the case $k = 2$. Suppose $\bar{v}_1$ and $\bar{v}_2$ are orthonormal and

$$\bar{u} = c_1\bar{v}_1 + c_2\bar{v}_2$$

We take the dot product of both sides with $\bar{v}_1$ and perform some elementary manipulations:

$$\bar{u}\cdot\bar{v}_1 = (c_1\bar{v}_1 + c_2\bar{v}_2)\cdot\bar{v}_1 = c_1(\bar{v}_1\cdot\bar{v}_1) + c_2(\bar{v}_2\cdot\bar{v}_1)$$

By assumption, $\bar{v}_1$ and $\bar{v}_2$ are orthonormal, and we can therefore substitute the relations $\bar{v}_1\cdot\bar{v}_2 = 0$ and $\bar{v}_1\cdot\bar{v}_1 = 1$ to obtain $c_1 = \bar{u}\cdot\bar{v}_1$.

A similar argument, using $\bar{v}_2$, shows that $c_2 = \bar{u}\cdot\bar{v}_2$.

We recall that if $|\bar{v}| = 1$ then the projection of $\bar{u}$ onto $\bar{v}$ is (*see* formula **5**, page 80) $(\bar{u}\cdot\bar{v})\bar{v}$; therefore, formula **2** gives us

3 *A vector* $\bar{u}$ *is a linear combination of the orthonormal vectors* $\bar{v}_1, \bar{v}_2, \ldots, \bar{v}_k$ *if and only if* $\bar{u}$ *is the sum of its projections onto each of the* $\bar{v}_i$.

We can restate formula **2** for orthogonal sets $\bar{u}_1,\bar{u}_2,\ldots,\bar{u}_k$ where each $\bar{u}_i \neq 0$, as follows: if

$$\bar{u} = c_1\bar{u}_1 + c_2\bar{u}_2 + \cdots + c_k\bar{u}_k$$

we can substitute, using

4 $$\bar{v}_i = (1/|\bar{u}_i|)\bar{u}_i \qquad i = 1,2,\ldots,k$$

and obtain

$$\bar{u} = (c_1|\bar{u}_1|)\bar{v}_1 + (c_2|\bar{u}_2|)\bar{v}_2 + \cdots + (c_k|\bar{u}_k|)\bar{v}_k$$

Since the vectors $\bar{v}_1,\bar{v}_2,\ldots,\bar{v}_k$ are orthonormal, we can apply formula **2** to obtain

$$c_1|\bar{u}_1| = \bar{u}\cdot\bar{v}_1,\ c_2|\bar{u}_2| = \bar{u}\cdot\bar{v}_2,\ \ldots,\ c_k|\bar{u}_k| = \bar{u}\cdot\bar{v}_k$$

We can now substitute formulas **4** in these relations and rewrite to obtain

5 $$c_1 = \frac{\bar{u}\cdot\bar{u}_1}{\bar{u}_1\cdot\bar{u}_1},\ c_2 = \frac{\bar{u}\cdot\bar{u}_2}{\bar{u}_2\cdot\bar{u}_2},\ \ldots,\ c_k = \frac{\bar{u}\cdot\bar{u}_k}{\bar{u}_k\cdot\bar{u}_k}$$

In particular, if

$$\bar{0} = c_1\bar{u}_1 + c_2\bar{u}_2 + \cdots + c_k\bar{u}_k$$

it must follow that $c_1 = 0,\ c_2 = 0,\ \ldots,\ c_k = 0$. We know, therefore, that

6 *An orthonormal set (or an orthogonal set of nonzero vectors) is independent.*

EXAMPLE 5 The standard basis for R^n is an orthonormal basis for R^n. For example, $\bar{v}_1 = (1,0,0)$, $\bar{v}_2 = (0,1,0)$, and $\bar{v}_3 = (0,0,1)$ are an orthonormal basis for R^3. In this case, formula **2** has a simple form, for we have

$$(x,y,z) = x\bar{v}_1 + y\bar{v}_2 + z\bar{v}_3$$

In other words

$$(x,y,z)\cdot\bar{v}_1 = x, \quad (x,y,z)\cdot\bar{v}_2 = y, \quad (x,y,z)\cdot\bar{v}_3 = z$$

EXAMPLE 6 The vectors $\bar{u}_1 = (1,1)$ and $\bar{u}_2 = (1,-1)$ are orthogonal, and thus statement **6** implies that they are independent. Since R^2 has dimension two we see from Theorem 10 that $\bar{u}_1$ and $\bar{u}_2$ are a basis for R^2. To express $\bar{u} = (x,y)$ in terms of this basis we can either use formula **5** directly or use the process by which we deduced formula **5** from formula **2**. It is often easier to remember formula **2** and to reconstruct this process.

We put

$$\bar{v}_1 = \frac{1}{\sqrt{2}}(1,1) \qquad \bar{v}_2 = \frac{1}{\sqrt{2}}(1,-1)$$

so that $\bar{v}_1$ and $\bar{v}_2$ are an orthonormal basis for R^2. For $\bar{u} = (x,y)$ we have

$$\bar{u}\cdot\bar{v}_1 = \frac{x+y}{\sqrt{2}} \qquad \bar{u}\cdot\bar{v}_2 = \frac{x-y}{\sqrt{2}}$$

and

$$(\bar{u}\cdot\bar{v}_1)\bar{v}_1 = \left[\frac{x+y}{\sqrt{2}}\right]\left[\frac{1}{\sqrt{2}}\right](1,1) = \frac{x+y}{2}\,\bar{u}_1$$

$$(\bar{u}\cdot\bar{v}_2)\bar{v}_2 = \left[\frac{x-y}{\sqrt{2}}\right]\left[\frac{1}{\sqrt{2}}\right](1,-1) = \frac{x-y}{2}\,\bar{u}_2$$

so that

$$\bar{u} = \frac{x+y}{2}\,\bar{u}_1 + \frac{x-y}{2}\,\bar{u}_2$$

EXAMPLE 7 We shall show that $\bar{u} = (1,2,3,4)$ is *not* a linear combination of the orthogonal vectors

$$\bar{u}_1 = (1,1,1,1) \qquad \bar{u}_2 = (1,-1,1,-1) \qquad \bar{u}_3 = (1,2,-1,-2)$$

by showing that $\bar{u}$ is not the sum of its projections onto $\bar{u}_1$, $\bar{u}_2$, and $\bar{u}_3$. Put

$$\bar{v}_1 = \tfrac{1}{2}\bar{u}_1 \qquad \bar{v}_2 = \tfrac{1}{2}\bar{u}_2 \qquad \bar{v}_3 = \left(\frac{1}{\sqrt{10}}\right)\bar{u}_3$$

so that the projections of $\bar{u}$ onto $\bar{u}_1$, $\bar{u}_2$, and $\bar{u}_3$ are, respectively,

$$(\bar{u}\cdot\bar{v}_1)\bar{v}_1 = \left(\frac{10}{2}\right)\left(\frac{1}{2}\right)\bar{u}_1 = \frac{5}{2}(1,1,1,1)$$

$$(\bar{u}\cdot\bar{v}_2)\bar{v}_2 = \left(\frac{-2}{2}\right)\left(\frac{1}{2}\right)\bar{u}_2 = \frac{-1}{2}(1,-1,1,-1)$$

$$(\bar{u}\cdot\bar{v}_3)\bar{v}_3 = \left(\frac{-6}{\sqrt{10}}\right)\left(\frac{1}{\sqrt{10}}\right)\bar{u}_3 = \frac{-3}{5}(1,2,-1,-2)$$

The sum of these projections is

$$\bar{v} = \tfrac{1}{5}(7,9,13,21)$$

which is not equal to ū, so that from result 3, ū is *not* a linear combination of $\bar{u}_1$, $\bar{u}_2$, and $\bar{u}_3$.

Put

$$\bar{w} = \bar{u} - \bar{v} = \tfrac{1}{5}(-2,1,2,-1)$$

By the usual computations we have

$$\bar{w} \cdot \bar{u}_1 = \bar{w} \cdot \bar{u}_2 = \bar{w} \cdot \bar{u}_3 = 0$$

The set $\bar{u}_1$, $\bar{u}_2$, $\bar{u}_3$, and $\bar{w}$ therefore is an orthogonal set. In general, if we subtract from ū its projections onto each member of an orthogonal set, we obtain a vector which is orthogonal to each member of the orthogonal set. This observation is the key to a general method of obtaining an orthonormal basis from any given basis. The method is called the Gram-Schmidt process and is outlined in Exercise 9.

EXERCISES

1 Show that each of the following sets of vectors is orthogonal.
   a (1,2), (−2,1)
   b (1,0,1), (1,1,−1), (−1,2,1)
   c (1,0,1,0), (1,1,−1,0), (1,−2,−1,1)

2c 2 Normalize each of the sets in Exercise 1 to obtain an orthonormal set.

3 Express (3,2,1) as a linear combination of (1,0,1), (1,1,−1), and (−1,2,1) by using statement 3.

4 Show that (1,4,1) is *not* a linear combination of (1,0,1) and (1,1,−1) by using statement 3. (*See* Example 7.)

5 By subtracting from (1,4,1) its projections onto (1,0,1) and (1,1,−1) find a nonzero vector which is orthogonal to (1,0,1) and (1,1,−1).

□ 6 Show that the functions sin πx, sin $2\pi x$, . . ., sin $n\pi x$ are orthogonal in $C[0,1]$. By normalizing obtain an orthonormal set of functions.

7 Find an orthogonal basis for R^4 that includes the vectors (1,0,1,0), (1,1,−1,0), and (1,−2,−1,1). (Hint: Find a vector ū that is not a linear combination of the given vectors and subtract from ū its projections onto the given vectors.)

8 Find an orthogonal basis for R^3 which includes $\bar{u}_1 = (1,2,3)$. (Hint: Select a vector which is not a multiple of $\bar{u}_1$ and let $\bar{u}_2$ be its projection orthogonal to $\bar{u}_1$. Construct a third vector $\bar{u}_3$ by proceeding as in Exercise 7.)

□ **9** Suppose $\overline{w}_1$, $\overline{w}_2$, and $\overline{w}_3$ are a basis for R^3. Find an orthogonal basis $\overline{u}_1$, $\overline{u}_2$, and $\overline{u}_3$ such that

a $\overline{w}_1$ is a multiple of $\overline{u}_1$.

b $\overline{w}_2$ is a linear combination of $\overline{u}_1$ and $\overline{u}_2$.

(Hint: Put $\overline{u}_1 = \overline{w}_1$, $\overline{u}_2 =$ projection of $\overline{w}_2$ orthogonal to $\overline{u}_1$, and $\overline{u}_3 = \overline{w}_3$ minus the projections of $\overline{w}_3$ onto $\overline{u}_1$ and $\overline{u}_2$. This process is called the *Gram-Schmidt process*.)

c Apply this process to the basis (1,1,1), (1,2,1), and (1,1,2).

d Apply this process to the functions 1, x, and x^2 to find three orthogonal polynomials of degree not exceeding 2, using the inner product of Example 4.

□ **10** Using the complex dot product of Exercise 17 of the previous section:

a Show that $(1,i,1)$, $(i,0,-i)$, and $(i,2,i)$ are orthogonal.

b Normalize the vectors of part **a** to obtain an orthonormal set of vectors.

c Express $(1,1,i)$ as a linear combination of the vectors of part **a** by using formula **2**.

CHAPTER 2

TRANSFORMATIONS AND MATRICES

The process of multiplying a column matrix by a matrix was introduced in Section 5 of Chapter 1. We then saw in Theorem 3 that this process satisfied the laws

$$A(\bar{u} + \bar{v}) = A\bar{u} + A\bar{v} \quad \text{and} \quad A(a\bar{u}) = a(A\bar{u})$$

These laws were particularly useful in obtaining the theorems about the solutions to linear systems given in Chapter 1.

Our task in this chapter is to study other processes or operations on vectors that satisfy the same laws. These operations are commonly known as linear transformations or linear operations and include such familiar and important geometric operations as rotation, reflection, and projection. In addition we shall see that the basic operations of calculus, differentiation and integration, are also linear operations satisfying these same laws. These examples will be discussed in Section 1. We shall then show in Section 2 that for the coordinate spaces R^n, every linear transformation is given by the process of multiplying by a matrix. We can then easily derive algebraic formulas for many geometric operations.

We introduce the concepts of sum, scalar multiple, and product of linear transformations in Sections 3 and 4. These concepts will enable us to combine various linear operations to obtain new linear operations, as well as to describe relationships among these processes. They will also lead to an analogous "arithmetic" for matrices, which will be studied further in Section 5. The concept of inverse will be discussed in Sections 6, 7, and 8, providing a certain kind of "division" process for reversing the effect of a transformation. The determinant and its relationship to matrix products and inverses will be discussed in Section 9.

SECTION 1 Linear Transformations

An operation T which is defined for all vectors $\bar{u}$ in a vector space V, resulting in vectors $T\bar{u}$ in a vector space W, is called a **transformation** from V into W. If this operation satisfies the conditions

1 $$T(\bar{u} + \bar{v}) = T\bar{u} + T\bar{v} \quad \text{and} \quad T(a\bar{u}) = a(T\bar{u})$$

it is called a **linear transformation** or **linear operation**.

Suppose A is a matrix with m rows and n columns and that we write our vectors as column matrices. We denote the operation of "multiplying by A" by the letter T. Thus the operation T is defined for vectors $\bar{u}$ in R^n by

2 $$T\bar{u} = A\bar{u}.$$

Since $A\bar{u}$ is then a vector in R^m, we see that T is a transformation from R^n into R^m. Furthermore, T is *linear*, for Theorem 3 tells us that

$$T(\bar{u} + \bar{v}) = T\bar{u} + T\bar{v} \qquad \text{and} \qquad T(a\bar{u}) = a(T\bar{u})$$

Therefore, the operation T satisfies the conditions **1**.

This is one of the primary examples of a linear transformation, namely, the operation defined by multiplication by a matrix. We shall, in Section 2, show that every linear transformation from R^n into R^m is really just multiplication by a suitable matrix. This is, however, not always the most convenient way to describe a linear transformation. For, as the examples below show, interesting and useful operations on vectors that also satisfy conditions **1** can be defined geometrically. In addition, the important processes of differentiation and integration will be seen, in fact, to be linear transformations defined for functions.

REMARK We shall usually denote a transformation by a single letter, such as T. In this case, T is the *name* of the operation, while $T\bar{u}$ denotes the *effect* of the operation on the vector $\bar{u}$. Thus, for example, the symbol T of formula **2** is a shorthand expression for the operation "multiply a column matrix by the matrix A," while $T\bar{u}$ is the *vector* obtained by multiplying $\bar{u}$ by A.

This is really a new way to think of a matrix. In the previous chapter we saw how systems of equations could be solved by reducing a matrix. We also saw how we could rewrite a system as a matrix equation, resulting in a simplification of notation, as well as providing a framework for treating the concepts of independence and bases. In this chapter we shall think of a matrix as defining the operation of multiplying by that matrix. Not only does this approach lead us to consider other operations with the same properties (the properties of conditions **1**), but it will also lead us to new concepts about vectors and matrices.

To distinguish between the matrix A and the operation of multiplying by A we shall generally denote the operation by a letter other than A, such as T.

EXAMPLE 1 *Projection.*

The operation of projection discussed in Section 10 of Chapter 1 is a linear operation, for it satisfies conditions **1**. We first give a geometric discussion of this fact and then show how we can use the dot product to obtain the same conclusions.

Suppose $\overline{w}$ is a unit vector in R^2 and that P is the name of the operation of projection onto the line through $\overline{w}$. For a given pair $\bar{u}$ and $\bar{v}$, Figure 1 shows that $P(\bar{u} + \bar{v})$ can be calculated in two ways: We can first find the sum $\bar{u} + \bar{v}$ and then project this onto $\bar{w}$; or we can project $\bar{u}$ and $\bar{v}$ each onto $\bar{w}$ and form the sum of these projections. In other words,

$$P(\bar{u} + \bar{v}) = P\bar{u} + P\bar{v}$$

We can also calculate $P(a\bar{u})$ in two ways: We can first multiply $\bar{u}$ by a and then project; or we can project $\bar{u}$ and then multiply by a, as shown in Figure 2. In other words, $P(a\bar{u}) = aP\bar{u}$.

Figure 1 $P(\bar{u} + \bar{v}) = P\bar{u} + P\bar{v}$.

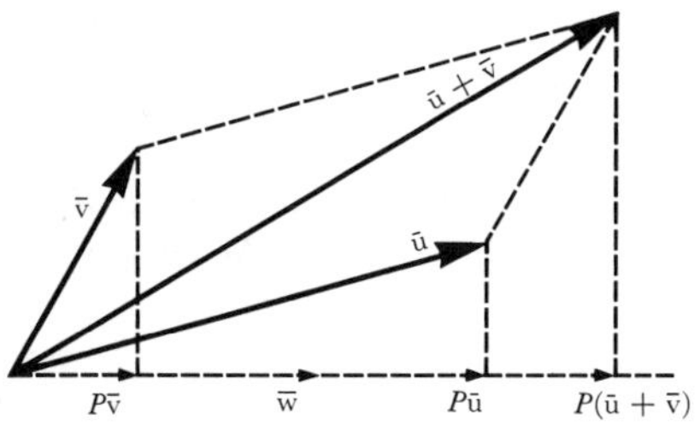

Figure 2 $P(a\bar{u}) = aP(\bar{u})$.

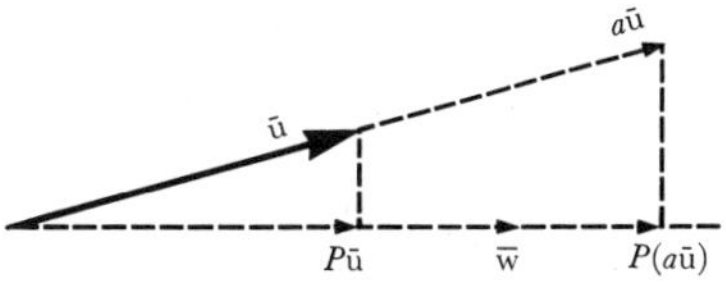

We have shown, therefore, that P does satisfy the linearity conditions **1**. Since the operation P is defined for vectors $\bar{u}$ in R^2 and results in vectors $P\bar{u}$ in R^2, we can conclude that the projection P is a *linear transformation* from R^2 into R^2. The same conclusion can be reached by using the dot product properties given in Section 10 of Chapter 1. We recall (*see* formula 5, page 80) that $P\bar{u} = (\bar{u} \cdot \bar{w})\bar{w}$. Since $(\bar{u} + \bar{v}) \cdot \bar{w} = \bar{u} \cdot \bar{w} + \bar{v} \cdot \bar{w}$, it follows that

$$\begin{aligned} P(\bar{u} + \bar{v}) &= [(\bar{u} + \bar{v}) \cdot \bar{w}]\bar{w} = (\bar{u} \cdot \bar{w} + \bar{v} \cdot \bar{w})\bar{w} \\ &= (\bar{u} \cdot \bar{w})\bar{w} + (\bar{v} \cdot \bar{w})\bar{w} \\ &= P\bar{u} + P\bar{v} \end{aligned}$$

We also have $(a\bar{u} \cdot \bar{w}) = a(\bar{u} \cdot \bar{w})$; therefore

$$P(a\bar{u}) = (a\bar{u} \cdot \bar{w})\bar{w} = a(\bar{u} \cdot \bar{w})\bar{w} = a(P\bar{u})$$

Thus the fact that the projection P satisfies the linearity conditions **1** is a consequence of properties of the dot product.

EXAMPLE 2 *Transformations of Coordinates.*

Transformations can also be defined by describing their effect on coordinates. For example, suppose T is the operation defined by the formula

$$T(x,y) = (-x,y)$$

In other words, the first coordinate of $T\bar{u}$ is just the negative of the first coordinate of $\bar{u}$, while the second coordinate of $T\bar{u}$ is the second coordinate of $\bar{u}$. This formula can be rewritten in column form as

$$T\begin{bmatrix} x \\ y \end{bmatrix} = \begin{bmatrix} -x \\ y \end{bmatrix}$$

Since

$$\begin{bmatrix} -x \\ y \end{bmatrix} = \begin{bmatrix} -1 & 0 \\ 0 & 1 \end{bmatrix} \begin{bmatrix} x \\ y \end{bmatrix}$$

we see that the transformation T is given by

$$T\bar{u} = A\bar{u} \qquad \text{where} \qquad A = \begin{bmatrix} -1 & 0 \\ 0 & 1 \end{bmatrix}$$

In other words, T is just the operation of multiplication by A; hence T is a linear transformation from R^2 into R^2. As we can see from Figure 3,

Figure 3

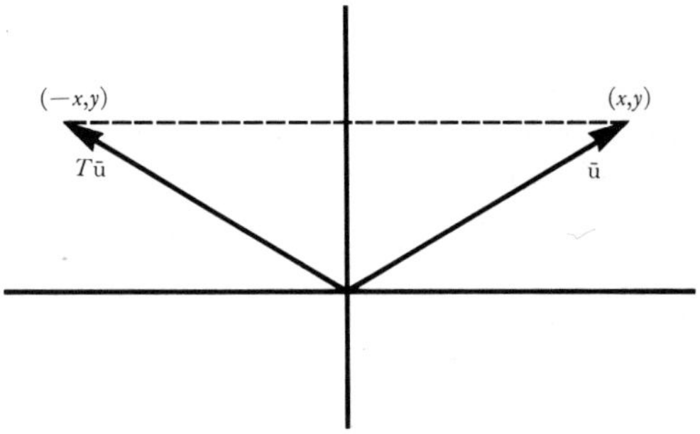

T can also be described as the operation which sends a vector into its reflection in the y-axis.

EXAMPLE 3 *Reflection.*

Suppose $\overline{w}$ is a unit vector in R^2. The operation T for vectors $\bar{u}$ in R^2 is defined as follows:

$T\bar{u}$ is the vector such that $\frac{1}{2}(T\bar{u} + \bar{u})$ is the projection of $\bar{u}$ onto $\overline{w}$.

As can be seen in Figure 4, $T\bar{u}$ is just the *reflection* of $\bar{u}$ in the line through $\overline{w}$. We therefore have $T\bar{u} = 2P\bar{u} - \bar{u}$. Arguments similar to those used in Example 1 can be given to show that T is linear, that is, that $T(\bar{u} + \bar{v})$

can be calculated by first calculating $\bar{u} + \bar{v}$ and reflecting; or it can be calculated by reflecting $\bar{u}$, reflecting $\bar{v}$, and then adding. Similar arguments show that $T(a\bar{u})$ can also be calculated in two ways: by first calculating $a\bar{u}$ and then reflecting, or by reflecting $\bar{u}$ and then multiplying by a.

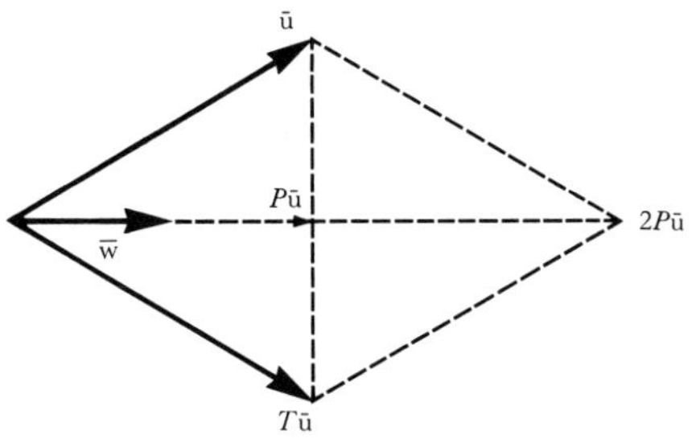

Figure 4 $\frac{1}{2}(T\bar{u} + \bar{u}) = P\bar{u}$.

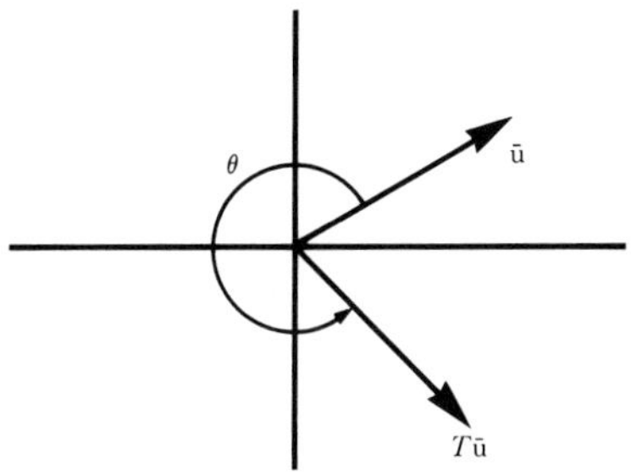

Figure 5 *The operation of counterclockwise rotation through the angle θ.*

EXAMPLE 4 *Rotation.*

The operation of rotation is a linear transformation. For example, suppose θ is a fixed number and that we represent vectors in R^2 as arrows issuing from the origin in the usual fashion. Let T denote the operation of counterclockwise rotation through the angle θ. In other words, $T\bar{u}$ is the arrow obtained by rotating $\bar{u}$ around the origin, as shown in Figure 5.

This operation T is a linear transformation, as indicated in Figs. 6a and 6b.

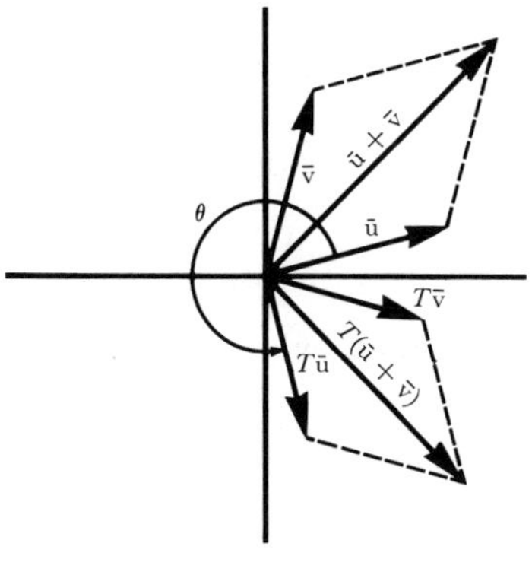

Figure 6a $T(\bar{u} + \bar{v}) = T\bar{u} + T\bar{v}$. *Therefore, the rotation of the sum is the sum of the rotations.*

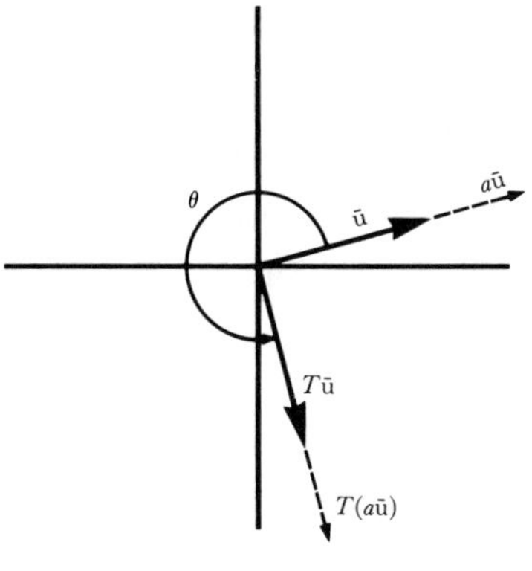

Figure 6b $T(a\bar{u}) = aT\bar{u}$. *Therefore, the multiple of a rotation is the rotation of the multiple.*

Figure 7 $T(1,0) = (\cos\theta, \sin\theta)$
$T(0,1) = (\cos(\theta + \pi/2), \sin(\theta + \pi/2))$.

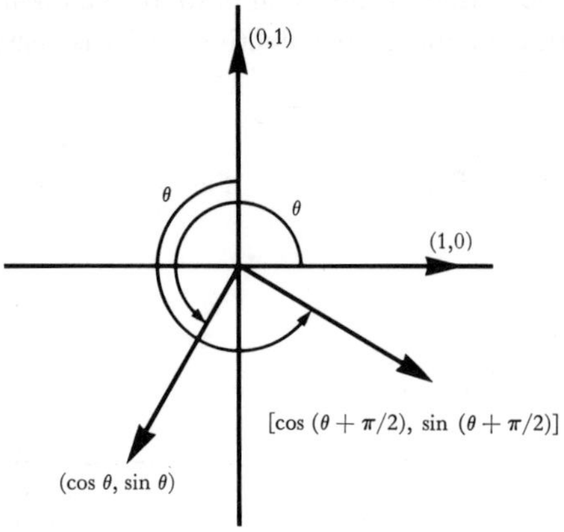

Figure 7 shows that

$$T\vec{i} = \cos\theta\,\vec{i} + \sin\theta\,\vec{j}$$
$$T\vec{j} = \cos(\theta + \pi/2)\vec{i} + \sin(\theta + \pi/2)\vec{j}$$

where $\vec{i}$ represents (1,0) and $\vec{j}$ represents (0,1). In the next section we shall give a general formula for calculating $T(x,y)$.

EXAMPLE 5 *Differentiation and Integration.*

Suppose $C[0,1]$ is the vector space of all functions f which are defined and continuous for $0 \leq x \leq 1$. (*See* Example 4, page 37.) Suppose further that M is the subspace of $C[0,1]$ consisting of the functions f such that both f and its derivative f' are defined and continuous for $0 \leq x \leq 1$.

In calculus it is shown that

$$(f + g)' = f' + g' \qquad \text{and} \qquad (af)' = af'$$

Thus, if we let D denote the differentiation operation, we have for f and g in M:

$$D(f + g) = Df + Dg \qquad \text{and} \qquad D(af) = aDf$$

In other words, the differentiation operator D is a linear transformation from M into $C[0,1]$.

Suppose T is the integration operation defined by

$$Tf(x) = \int_0^x f(t)\,dt, \qquad 0 \leq x \leq 1$$

For example,

$$T(\sin x) = 1 - \cos x \qquad \text{since} \int_0^x \sin t \, dt = -\cos t \Big|_0^x = 1 - \cos x$$

From calculus, again, we know that

$$\int_0^x (f(t) + g(t)) \, dt = \int_0^x f(t) \, dt + \int_0^x g(t) \, dt,$$

and

$$\int_0^x af(t) \, dt = a \int_0^x f(t) \, dt$$

or, in other words, that

$$T(f + g) = Tf + Tg \qquad \text{and} \qquad T(af) = aTf$$

If f is continuous, then it also follows that for each x

$$\int_0^x f(t) \, dt \text{ is continuous}$$

These observations can be summarized by stating that the integral operator T is a linear transformation from $C[0,1]$ into $C[0,1]$.

EXAMPLE 6 *Linear Differential Operators.*

Suppose $a_1, a_2, \ldots, a_n$ are numbers and f is a function such that $f, f', f'', f''', \ldots, f^{(n)}$ are all defined and continuous for $0 \leq x \leq 1$. We define the *linear differential operator* L by

$$Lf = f^{(n)} + a_n f^{(n-1)} + \cdots + a_2 f' + a_1 f$$

An extension of the arguments used in Example 5 can be given to establish that

3
$$L(f + g) = Lf + Lg$$
$$L(af) = aLf$$

Therefore L is a *linear transformation* from the vector space of n times continuously differentiable functions into $C[0,1]$. As the student will see in Chapter 4 this fact allows us to use many of the concepts of linear algebra to discuss linear differential equations, which are equations of the form $Lf = g$. For example, just as Theorem 3 was used to obtain Theorem 4, properties **3** can be used to show that

4 *The null space of L, that is, the set of all functions f such that $Lf = 0$ is a subspace of $C[0,1]$.*

We can also use properties 3, just as we used Theorem 3 to prove Theorem 6, to show that

5 *If g is a given function and if $Lf_1 = g$, then every solution to the equation $Lf = g$ is of the form $f_1 + h$, where h is in the null space of L.*

We shall also show that the null space of L has dimension n; that is, there are n independent functions

$$h_1, h_2, \ldots, h_n$$

such that the null space of L consists of all functions of the form

$$c_1h_1 + c_2h_2 + \cdots + c_nh_n$$

where $c_1, c_2, \ldots, c_n$, are arbitrary constants.

EXERCISES

1 Suppose P is projection onto the vector $\bar{w} = \frac{1}{3}(1,2,2)$. For $\bar{u} = (1,3,-1)$, $\bar{v} = (0,-1,2)$ calculate
a $P\bar{u}$ **b** $P\bar{v}$ **c** $P(\bar{u} + \bar{v})$ **d** $P(4\bar{u})$ **e** $4P\bar{u}$

2 For the transformation T defined by $T(x,y) = (-x,y)$ calculate
a $T(3,2)$ **b** $T(-1,-4)$
c $T((3,2) + (-1,-4))$ **d** $T(3,2) + T(-1,-4)$

3 Suppose T and P are as in Example 3, so that $P\bar{u} = (\bar{u} \cdot \bar{w})\bar{w}$, $T\bar{u} = 2P\bar{u} - \bar{u}$. Show that $T(\bar{u} + \bar{v}) = T\bar{u} + T\bar{v}$ and $T(a\bar{u}) = aT(\bar{u})$. Illustrate these facts with a figure.

4 Suppose T is reflection in the line through $\bar{w} = \frac{1}{3}(1,-2,2)$ and that P is projection onto $\bar{w}$. For $\bar{u} = (2,-3,1)$, $\bar{v} = (2,-1,-1)$, calculate
a $P\bar{u}$ **b** $P\bar{v}$ **c** $T\bar{u}$ **d** $T\bar{v}$
Verify that $T(\bar{u} + \bar{v}) = T\bar{u} + T\bar{v}$.

5 Suppose T is a counterclockwise rotation in R^2 through the angle $\pi/4$. Draw figures similar to Figures 6a and 6b to indicate that T is linear. Calculate $T(1,0)$, $T(0,1)$, and $T(1,1)$.

6 Give a geometric description of each of the following transformations.
a $T(x,y) = (y,x)$ **b** $T(x,y,z) = (0,y,z)$
c $T(x,y) = (x,-y)$ **d** $T(x,y,z,w) = (x,0,0,0)$

7 Suppose P is projection orthogonal to the unit vector $\bar{w}$. Find a formula for $P\bar{u}$ and use this to show that P is linear.

8 Show that if T is linear, then $T(a\bar{u} + b\bar{v}) = aT\bar{u} + bT\bar{v}$.

9 Suppose $T(x,y) = (|x|,y)$. Calculate $T(1,2)$ and $T(-1,2)$. Does $T(1,2) = -T(-1,-2)$? Is T linear?

10 Suppose T is a linear transformation. Show that $T\bar{0} = \bar{0}$. (Hint: $T\bar{0} = T(a\bar{0})$ for any scalar a.)

11 For $Df = f'$ calculate
a $D(\sin x)$ **b** $D(e^x)$ **c** $D(e^x + \sin x)$ **d** $D(ae^x + b \sin x)$

12 For T, the integration operator defined in Example 5, calculate
a $T(\cos x)$ **b** $T(x^2)$ **c** $T(e^x)$ **d** $T(x^2 + 3\cos x + 2e^x)$

13 **a** Find a basis for the null space of the differential operator $Lf = f'''$.
b Describe the solutions to $Lf = \sin x$, where L is as in part **a**.

14 Consider the operator $Lf = f'' - f$. Show that e^x and e^{-x} are in the null space of L. Show that these two functions are independent. (Hence, from more advanced techniques, they form a basis for the null space of L.) Show that $Lx = -x$ and describe the solutions to $Lf = x$.

15 Proceed as in Exercise 14 for the operator $Lf = f'' + f$ and the functions $\sin x$, $\cos x$. Describe also the solutions to $Lf = 2 + x^2$. (Hint: $L(x^2) = 2 + x^2$.)

16 Suppose g is in $C[0,1]$ and that Tf is defined to be that function whose value at x is $Tf(x) = f(x)g(x)$. Show that T is a linear transformation from $C[0,1]$ into $C[0,1]$ and find the null space of T. (T is called a *multiplication operator*.)

□ 17 The discussion of this section also extends to complex vector spaces. For the transformation T defined by

$$T(x,y) = (ix + (2 + i)y, -3ix)$$

verify that $T[(2, i) + i(3, 1 - i)] = T(2, i) + iT(3, 1 - i)$. Then verify that T is a linear transformation from C^2 into C^2.

SECTION 2 The Matrix of a Linear Transformation

We noted in the previous section that the transformation T defined by $T\bar{u} = A\bar{u}$, where A has m rows and n columns, is a linear transformation from R^n into R^m. In this section we establish the converse of this result, that every linear transformation from R^n into R^m is just multiplication by a suitable matrix. This will give us a useful tool for calculating the effect of a linear transformation, enabling us, for example, to obtain formulas for rotations, reflections, and projections.

In the following theorem we assume that vectors are expressed as column matrices.

THEOREM 12 If T is a linear transformation from R^n into R^m, there is a *unique* matrix A, with m rows and n columns, such that $T\bar{u} = A\bar{u}$, for all $\bar{u}$ in R^n.

The matrix A is called the **matrix** of T. We shall prove this result for the case when $n = m = 2$, and, in the process, a method for calculating A will be shown.

Suppose T is a linear transformation from R^2 into R^2, so that for each $\bar{u}$ in R^2, $T\bar{u}$ is a vector in R^2 and

1 $$T(\bar{u} + \bar{v}) = T\bar{u} + T\bar{v} \qquad T(a\bar{u}) = aT\bar{u}$$

We have

$$\begin{bmatrix} x \\ y \end{bmatrix} = x\begin{bmatrix} 1 \\ 0 \end{bmatrix} + y\begin{bmatrix} 0 \\ 1 \end{bmatrix}, \qquad \text{so that } T\begin{bmatrix} x \\ y \end{bmatrix} = T\left\{x\begin{bmatrix} 1 \\ 0 \end{bmatrix} + y\begin{bmatrix} 0 \\ 1 \end{bmatrix}\right\}$$

We now apply the first part and then the second part of conditions **1** to obtain

$$T\left\{x\begin{bmatrix} 1 \\ 0 \end{bmatrix} + y\begin{bmatrix} 0 \\ 1 \end{bmatrix}\right\} = T\left\{x\begin{bmatrix} 1 \\ 0 \end{bmatrix}\right\} + T\left\{y\begin{bmatrix} 0 \\ 1 \end{bmatrix}\right\}$$
$$= xT\begin{bmatrix} 1 \\ 0 \end{bmatrix} + yT\begin{bmatrix} 0 \\ 1 \end{bmatrix}$$

This shows that

2 $$T\begin{bmatrix} x \\ y \end{bmatrix} = xT\begin{bmatrix} 1 \\ 0 \end{bmatrix} + yT\begin{bmatrix} 0 \\ 1 \end{bmatrix}$$

We now put

3 $$T\begin{bmatrix} 1 \\ 0 \end{bmatrix} = \begin{bmatrix} A_{11} \\ A_{21} \end{bmatrix}, \qquad T\begin{bmatrix} 0 \\ 1 \end{bmatrix} = \begin{bmatrix} A_{12} \\ A_{22} \end{bmatrix}, \qquad A = \begin{bmatrix} A_{11} & A_{12} \\ A_{21} & A_{22} \end{bmatrix}$$

so that

$$A\begin{bmatrix} x \\ y \end{bmatrix} = \begin{bmatrix} A_{11}x + A_{12}y \\ A_{21}x + A_{22}y \end{bmatrix} = x\begin{bmatrix} A_{11} \\ A_{21} \end{bmatrix} + y\begin{bmatrix} A_{12} \\ A_{22} \end{bmatrix}$$

Comparing this result with the right-hand side of equation **2** we see that for all pairs (x,y)

4 $$T\begin{bmatrix} x \\ y \end{bmatrix} = A\begin{bmatrix} x \\ y \end{bmatrix}$$

We have therefore shown that every linear operation from R^2 into R^2 can, in fact, be expressed as multiplication by a suitable matrix.

To complete the proof of Theorem 12 we need to show that formula **4** uniquely determines A; in other words, if B is a matrix such that

$$T\begin{bmatrix} x \\ y \end{bmatrix} = B\begin{bmatrix} x \\ y \end{bmatrix} \qquad \text{then we must have } B = A$$

This is a consequence of the fact that

$$B\begin{bmatrix}1\\0\end{bmatrix} \quad \text{and} \quad B\begin{bmatrix}0\\1\end{bmatrix}$$

are the first and second columns of B.

From formulas 2 we conclude that A and B have the same columns and thus are identical. The proof of Theorem 12 in the case when $m = n = 2$ is thus complete. We have also shown that

5 *The columns of the matrix of T are* $T\begin{bmatrix}1\\0\end{bmatrix}$ *and* $T\begin{bmatrix}0\\1\end{bmatrix}$

In the general case, similar arguments can be used to show that the columns of the matrix of T are

$$T\begin{bmatrix}1\\0\\0\\\vdots\\0\end{bmatrix}, \quad T\begin{bmatrix}0\\1\\0\\\vdots\\0\end{bmatrix}, \ldots, T\begin{bmatrix}0\\0\\0\\\vdots\\1\end{bmatrix}$$

REMARK The above theorem establishes a one-to-one correspondence between linear operations on coordinate spaces and matrices whereby each such operation can be represented as the operation of multiplication by a matrix. Therefore, each statement about linear operations on coordinate spaces can be translated into a statement about matrices, and each statement about matrices can be translated into a statement about linear operations. We shall make full use of this identification in this chapter and in Chapter 3. In some cases we shall find it easier to discuss linear operations first, and then translate our ideas into matrix form; in other cases we will find it convenient to reverse this procedure.

Note that the construction of the matrix of T was given in terms of the effect of T upon the standard basis vectors. In the next chapter, a similar construction in terms of the effect of T upon other bases will be discussed.

EXAMPLE 1 Suppose $\bar{v} = \frac{1}{3}(1,2,2)$ and $P\bar{u}$ is the projection of $\bar{u}$ onto $\bar{v}$. Then $P\bar{u} = (\bar{u} \cdot \bar{v})\bar{v}$, and P is a linear transformation from R^3 into R^3. To find the matrix of P we need to calculate

$$P\begin{bmatrix}1\\0\\0\end{bmatrix} \quad P\begin{bmatrix}0\\1\\0\end{bmatrix} \quad P\begin{bmatrix}0\\0\\1\end{bmatrix}$$

We have

$$\left\{\begin{bmatrix}1\\0\\0\end{bmatrix}\cdot\bar{v}\right\}\bar{v} = \tfrac{1}{3}\cdot\tfrac{1}{3}\begin{bmatrix}1\\2\\2\end{bmatrix} = \tfrac{1}{9}\begin{bmatrix}1\\2\\2\end{bmatrix}$$

$$\left\{\begin{bmatrix}0\\1\\0\end{bmatrix}\cdot\bar{v}\right\}\bar{v} = \tfrac{2}{3}\cdot\tfrac{1}{3}\begin{bmatrix}1\\2\\2\end{bmatrix} = \tfrac{2}{9}\begin{bmatrix}1\\2\\2\end{bmatrix}$$

$$\left\{\begin{bmatrix}0\\0\\1\end{bmatrix}\cdot\bar{v}\right\}\bar{v} = \tfrac{2}{3}\cdot\tfrac{1}{3}\begin{bmatrix}1\\2\\2\end{bmatrix} = \tfrac{2}{9}\begin{bmatrix}1\\2\\2\end{bmatrix}$$

Therefore the matrix of P is

$$P_0 = \begin{bmatrix}\tfrac{1}{9} & \tfrac{2}{9} & \tfrac{2}{9}\\ \tfrac{2}{9} & \tfrac{4}{9} & \tfrac{4}{9}\\ \tfrac{2}{9} & \tfrac{4}{9} & \tfrac{4}{9}\end{bmatrix}$$

and the formula for P can be rewritten as $P\bar{u} = P_0\bar{u}$.

EXAMPLE 2 If T is defined by

$$T(x,y) = (ax + by,\ cx + dy)$$

we can rewrite both parts of this expression as column matrices:

$$T\begin{bmatrix}x\\y\end{bmatrix} = \begin{bmatrix}ax + by\\cx + dy\end{bmatrix}$$

Since the right-hand side is the same as

$$\begin{bmatrix}a & b\\c & d\end{bmatrix}\begin{bmatrix}x\\y\end{bmatrix}$$

it follows that

$$T\begin{bmatrix}x\\y\end{bmatrix} = \begin{bmatrix}a & b\\c & d\end{bmatrix}\begin{bmatrix}x\\y\end{bmatrix}$$

We conclude that T is a linear transformation from R^2 into R^2 and that the matrix of T is

$$\begin{bmatrix}a & b\\c & d\end{bmatrix}$$

For example, suppose T is the reflection of Example 2, page 99, so that $T(x,y) = (-x,y)$, which can be rewritten as

$$T\begin{bmatrix} x \\ y \end{bmatrix} = \begin{bmatrix} -1 & 0 \\ 0 & 1 \end{bmatrix}\begin{bmatrix} x \\ y \end{bmatrix}$$

From this we conclude that the matrix of T is

$$\begin{bmatrix} -1 & 0 \\ 0 & 1 \end{bmatrix}$$

EXAMPLE 3 Suppose T is a counterclockwise rotation in R^2 through the angle θ. Then, as shown in Example 4, page 101, T is a linear transformation and

$$T(1,0) = (\cos\theta, \sin\theta)$$
$$T(0,1) = [\cos(\theta + \pi/2), \sin(\theta + \pi/2)]$$

Writing these as columns, we have

$$T\begin{bmatrix} 1 \\ 0 \end{bmatrix} = \begin{bmatrix} \cos\theta \\ \sin\theta \end{bmatrix} \qquad T\begin{bmatrix} 0 \\ 1 \end{bmatrix} = \begin{bmatrix} \cos(\theta + \pi/2) \\ \sin(\theta + \pi/2) \end{bmatrix}$$

Since $\cos(\theta + \pi/2) = -\sin\theta$ and $\sin(\theta + \pi/2) = \cos\theta$, we have shown that the matrix of T is

$$A = \begin{bmatrix} \cos\theta & -\sin\theta \\ \sin\theta & \cos\theta \end{bmatrix}$$

Therefore

$$T\begin{bmatrix} x \\ y \end{bmatrix} = A\begin{bmatrix} x \\ y \end{bmatrix}$$

This gives the formula

$$T\begin{bmatrix} x \\ y \end{bmatrix} = \begin{bmatrix} x\cos\theta - y\sin\theta \\ x\sin\theta + y\cos\theta \end{bmatrix}$$

which enables us to calculate the effect of rotating

$$\begin{bmatrix} x \\ y \end{bmatrix}$$

through the angle θ.

EXAMPLE 4 Suppose $\overline{w} = \frac{1}{3}(1,2,2)$ and T is reflection in the line through $\overline{w}$. As shown in Example 3, page 100, we have

$$T\bar{u} = 2P\bar{u} - \bar{u}$$

where P is the projection onto $\overline{w}$. In Example 1 it was shown that

$$P\begin{bmatrix}1\\0\\0\end{bmatrix} = \begin{bmatrix}\frac{1}{9}\\\frac{2}{9}\\\frac{2}{9}\end{bmatrix}, \quad P\begin{bmatrix}0\\1\\0\end{bmatrix} = \begin{bmatrix}\frac{2}{9}\\\frac{4}{9}\\\frac{4}{9}\end{bmatrix}, \quad P\begin{bmatrix}0\\0\\1\end{bmatrix} = \begin{bmatrix}\frac{2}{9}\\\frac{4}{9}\\\frac{4}{9}\end{bmatrix}$$

so that

$$T\begin{bmatrix}1\\0\\0\end{bmatrix} = \begin{bmatrix}-\frac{7}{9}\\\frac{4}{9}\\\frac{4}{9}\end{bmatrix}, \quad T\begin{bmatrix}0\\1\\0\end{bmatrix} = \begin{bmatrix}\frac{4}{9}\\-\frac{1}{9}\\\frac{8}{9}\end{bmatrix}, \quad T\begin{bmatrix}0\\0\\1\end{bmatrix} = \begin{bmatrix}\frac{4}{9}\\\frac{8}{9}\\-\frac{1}{9}\end{bmatrix}$$

Thus we have the formula

$$T\begin{bmatrix}x\\y\\z\end{bmatrix} = \begin{bmatrix}-\frac{7}{9} & \frac{4}{9} & \frac{4}{9}\\\frac{4}{9} & -\frac{1}{9} & \frac{8}{9}\\\frac{4}{9} & \frac{8}{9} & -\frac{1}{9}\end{bmatrix}\begin{bmatrix}x\\y\\z\end{bmatrix}$$

which can be rewritten in coordinate form as

$$T(x,y,z) = \tfrac{1}{9}(-7x + 4y + 4z,\ 4x - y + 8z,\ 4x + 8y - z)$$

EXAMPLE 5 Suppose T is a linear transformation from R^1 into R^1. The matrix of T is a matrix with one row and one column; that is, the matrix of T is a number. Theorem 12 then tells us that for all x in R^1, $Tx = ax$, where $a = T1$.

In other words, if $f(x)$ is a real-valued function of a real variable such that $f(x + y) = f(x) + f(y)$ and $f(bx) = bf(x)$, for all real numbers x, y, b, then f is of the form $f(x) = ax$, where $a = f(1)$.

EXAMPLE 6 All the above examples discuss transformations from R^n into R^m where $m = n$, in which case the matrix of the transformation is square. In general, the matrix of a linear transformation from R^n into R^m has n columns and m rows. For example, consider

$$T(x,y,z) = (x - y,\ 2y + z)$$

Since

$$T\begin{bmatrix}1\\0\\0\end{bmatrix} = \begin{bmatrix}1\\0\end{bmatrix}, \quad T\begin{bmatrix}0\\1\\0\end{bmatrix} = \begin{bmatrix}-1\\2\end{bmatrix}, \quad T\begin{bmatrix}0\\0\\1\end{bmatrix} = \begin{bmatrix}0\\1\end{bmatrix}$$

we see that

$$T\begin{bmatrix}x\\y\\z\end{bmatrix} = \begin{bmatrix}1 & -1 & 0\\0 & 2 & 1\end{bmatrix}\begin{bmatrix}x\\y\\z\end{bmatrix}$$

EXERCISES

1 Find the matrix of each of the following linear transformations.
  a $T(x,y,z,w) = (x, x + y, x + y + z, x + y + z + w)$
  b $T(x,y,z) = (x - y, z)$
  c $T(x,y,z,w) = (x,x,x,x,x)$

2 Find the matrix of a counterclockwise rotation in R^2 through the angle
  a $\pi/4$ **b** $\pi/2$ **c** π **d** $-\pi$ **e** 0

3 For each of the rotations T of Exercise 2, calculate $T(1,1)$ and $T(2,-3)$.

4 Suppose P is projection onto $\overline{w} = \frac{1}{\sqrt{2}}(1,1)$. Find the matrix of P.

5 Suppose T is a reflection in the line through $\overline{w} = \frac{1}{\sqrt{2}}(1,1)$. Find the matrix of T.

6 Suppose P is projection orthogonal to $\overline{w} = \frac{1}{3}(1,2,2)$. Find the matrix of P.

7 Suppose T is the linear transformation from R^2 into R^2 defined by $T\bar{u} = \bar{0}$. What is the matrix of T?

8 Suppose T is the linear transformation from R^2 into R^2 defined by $T\bar{u} = \bar{u}$. What is the matrix of T?

9 Suppose $T\bar{u} = A\bar{u}$, where $A = \begin{bmatrix}2 & 1 & 3\\0 & -1 & 1\end{bmatrix}$. What is $T(x,y,z)$?

10 Give a geometric description of the linear transformation T if the matrix of T is

  a $\begin{bmatrix}0 & 1\\1 & 0\end{bmatrix}$ **b** $\begin{bmatrix}1 & 0\\0 & 0\end{bmatrix}$ **c** $\begin{bmatrix}0 & -1\\-1 & 0\end{bmatrix}$ **d** $\begin{bmatrix}-1 & 0\\0 & -1\end{bmatrix}$

11 We noted in the proof of Theorem 12 that $A\begin{bmatrix}1\\0\end{bmatrix}$ and $A\begin{bmatrix}0\\1\end{bmatrix}$ are the columns of A. This fact enables quick calculation of certain products.

a Find $\begin{bmatrix} 3 & 1 & 2 & 1 \\ 0 & 1 & 1 & -1 \\ 0 & 0 & 0 & 1 \end{bmatrix} \begin{bmatrix} 0 \\ 1 \\ 0 \\ 0 \end{bmatrix}$ and $\begin{bmatrix} 2 & 1 \\ 0 & 1 \end{bmatrix} \begin{bmatrix} 0 \\ 1 \end{bmatrix}$.

b Suppose A has five columns and $\bar{u} = \begin{bmatrix} 0 \\ 0 \\ 1 \\ 0 \\ 0 \end{bmatrix}$. What is $A\bar{u}$?

c Suppose A has five columns. Find a vector $\bar{u}$ such that $A\bar{u}$ is the fifth column of A.

N B

12 Suppose T is a linear transformation from R^2 in R^2 and that

$$T\begin{bmatrix} 3 \\ 1 \end{bmatrix} = \begin{bmatrix} -2 \\ 6 \end{bmatrix}, \quad T\begin{bmatrix} -1 \\ 4 \end{bmatrix} = \begin{bmatrix} 0 \\ 5 \end{bmatrix}$$

Find the matrix of T. (Hint: Express the standard basis vectors as linear combinations of

$$\begin{bmatrix} 3 \\ 1 \end{bmatrix} \text{ and } \begin{bmatrix} -1 \\ 4 \end{bmatrix} \text{ in order to find } T\begin{bmatrix} 1 \\ 0 \end{bmatrix} \text{ and } T\begin{bmatrix} 0 \\ 1 \end{bmatrix}\text{)}$$

13 Suppose $\bar{u}_1$ and $\bar{u}_2$ are a basis for R^2 and that S and T are linear transformations from R^2 into R^2 such that $S\bar{u}_1 = T\bar{u}_1$ and $S\bar{u}_2 = T\bar{u}_2$. Show that S and T must be the same. (Hint: By expressing $\bar{u}$ in terms of $\bar{u}_1$ and $\bar{u}_2$ show that $S\bar{u} = T\bar{u}$.)

□ **14** The concepts of this section extend to complex vector spaces. Find the matrix of each of the following linear transformations.

a $T(x,y) = (ix - y, (1 + i)x)$

b $T(x,y) = (0, 0, ix, (i - 1)x + 2y)$

c T is projection onto $\frac{1}{\sqrt{2}}(i, 1)$

SECTION 3 Sums and Scalar Multiples

Our next task is to define the sum of two matrices (or two transformations) and the scalar multiple of a matrix (or a transformation). These definitions, along with the definition of a product given in the next section, will provide us with a formal algebra of matrices (and transformations). This transformation (or matrix) algebra is of central importance in modern mathematics. For example, we shall use these formal concepts in Chapter 4 to show how the study of certain differential equations can be converted into the study of roots of polynomials.

If

$$A = \begin{bmatrix} a_1 & b_1 \\ c_1 & d_1 \end{bmatrix} \quad \text{and} \quad B = \begin{bmatrix} a_2 & b_2 \\ c_2 & d_2 \end{bmatrix}$$

then the **sum** $A + B$ is defined by

$$A + B = \begin{bmatrix} a_1+a_2 & b_1+b_2 \\ c_1+c_2 & d_1+d_2 \end{bmatrix}$$

Note that we merely add together the corresponding entries of A and B. For larger matrices, the definition of sum is analogous. For example

$$\begin{bmatrix} 2 & 1 & -1 & 3 \\ 2 & 1 & 14 & 2 \\ -3 & 0 & -2 & 1 \end{bmatrix} + \begin{bmatrix} -1 & 0 & 2 & -3 \\ -6 & 7 & 0 & -9 \\ 5 & -1 & 0 & 0 \end{bmatrix} = \begin{bmatrix} 1 & 1 & 1 & 0 \\ -4 & 8 & 14 & -7 \\ 2 & -1 & -2 & 1 \end{bmatrix}$$

We note that the sum $A + B$ is defined only when A and B are of the same size, that is, when the number of rows of A equals the number of rows of B and the number of columns of A equals the number of columns of B. It is evident from our definition of matrix sum that the following rules hold:

1 $$A+B = B + A, \qquad A + (B + C) = (A + B) + C$$

A matrix, all of whose entries are zeros, is called a **zero matrix** and usually denoted by 0. We note that if A and the zero matrix 0 have the same size then

2 $$A + 0 = A$$

If

$$A = \begin{bmatrix} a_1 & b_1 \\ c_1 & d_1 \end{bmatrix}$$

and a is any scalar, the **scalar multiple** aA is defined by

$$aA = \begin{bmatrix} aa_1 & ab_1 \\ ac_1 & ad_1 \end{bmatrix}$$

In other words we merely multiply each entry of A by the scalar a. The definition for larger matrices is analogous. For example

$$5\begin{bmatrix} 2 & 1 & -1 & 3 \\ 2 & 1 & 14 & 2 \\ -3 & 0 & -2 & 1 \end{bmatrix} = \begin{bmatrix} 10 & 5 & -5 & 15 \\ 10 & 5 & 70 & 10 \\ -15 & 0 & -10 & 5 \end{bmatrix}$$

The following rules should be evident.

3
$$a(A + B) = aA + aB, \qquad (a + b)A = aA + bA$$
$$(ab)A = a(bA)$$
$$1A = A, \qquad 0A = 0$$

We also observe that the matrix $-A$ [defined by the rule $-A = (-1)A$] satisfies the relation

4
$$A + (-A) = 0$$

From these definitions and observations it follows that the collection of all matrices with m rows and n columns is in fact a vector space. In other words, rules **1**, page 32, are satisfied. (*See also* Exercise 11, below.)

EXAMPLE 1

a
$$\begin{bmatrix} 3 & 1 & 1 \\ 2 & -1 & 1 \end{bmatrix} + \begin{bmatrix} 4 & 2 & -1 \\ 0 & 0 & 2 \end{bmatrix} = \begin{bmatrix} 7 & 3 & 0 \\ 2 & -1 & 3 \end{bmatrix}$$

and
$$\begin{bmatrix} 4 & 2 & -1 \\ 0 & 0 & 2 \end{bmatrix} + \begin{bmatrix} 3 & 1 & 1 \\ 2 & -1 & 1 \end{bmatrix} = \begin{bmatrix} 7 & 3 & 0 \\ 2 & -1 & 3 \end{bmatrix}$$

This illustrates the general law $A + B = B + A$.

b
$$\begin{bmatrix} 2 & 1 \\ 0 & 3 \end{bmatrix} + \begin{bmatrix} -1 & 0 \\ 7 & 2 \end{bmatrix} = \begin{bmatrix} 1 & 1 \\ 7 & 5 \end{bmatrix}$$

and
$$\begin{bmatrix} -2 & 6 \\ 2 & 1 \end{bmatrix} + \begin{bmatrix} 1 & 1 \\ 7 & 5 \end{bmatrix} = \begin{bmatrix} -1 & 7 \\ 9 & 6 \end{bmatrix}$$

We also have

$$\begin{bmatrix} -2 & 6 \\ 2 & 1 \end{bmatrix} + \begin{bmatrix} 2 & 1 \\ 0 & 3 \end{bmatrix} = \begin{bmatrix} 0 & 7 \\ 2 & 4 \end{bmatrix}$$

and
$$\begin{bmatrix} 0 & 7 \\ 2 & 4 \end{bmatrix} + \begin{bmatrix} -1 & 0 \\ 7 & 2 \end{bmatrix} = \begin{bmatrix} -1 & 7 \\ 9 & 6 \end{bmatrix}$$

This is an example of the law $(A + B) + C = A + (B + C)$.

c
$$\begin{bmatrix} 2 & 1 \\ 1 & 2 \end{bmatrix} + \begin{bmatrix} 0 & 0 \\ 0 & 0 \end{bmatrix} = \begin{bmatrix} 2 & 1 \\ 1 & 2 \end{bmatrix}$$

and
$$\begin{bmatrix} 2 & 1 \\ 1 & 2 \end{bmatrix} + \begin{bmatrix} -2 & -1 \\ -1 & -2 \end{bmatrix} = \begin{bmatrix} 0 & 0 \\ 0 & 0 \end{bmatrix}$$

These illustrate principles **2** and **4**.

d
$$3\begin{bmatrix} 6 & -1 & 0 \\ 1 & 2 & 1 \end{bmatrix} = \begin{bmatrix} 18 & -3 & 0 \\ 3 & 6 & 3 \end{bmatrix}$$

and
$$-5\begin{bmatrix} 18 & -3 & 0 \\ 3 & 6 & 3 \end{bmatrix} = \begin{bmatrix} -90 & 15 & 0 \\ -15 & -30 & -15 \end{bmatrix}$$

We also have
$$-15\begin{bmatrix} 6 & -1 & 0 \\ 1 & 2 & 1 \end{bmatrix} = \begin{bmatrix} -90 & 15 & 0 \\ -15 & -30 & -15 \end{bmatrix}$$

This is just a special case of the principle $(ab)A = a(bA)$.

e
$$\text{If } A = \begin{bmatrix} -1 & 3 \\ 0 & 0 \end{bmatrix} \quad \text{and} \quad C = \begin{bmatrix} -2 & -1 \\ -1 & 1 \end{bmatrix}$$

then the solution B to $2A - 3B + C = 0$ is
$$B = \tfrac{2}{3}A + \tfrac{1}{3}C = \begin{bmatrix} -\frac{4}{3} & \frac{5}{3} \\ -\frac{1}{3} & \frac{1}{3} \end{bmatrix}$$

DISCUSSION

We now give the corresponding definitions for linear transformations from V into W. In order to define $S + T$ and aT we need to show what effect each has on a given vector in V. We define $S + T$ as that transformation whose value at $\bar{u}$ is $S\bar{u} + T\bar{u}$. We define aT as that transformation whose value at $\bar{u}$ is $a(T\bar{u})$. In other words, the **sum** $S + T$ is defined by $(S + T)\bar{u} = S\bar{u} + T\bar{u}$ for each $\bar{u}$ in V, and the **scalar multiple** aT is defined by $(aT)\bar{u} = a(T\bar{u})$.

The proof that the sum $S + T$ and multiple aT are each linear if S and T are linear is left to Exercise 10 below. If S and T are both linear transformations from R^n into R^m we have

5 *The matrix of* S + T *is the sum of the matrix of* S *and the matrix of* T. *The matrix of* aT *is* a *times the matrix of* T.

In order to establish this we need to show that if A and B are matrices such that $S\bar{u} = A\bar{u}$ and $T\bar{u} = B\bar{u}$ for all $\bar{u}$ in R^n, then $(S + T)\bar{u} = (A + B)\bar{u}$

for all ū in R^n. From the definition of transformation sum we have $(S + T)\bar{u} = S\bar{u} + T\bar{u}$, which is equal to $A\bar{u} + B\bar{u}$. To complete the proof of property **5** we need to show that

6 $$A\bar{u} + B\bar{u} = (A + B)\bar{u}$$

This is proved by direct calculation. For example, if

$$A = \begin{bmatrix} a_1 & b_1 \\ c_1 & d_1 \end{bmatrix}, \qquad B = \begin{bmatrix} a_2 & b_2 \\ c_2 & d_2 \end{bmatrix}, \qquad \bar{u} = \begin{bmatrix} x \\ y \end{bmatrix}$$

it follows that

$$\begin{aligned} A\bar{u} + B\bar{u} &= \begin{bmatrix} a_1 & b_1 \\ c_1 & d_1 \end{bmatrix} \begin{bmatrix} x \\ y \end{bmatrix} + \begin{bmatrix} a_2 & b_2 \\ c_2 & d_2 \end{bmatrix} \begin{bmatrix} x \\ y \end{bmatrix} \\ &= \begin{bmatrix} a_1x + b_1y \\ c_1x + d_1y \end{bmatrix} + \begin{bmatrix} a_2x + b_2y \\ c_2x + d_2y \end{bmatrix} \\ &= \begin{bmatrix} a_1x + b_1y + a_2x + b_2y \\ c_1x + d_1y + c_2x + d_2y \end{bmatrix} \\ &= \begin{bmatrix} (a_1 + a_2)x + (b_1 + b_2)y \\ (c_1 + c_2)x + (d_1 + d_2)y \end{bmatrix} \\ &= \begin{bmatrix} a_1 + a_2 & b_1 + b_2 \\ c_1 + c_2 & d_1 + d_2 \end{bmatrix} \begin{bmatrix} x \\ y \end{bmatrix} \\ &= (A + B)\bar{u} \end{aligned}$$

which establishes statement **6** in this case. The proof that the matrix of aT is aB is even easier and will be omitted.

EXAMPLE 2 Suppose S and T are defined by

$$S(x,y) = (x - 2y, 2x + 7y) \qquad \text{and} \qquad T(x,y) = (3x + 2y, x - y)$$

Then
$$\begin{aligned} (S + T)(x,y) &= S(x,y) + T(x,y) \\ &= (x - 2y, 2x + 7y) + (3x + 2y, x - y) \\ &= (4x, 3x + 6y) \end{aligned}$$

and
$$\begin{aligned} (3T)(x,y) &= 3[T(x,y)] \\ &= 3(3x + 2y, x - y) \\ &= (9x + 6y, 3x - 3y) \end{aligned}$$

To express these facts in matrix form we rewrite our vectors as column matrices:

$$S\begin{bmatrix} x \\ y \end{bmatrix} = \begin{bmatrix} x - 2y \\ 2x + 7y \end{bmatrix} = \begin{bmatrix} 1 & -2 \\ 2 & 7 \end{bmatrix} \begin{bmatrix} x \\ y \end{bmatrix}$$

$$T\begin{bmatrix} x \\ y \end{bmatrix} = \begin{bmatrix} 3x + 2y \\ x - y \end{bmatrix} = \begin{bmatrix} 3 & 2 \\ 1 & -1 \end{bmatrix} \begin{bmatrix} x \\ y \end{bmatrix}$$

so that the matrices of S and T are, respectively,

$$A = \begin{bmatrix} 1 & -2 \\ 2 & 7 \end{bmatrix} \quad \text{and} \quad B = \begin{bmatrix} 3 & 2 \\ 1 & -1 \end{bmatrix}$$

Thus $$A + B = \begin{bmatrix} 4 & 0 \\ 3 & 6 \end{bmatrix} \quad \text{and} \quad 3B = \begin{bmatrix} 9 & 6 \\ 3 & -3 \end{bmatrix}$$

are the matrices of $S + T$ and $3T$, respectively. This can also be verified by observing that

$$(S + T)\begin{bmatrix} x \\ y \end{bmatrix} = \begin{bmatrix} 4x \\ 3x + 6y \end{bmatrix} = \begin{bmatrix} 4 & 0 \\ 3 & 6 \end{bmatrix} \begin{bmatrix} x \\ y \end{bmatrix}$$

$$(3T)\begin{bmatrix} x \\ y \end{bmatrix} = \begin{bmatrix} 9x + 6y \\ 3x - 3y \end{bmatrix} = \begin{bmatrix} 9 & 6 \\ 3 & -3 \end{bmatrix} \begin{bmatrix} x \\ y \end{bmatrix}$$

EXAMPLE 3 *The Zero and Identity Transformations.*

The **zero transformation** 0 from V into W is the transformation defined by

$$0\bar{u} = \bar{0}, \text{ for each } \bar{u} \text{ in } V$$

where $\bar{0}$ denotes the zero vector in W. If V and W are coordinate spaces then the matrix of 0 is the zero matrix 0 of appropriate size.

The **identity transformation** I from V into V is defined by $I\bar{u} = \bar{u}$, for each $\bar{u}$ in V. The matrix of the identity transformation from R^n into R^n is the identity matrix with n rows and n columns. For example, if $n = 2$ and $I\bar{u} = \bar{u}$, for each $\bar{u}$ in R^2, then, certainly we have

$$I\begin{bmatrix} 1 \\ 0 \end{bmatrix} = \begin{bmatrix} 1 \\ 0 \end{bmatrix} \quad \text{and} \quad I\begin{bmatrix} 0 \\ 1 \end{bmatrix} = \begin{bmatrix} 0 \\ 1 \end{bmatrix}$$

so that the matrix of I is

$$\begin{bmatrix} 1 & 0 \\ 0 & 1 \end{bmatrix}$$

We note that for any transformation T,

$$T + (-1)T = 0$$

This follows from the definitions of sum, scalar multiple, and the zero transformation, for

$$\begin{aligned}[T + (-1)T]\bar{u} &= T\bar{u} + (-1)T\bar{u} = T\bar{u} - T\bar{u} = \bar{0} \\ &= 0\bar{u}\end{aligned}$$

The various rules **1**, **2**, and **3** also can be shown to be true for transformations by using the appropriate definitions. In particular, the collection of all linear transformations from V into W is a vector space with these definitions. In more advanced courses, the student will study many of the properties of this vector space.

EXAMPLE 4 Suppose $\overline{w}$ is a unit vector and P is projection onto $\overline{w}$. Suppose further that Q is projection orthogonal to $\overline{w}$. Then (*see* formulas **5**,**6**; pages 80, 81)

$$\begin{aligned} P\bar{u} &= (\bar{u} \cdot \overline{w})\overline{w} \\ Q\bar{u} &= \bar{u} - (\bar{u} \cdot \overline{w})\overline{w} \end{aligned}$$

so that $P\bar{u} + Q\bar{u} = \bar{u}$. In other words, $P + Q = I$.

For example, suppose $\overline{w} = \frac{1}{3}(1,2,2)$, so that the matrix of P is (*see* Example 1, page 107)

$$P_0 = \begin{bmatrix} \frac{1}{9} & \frac{2}{9} & \frac{2}{9} \\ \frac{2}{9} & \frac{4}{9} & \frac{4}{9} \\ \frac{2}{9} & \frac{4}{9} & \frac{4}{9} \end{bmatrix}$$

Denote the matrix of Q by Q_0. Since $P + Q = I$, we have $Q = I - P$; therefore

$$Q_0 = I - P_0 = \begin{bmatrix} \frac{8}{9} & -\frac{2}{9} & -\frac{2}{9} \\ -\frac{2}{9} & \frac{5}{9} & -\frac{4}{9} \\ -\frac{2}{9} & -\frac{4}{9} & \frac{5}{9} \end{bmatrix}$$

EXAMPLE 5 Suppose $\overline{w}_1$, $\overline{w}_2$, and $\overline{w}_3$ are an orthonormal basis for R^3 and P_1, P_2, and P_3 are the projections onto $\overline{w}_1$, $\overline{w}_2$, and $\overline{w}_3$, respectively. We then have the formulas

$$P_1\bar{u} = (\bar{u} \cdot \overline{w}_1)\overline{w}_1$$
$$P_2\bar{u} = (\bar{u} \cdot \overline{w}_2)\overline{w}_2$$
$$P_3\bar{u} = (\bar{u} \cdot \overline{w}_3)\overline{w}_3$$

Since $\bar{u} = (\bar{u} \cdot \overline{w}_1)\overline{w}_1 + (\bar{u} \cdot \overline{w}_2)\overline{w}_2 + (\bar{u} \cdot \overline{w}_3)\overline{w}_3$ (*see* formula 2, page 92) we have

$$P_1 + P_2 + P_3 = I.$$

Thus, for example, $P_1 + P_2 = I - P_3$. Example 4 shows that $I - P_3$ is the projection orthogonal to $\overline{w}_3$; therefore, the sum of the projections onto $\overline{w}_1$ and $\overline{w}_2$ is the projection orthogonal to $\overline{w}_3$.

EXAMPLE 6 Suppose T is reflection in the line through $\overline{w}$ and P is projection onto $\overline{w}$. Then, as shown in Example 3, page 100, we have $T\bar{u} = 2P\bar{u} - \bar{u}$, and, consequently, $T = 2P - I$. Solving for P we have

$$P = \tfrac{1}{2}(T + I)$$

EXAMPLE 7 The differential operator L defined by $Lf = f'' - f$ is the difference of the two operators D_1 and I, where $D_1f = f''$. In fact, a linear differential operator is simply a linear transformation that is a sum of transformations of the form L_i, where

$$L_if = a_if^{(i)}$$

(*See* Example 6, page 103.)

EXERCISES

1 Express as a single matrix

a $\begin{bmatrix} 2 & 0 \\ 1 & 1 \end{bmatrix} + 3\begin{bmatrix} -1 & 1 \\ 0 & 1 \end{bmatrix}$

b $-\begin{bmatrix} 1 & 2 & 1 & 0 \\ 1 & 1 & 1 & 0 \end{bmatrix} + 4\begin{bmatrix} -1 & 0 & 0 & 1 \\ 1 & 2 & 0 & 0 \end{bmatrix}$

c $-2\begin{bmatrix} 1 & 1 \\ 1 & 1 \\ 1 & 1 \end{bmatrix} - \frac{1}{2}\begin{bmatrix} -4 & -4 \\ -4 & -4 \\ -4 & -4 \end{bmatrix}$

2 For $A = \begin{bmatrix} 2 & 1 & 3 \\ 1 & -1 & 2 \end{bmatrix}$, $B = \begin{bmatrix} -1 & 0 & -2 \\ 4 & 1 & 2 \end{bmatrix}$, $\bar{u} = \begin{bmatrix} x \\ y \\ z \end{bmatrix}$

verify that

a $A\bar{u} + B\bar{u} = (A + B)\bar{u}$ b $(-5A)\bar{u} = (-5)A\bar{u}$

c $(aB)\bar{u} = a(B\bar{u})$.

3 Suppose $T(x,y) = (3x - y, 2x)$ and $S(x,y) = (2x + y, 0)$. Find

a $(S + T)(3,4)$

b $(2T - 4S)(1,1)$

c The matrix of S, the matrix of T, and the matrix of $S + T$

4 Suppose $T(x,y,z) = (4x, 0, x + y + z, z)$, $S(x,y,z) = (x,x,x,x)$. Find the matrix of $S + T$, $S - T$, $2T$ and $3S - 2T$.

5 Suppose A has m rows and n columns and B has p rows and q columns. What relations must hold among m, n, p, and q for $A + B$ to be defined?

6 Suppose M is a plane through $(0,0,0)$ perpendicular to the unit vector $\bar{w}$. Describe projection onto M and reflection in M in terms of projection onto $\bar{w}$, as in Examples 5 and 6.

7 Suppose $Df = f'$ and $Tf = \int_0^x f(t)\,dt$. Calculate

a $(D + T)(\cos x)$ b $(3D)x^2$ c $(-2T + 4D)e^{2x}$

Find a nonzero function in the null space of $T + D$.

8 Suppose R, S, and T are linear transformations which satisfy $3R + 2S - (4S + 2T + I) = 0$. Express T in terms of R, S, and I.

9 Suppose $A = \begin{bmatrix} a_{11} & a_{12} \\ a_{21} & a_{22} \end{bmatrix}$

Find $\lambda I - A$. If $\bar{u}$ is in the null space of $\lambda I - A$, what is $A\bar{u}$?

10 Show that if S and T are linear transformations from V into W, then $S + T$ and aT are linear. (Hint: Calculate $(S + T)(\bar{u} + \bar{v})$, and so on.)

☐ 11 Suppose V is the set of all matrices with m rows and n columns. What is the dimension of V?

☐ 12 Suppose P is projection onto $\bar{w}$ and Q is projection orthogonal to $\bar{w}$. Are P, Q, and I independent?

☐ 13 Suppose S and T are the linear transformations from the complex space C^2 into C^2 defined by

$$S(x,y) = ((i + 2)y, -x - iy)$$
$$T(x,y) = ((3i + 1)x + iy, 0)$$

a What is $(S + T)(x, y)$?

b Verify that the matrix of $S + T$ is the sum of the matrix of S and the matrix of T.

c Find the matrix of iT.

SECTION 4 Transformation and Matrix Products

We continue our discussion of transformation and matrix algebra by defining a product. In Section 3 we first defined matrix sums and scalar multiples and then extended our definitions to transformations. In defining the product we find it more natural to begin with transformations.

Suppose T is a transformation from V into W and S is a transformation from W into U. For each $\bar{u}$ in V, the vector $T\bar{u}$ is in W; therefore, S can be applied to $T\bar{u}$, resulting in a vector $S(T\bar{u})$ which is in U. We define the **product** ST as the transformation from V into U whose value at each $\bar{u}$ in V is given by

$$(ST)\bar{u} = S(T\bar{u}).$$

Thus, the operation ST is the operation obtained by first applying T, then applying S.

We wish to show that ST is linear if S and T are linear. To do this, suppose S and T are linear and $\bar{u}$ and $\bar{v}$ are in V. Then, since T is linear, we have

$$T(\bar{u} + \bar{v}) = T\bar{u} + T\bar{v}$$

Since S is linear, we have

$$S(T(\bar{u} + \bar{v})) = S(T\bar{u} + T\bar{v}) = S(T\bar{u}) + S(T\bar{v})$$

The definition of transformation product tells us that

$$S(T(\bar{u} + \bar{v})) = (ST)(\bar{u} + \bar{v}) \quad \text{and} \quad S(T\bar{u}) + S(T\bar{v}) = (ST)\bar{u} + (ST)\bar{v}$$

We have therefore shown that

$$(ST)(\bar{u} + \bar{v}) = (ST)\bar{u} + (ST)\bar{v}$$

A similar argument shows that

$$(ST)(a\bar{u}) = a(ST)\bar{u}$$

demonstrating that ST is linear if S and T are linear.

EXAMPLE 1 The product ST is defined by the process of composition, that is, by first performing the operation T, then the operation S. This is an extension of the idea of function composition discussed in calculus. For example, if

$$f(x) = \sin x \qquad \text{and} \qquad g(x) = x^2$$

then the composition $f \circ g$ is the function defined by

$$(f \circ g)(x) = f(g(x)) = \sin x^2$$

EXAMPLE 2 Suppose S is a counterclockwise rotation in R^2 through the angle θ and T is a counterclockwise rotation in R^2 through the angle φ. The product ST is then a counterclockwise rotation through φ followed by a counterclockwise rotation through θ. In other words,

ST is a counterclockwise rotation through $\varphi + \theta$.

We can also rotate first through θ, then through φ. This is the product TS. Clearly, TS is also a counterclockwise rotation through $\varphi + \theta$, and, therefore, $ST = TS$. The operations S, T, ST, and TS are indicated in Figure 8.

Figure 8 *Rotation product.*

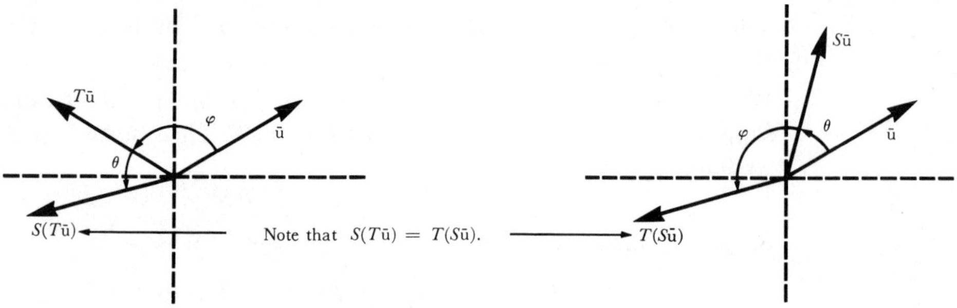

We say that two operators S and T **commute** if $ST = TS$. Thus we have shown that any two rotations of R^2 must commute. The next example shows that, in general, two operators *do not commute.*

EXAMPLE 3 Suppose S is a counterclockwise rotation in R^2 through the angle $\pi/4$ and that T is reflection in the y-axis. Then ST is reflection in the y-axis

Figure 9

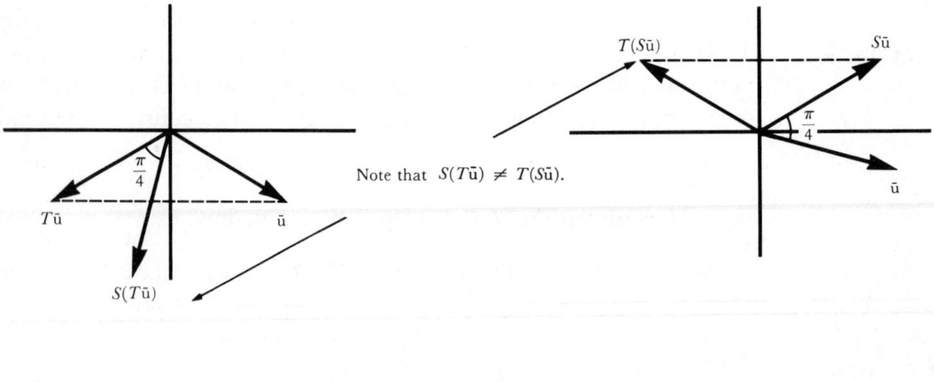

followed by rotation through $\pi/4$. The product TS is rotation through $\pi/4$ followed by reflection in the y-axis. As is shown in Figure 9, the two operations ST and TS are *not* the same.

EXAMPLE 4 Suppose V is the collection of all functions f such that f and *each* of its derivatives $f', f'', \ldots, f^{(n)}, \ldots$, are defined and continuous for $0 \leq x \leq 1$. We denote the differentiation operator by D, so that $Df = f'$.

The operator DD is the operation of differentiating twice. We usually denote this operator by D^2. For example,

$$\begin{aligned} D^2(x^3 + 3x^2) &= D[D(x^3 + 3x^2)] \\ &= D(3x^2 + 6x) \\ &= 6x + 6 \end{aligned}$$

The operator $D^3 = D(DD)$ is just the operation of differentiating three times. A systematic study of the operator D and its powers $D^2, D^3, \ldots$, will be given in Chapter 4.

EXAMPLE 5 Suppose $\bar{v}$ is a unit vector and P is the operation of projection onto $\bar{v}$. As we saw in Example 1, page 98, $P\bar{u}$ is given by the formula

1 $$P\bar{u} = (\bar{u} \cdot \bar{v})\bar{v}$$

Suppose $\bar{u}_1$ is parallel to $\bar{v}$. We should then expect that $P\bar{u}_1 = \bar{u}_1$. We can establish this fact using formula **1**, since saying that $\bar{u}_1$ is parallel to $\bar{v}$ means that $\bar{u}_1 = a\bar{v}$, for some scalar a. We therefore have

$$P\bar{u}_1 = P(a\bar{v}) = a(P\bar{v}) = a(\bar{v} \cdot \bar{v})\bar{v}$$

Since $\bar{v} \cdot \bar{v} = 1$ (by assumption, $\bar{v}$ is a unit vector) we have

$$P\bar{u}_1 = a(\bar{v} \cdot \bar{v})\bar{v} = a\bar{v} = \bar{u}_1$$

We now consider the operation of projecting twice, namely, $P^2 = PP$. For each $\bar{u}$ we know that $P\bar{u}$ is parallel to $\bar{v}$ (since formula **1** tells us that $P\bar{u}$ is a multiple of $\bar{v}$). Thus, since $P\bar{u}$ is parallel to $\bar{v}$, the above argument shows that $P(P\bar{u}) = P\bar{u}$.

We know from the definition of product that

$$P^2\bar{u} = (PP)\bar{u} = P(P\bar{u}) = P\bar{u}$$

Consequently, $P^2 = P$. This statement is equivalent to saying that projecting twice in the same direction is the same as projecting once.

DISCUSSION The student may wish to do some of the initial exercises at this point to clarify further his understanding of transformation products.

We will now show how to define a matrix product. We shall define it so that the matrix of ST is the product of the matrix of S and the matrix of T. We do this first for matrices with two rows and two columns. Suppose

$$A = \begin{bmatrix} A_{11} & A_{12} \\ A_{21} & A_{22} \end{bmatrix} \quad \text{and} \quad B = \begin{bmatrix} B_{11} & B_{12} \\ B_{21} & B_{22} \end{bmatrix}$$

and that S and T are the linear transformations defined by $S\bar{u} = A\bar{u}$ and $T\bar{u} = B\bar{u}$.

We have shown that ST is linear. Furthermore, we know that the matrix of ST is the matrix with the columns

$$(ST)\begin{bmatrix} 1 \\ 0 \end{bmatrix} \quad \text{and} \quad (ST)\begin{bmatrix} 0 \\ 1 \end{bmatrix}$$

as shown in formula 5, page 107. We know from this formula that

$$T\begin{bmatrix} 1 \\ 0 \end{bmatrix} = \begin{bmatrix} B_{11} \\ B_{21} \end{bmatrix} \quad \text{and} \quad T\begin{bmatrix} 0 \\ 1 \end{bmatrix} = \begin{bmatrix} B_{12} \\ B_{22} \end{bmatrix}$$

We now use the definition of ST and the above relations along with the fact that $S\bar{u} = A\bar{u}$ to obtain

$$ST\begin{bmatrix} 1 \\ 0 \end{bmatrix} = S\left\{T\begin{bmatrix} 1 \\ 0 \end{bmatrix}\right\} = S\begin{bmatrix} B_{11} \\ B_{21} \end{bmatrix} = A\begin{bmatrix} B_{11} \\ B_{21} \end{bmatrix}$$

$$ST\begin{bmatrix} 0 \\ 1 \end{bmatrix} = S\left\{T\begin{bmatrix} 0 \\ 1 \end{bmatrix}\right\} = S\begin{bmatrix} B_{12} \\ B_{22} \end{bmatrix} = A\begin{bmatrix} B_{12} \\ B_{22} \end{bmatrix}$$

In other words, the columns of the matrix of ST are given by

$$A\begin{bmatrix} B_{11} \\ B_{21} \end{bmatrix} = \begin{bmatrix} A_{11}B_{11} + A_{12}B_{21} \\ A_{21}B_{11} + A_{22}B_{21} \end{bmatrix}$$

and

$$A\begin{bmatrix} B_{12} \\ B_{22} \end{bmatrix} = \begin{bmatrix} A_{11}B_{12} + A_{12}B_{22} \\ A_{21}B_{12} + A_{22}B_{22} \end{bmatrix}$$

The matrix of ST, then, is

$$\begin{bmatrix} A_{11}B_{11} + A_{12}B_{21} & A_{11}B_{12} + A_{12}B_{22} \\ A_{21}B_{11} + A_{22}B_{21} & A_{21}B_{12} + A_{22}B_{22} \end{bmatrix}$$

We call this matrix the **product** AB. We defined the product in such a way that

2 *If A is the matrix of S and B is the matrix of T, then AB is the matrix of ST.*

We follow this same procedure for larger matrices, obtaining the definition: If A has m rows and n columns and B has n rows and k columns, then the **product** AB is the matrix with m rows and k columns such that

3 *Each column of AB is A times the corresponding column of B.*

This product is so defined that property 2 holds in this general case. Since the student must become adept at computing matrix products before proceeding further, we now give several examples. Also, much of the next section is devoted to practice with matrix products.

EXAMPLE 6

$$\begin{bmatrix} 2 & 1 \\ 3 & 2 \end{bmatrix}\begin{bmatrix} 1 & 2 & -1 \\ 1 & 1 & 1 \end{bmatrix} = \begin{bmatrix} 3 & 5 & -1 \\ 5 & 8 & -1 \end{bmatrix} \quad \text{since}$$

$$\begin{bmatrix} 2 & 1 \\ 3 & 2 \end{bmatrix}\begin{bmatrix} 1 \\ 1 \end{bmatrix} = \begin{bmatrix} 3 \\ 5 \end{bmatrix}, \quad \begin{bmatrix} 2 & 1 \\ 3 & 2 \end{bmatrix}\begin{bmatrix} 2 \\ 1 \end{bmatrix} = \begin{bmatrix} 5 \\ 8 \end{bmatrix}, \quad \begin{bmatrix} 2 & 1 \\ 3 & 2 \end{bmatrix}\begin{bmatrix} -1 \\ 1 \end{bmatrix} = \begin{bmatrix} -1 \\ -1 \end{bmatrix}$$

EXAMPLE 7

$$\begin{bmatrix} 6 & 1 & 2 & 1 \\ 4 & 0 & 1 & -1 \\ 2 & 1 & 3 & 0 \end{bmatrix}\begin{bmatrix} 4 & 2 & 1 \\ 1 & 1 & 0 \\ 2 & -3 & -1 \\ 6 & 1 & 1 \end{bmatrix} = \begin{bmatrix} 35 & 8 & 5 \\ 12 & 4 & 2 \\ 15 & -4 & -1 \end{bmatrix}$$

EXAMPLE 8 The product

$$\begin{bmatrix} 2 & 1 \\ 1 & 2 \end{bmatrix}\begin{bmatrix} 1 & 2 \\ 3 & 1 \\ -1 & 4 \end{bmatrix}$$

is not defined, for the left matrix is the matrix of a linear transformation S from R^2 into R^2, and the right matrix is the matrix of a linear transformation T from R^2 into R^3. Thus, ST is not defined, for after applying T, we obtain a vector in R^3, and hence (since S is not defined for vectors in R^3) we cannot then apply S.

If we reverse the order, we have

$$\begin{bmatrix} 1 & 2 \\ 3 & 1 \\ -1 & 4 \end{bmatrix}\begin{bmatrix} 2 & 1 \\ 1 & 2 \end{bmatrix} = \begin{bmatrix} 4 & 5 \\ 7 & 5 \\ 2 & 7 \end{bmatrix}$$

This shows that it may be possible to find BA but not AB. In general, even this may not be possible. For example, neither product

$$\begin{bmatrix} 2 & 1 \\ 1 & 2 \end{bmatrix} \begin{bmatrix} 1 & 2 & 1 \\ 3 & 1 & 0 \\ -1 & 4 & 0 \end{bmatrix} \quad \text{nor} \quad \begin{bmatrix} 1 & 2 & 1 \\ 3 & 1 & 0 \\ -1 & 4 & 0 \end{bmatrix} \begin{bmatrix} 2 & 1 \\ 1 & 2 \end{bmatrix}$$

is defined. We also note that

$$\begin{bmatrix} 1 & 1 \\ 0 & 1 \end{bmatrix} \begin{bmatrix} 1 & -3 \\ 0 & 2 \end{bmatrix} = \begin{bmatrix} 1 & -1 \\ 0 & 2 \end{bmatrix}$$

and

$$\begin{bmatrix} 1 & -3 \\ 0 & 2 \end{bmatrix} \begin{bmatrix} 1 & 1 \\ 0 & 1 \end{bmatrix} = \begin{bmatrix} 1 & -2 \\ 0 & 2 \end{bmatrix}$$

This shows that AB is not generally equal to BA, even if both are defined. (Example 3 should lead us to expect this.)

EXAMPLE 9 In the next section we shall establish the associative law $A(BC) = (AB)C$, from which it follows that $A(AA) = (AA)A$. We therefore can use exponent notation without ambiguity, writing A^2 for AA, A^3 for $(AA)A$, and so forth. The usual laws for exponents will then hold, such as $A^mA^n = A^{m+n}$ and $(A^m)^n = A^{mn}$. It is not true in general, however, that $A^2 = 0$ must imply that $A = 0$. The following examples illustrate some of these considerations.

$$\begin{bmatrix} 1 & 2 \\ -1 & 1 \end{bmatrix}^2 = \begin{bmatrix} 1 & 2 \\ -1 & 1 \end{bmatrix} \begin{bmatrix} 1 & 2 \\ -1 & 1 \end{bmatrix} = \begin{bmatrix} -1 & 4 \\ -2 & -1 \end{bmatrix}$$

$$\begin{bmatrix} 1 & 2 \\ -1 & 1 \end{bmatrix}^3 = \begin{bmatrix} -1 & 4 \\ -2 & -1 \end{bmatrix} \begin{bmatrix} 1 & 2 \\ -1 & 1 \end{bmatrix} = \begin{bmatrix} -5 & 2 \\ -1 & -5 \end{bmatrix}$$

$$\begin{bmatrix} 1 & 2 \\ -1 & 1 \end{bmatrix}^4 = \begin{bmatrix} -5 & 2 \\ -1 & -5 \end{bmatrix} \begin{bmatrix} 1 & 2 \\ -1 & 1 \end{bmatrix} = \begin{bmatrix} -7 & -8 \\ 4 & -7 \end{bmatrix}$$

Note that

$$\begin{bmatrix} 1 & 2 \\ -1 & 1 \end{bmatrix}^4 = \begin{bmatrix} -1 & 4 \\ -2 & -1 \end{bmatrix} \begin{bmatrix} -1 & 4 \\ -2 & -1 \end{bmatrix} = \begin{bmatrix} -7 & -8 \\ 4 & -7 \end{bmatrix}$$

so that, indeed, $A^4 = (A^2)^2$.

The following is an example of a nonzero matrix whose square is the zero matrix.

$$\begin{bmatrix} 1 & -1 \\ 1 & -1 \end{bmatrix}^2 = \begin{bmatrix} 1 & -1 \\ 1 & -1 \end{bmatrix} \begin{bmatrix} 1 & -1 \\ 1 & -1 \end{bmatrix} = \begin{bmatrix} 0 & 0 \\ 0 & 0 \end{bmatrix}$$

We have defined the matrix product in terms of the transformation product. The remaining two examples further illustrate this interconnection.

EXAMPLE 10 Suppose S and T are counterclockwise rotations in R^2 through the angles θ and φ respectively. (*See* Example 2, page 122.) The respective matrices of S and T are

$$A = \begin{bmatrix} \cos\theta & -\sin\theta \\ \sin\theta & \cos\theta \end{bmatrix} \quad \text{and} \quad B = \begin{bmatrix} \cos\varphi & -\sin\varphi \\ \sin\varphi & \cos\varphi \end{bmatrix}$$

as shown in Example 3, page 109.

We have

$$AB = \begin{bmatrix} \cos\theta\cos\varphi - \sin\theta\sin\varphi & -\cos\theta\sin\varphi - \sin\theta\cos\varphi \\ \sin\theta\cos\varphi + \cos\theta\sin\varphi & -\sin\theta\sin\varphi + \cos\theta\cos\varphi \end{bmatrix}$$

Because of property 2, the matrix AB is the matrix of ST. We showed in Example 2 that ST is just counterclockwise rotation through the angle $\theta + \varphi$, so its matrix is

$$\begin{bmatrix} \cos(\theta+\varphi) & -\sin(\theta+\varphi) \\ \sin(\theta+\varphi) & \cos(\theta+\varphi) \end{bmatrix}$$

Since this must be equal to AB (for Theorem 12 tells us that the matrix of a transformation is unique) we have derived the familiar formulas

$$\cos(\theta+\varphi) = \cos\theta\cos\varphi - \sin\theta\sin\varphi$$
$$\sin(\theta+\varphi) = \cos\theta\sin\varphi + \sin\theta\cos\varphi$$

This derivation provides a convenient device for reconstructing these formulas.

EXAMPLE 11 Suppose S and T are defined by the formulas

$$T(x,y) = (2x - y,\ 3x + y) \quad \text{and} \quad S(x,y) = (3x + 2y,\ -x - 2y)$$

Then, rewriting these in column form,

$$T\begin{bmatrix} x \\ y \end{bmatrix} = \begin{bmatrix} 2 & -1 \\ 3 & 1 \end{bmatrix} \begin{bmatrix} x \\ y \end{bmatrix} \quad \text{and} \quad S\begin{bmatrix} x \\ y \end{bmatrix} = \begin{bmatrix} 3 & 2 \\ -1 & -2 \end{bmatrix} \begin{bmatrix} x \\ y \end{bmatrix}$$

Therefore

$$ST\begin{bmatrix} x \\ y \end{bmatrix} = \begin{bmatrix} 3 & 2 \\ -1 & -2 \end{bmatrix} \begin{bmatrix} 2 & -1 \\ 3 & 1 \end{bmatrix} \begin{bmatrix} x \\ y \end{bmatrix} = \begin{bmatrix} 12 & -1 \\ -8 & -1 \end{bmatrix} \begin{bmatrix} x \\ y \end{bmatrix}$$

which can be rewritten as

$$ST(x,y) = (12x - y, -8x - y)$$

This formula can also be computed directly from the given formulas for S and T:

$$\begin{aligned} ST(x,y) &= S[T(x,y)] \\ &= S(2x - y, 3x + y) \\ &= (3(2x - y) + 2(3x + y), -(2x - y) - 2(3x + y)) \\ &= (12x - y, -8x - y) \end{aligned}$$

EXERCISES

1 If S is counterclockwise rotation through the angle $\pi/4$, and T is counterclockwise rotation through the angle π, describe each of the following:

a S^2 **b** T^2 **c** S^4 **d** ST **e** $(ST)^2$ **f** S^4T

2 Suppose S is a counterclockwise rotation through $\pi/2$ and T is a reflection in the line $y = x$. Draw figures such as those in Figures 8 and 9 indicating $(ST)\bar{u}$ and $(TS)\bar{u}$. Do S and T commute?

3 **a** Suppose S is a reflection in the y-axis and T is a projection onto the line $y = x$. Draw figures illustrating $(ST)\bar{u}$ and $(TS)\bar{u}$. Do S and T commute?

b Suppose S is as given in part **a** and S_1 is reflection in the x-axis. What is S_1S? Do S_1 and S commute? (A figure may be helpful.)

c For S, S_1, and T as in parts **a** and **b** let T_1 denote S_1S. Do T_1 and T commute? (A figure may be helpful.)

4 Suppose $\bar{v}$ is a unit vector in R^2 and P is the projection onto $\bar{v}$, while Q is the projection orthogonal to $\bar{v}$. We showed that $P^2 = P$ in Example 5. Show that

a $Q^2 = Q$ **b** $P + Q = I$ **c** $PQ = 0$ **d** $QP = 0$.

(The use of figures or the dot product formulas might be helpful.)

5 Suppose P is the projection onto the unit vector $\bar{v}$ in R^2 and T is the reflection in the line through $\bar{v}$.

a Show that $T^2 = I$. (A figure may be helpful.)

b Show that $T^2 = I$ by using the fact that $P^2 = P$ and $T = 2P - I$ and calculating $(2P - I)^2$.

6 For $Df = f'$ and $Tf(x) = \int_0^x f(t)\,dt$ find

a Dx **b** Tx^2 **c** $D^3 \sin x$ **d** $T^2 (\sin 2x)$ **e** $TD (\cos x)$ **f** $DT (\cos x)$ **g** $(3D^2 + 2T)x^2$

Do D and T commute?

7 Calculate

a $\begin{bmatrix} 2 & 0 \\ 1 & 1 \end{bmatrix} \begin{bmatrix} -1 & 1 \\ 0 & 1 \end{bmatrix}$ **b** $\begin{bmatrix} 3 & 1 \\ -1 & 0 \end{bmatrix} \begin{bmatrix} 0 & 1 \\ 0 & 2 \end{bmatrix}$

c $\begin{bmatrix} 1 & 2 \\ 3 & 4 \end{bmatrix} \begin{bmatrix} 5 & 6 \\ 7 & 8 \end{bmatrix}$ **d** $\begin{bmatrix} 1 & 1 \\ 0 & 1 \end{bmatrix} \begin{bmatrix} 1 & -1 \\ 0 & 1 \end{bmatrix}$

8 Calculate

a $\begin{bmatrix} 3 & 1 & -4 \\ 1 & 1 & 0 \\ -1 & 1 & 2 \end{bmatrix} \begin{bmatrix} 1 & -2 & -1 \\ 6 & -1 & 0 \\ 1 & 0 & 0 \end{bmatrix}$

b $\begin{bmatrix} -1 & 1 & 1 \\ 1 & -1 & 1 \\ 1 & 1 & -1 \end{bmatrix} \begin{bmatrix} 1 & -1 & -1 \\ -1 & 1 & -1 \\ -1 & -1 & 1 \end{bmatrix}$

c $\begin{bmatrix} 1 & 2 & 3 \\ 4 & 5 & 6 \\ 7 & 8 & 9 \end{bmatrix} \begin{bmatrix} 1 & -2 & 3 \\ -4 & 5 & -6 \\ 7 & -8 & 9 \end{bmatrix}$ **d** $\begin{bmatrix} 0 & 0 & 1 \\ 0 & 1 & 0 \\ 1 & 0 & 0 \end{bmatrix} \begin{bmatrix} 1 & 2 & 1 \\ 2 & 1 & 1 \\ 1 & 1 & 2 \end{bmatrix}$

9 Calculate

a $\begin{bmatrix} 2 & 1 & 0 \\ 0 & 1 & 1 \end{bmatrix} \begin{bmatrix} 1 & -1 & 2 \\ 1 & 2 & 3 \\ 0 & 1 & 1 \end{bmatrix}$ **b** $\begin{bmatrix} 2 & 1 & 0 \end{bmatrix} \begin{bmatrix} 1 \\ -1 \\ 1 \end{bmatrix}$

c $\begin{bmatrix} 4 & 1 & 1 & 2 & -6 \\ 1 & 2 & 1 & 1 & 0 \\ 0 & 0 & -3 & -2 & -1 \\ 1 & 1 & 2 & -1 & 0 \\ 0 & 0 & 0 & 1 & 1 \end{bmatrix} \begin{bmatrix} 0 & 1 & -1 & 1 & 1 \\ 2 & 1 & 4 & 1 & -6 \\ 0 & 3 & 0 & 2 & 1 \\ 2 & 1 & 0 & -1 & 1 \\ 1 & 1 & 1 & 1 & 1 \end{bmatrix}$

d $\begin{bmatrix} 2 & 0 & 1 & 4 & 1 \\ 1 & 2 & 1 & 0 & 6 \\ 0 & 3 & 1 & 2 & 1 \end{bmatrix} \begin{bmatrix} -1 & 1 \\ -1 & 1 \\ -1 & 1 \\ -1 & 1 \\ 0 & 0 \end{bmatrix}$

10 For each of the following matrices A find A^2, A^3, A^4, and $(A^2)^2$.

a $A = \begin{bmatrix} 1 & 1 \\ 0 & 1 \end{bmatrix}$ **b** $A = \begin{bmatrix} 0 & 1 \\ 1 & 0 \end{bmatrix}$

c $A = \begin{bmatrix} 1 & 2 \\ 3 & 4 \end{bmatrix}$ **d** $A = \begin{bmatrix} 2 & 1 & 0 \\ 1 & -1 & 1 \\ 1 & 2 & 1 \end{bmatrix}$

11 For $A = \begin{bmatrix} 2 & 1 & 0 \\ -1 & 1 & 2 \end{bmatrix}$ $B = \begin{bmatrix} 3 & 1 \\ 2 & -1 \\ 0 & 1 \end{bmatrix}$ $C = \begin{bmatrix} 2 & 0 \\ -1 & 1 \end{bmatrix}$

which of the following are defined? Calculate those that are defined.

a AB **b** $(AB)C$ **c** $A(BC)$
d $C(AB)$ **e** BA **f** AC
g A^2 **h** B^2 **i** $AB - C^2$
j $BA - C^2$

12 What relationship must hold between the number of columns of A and rows of B in order that AB is defined? How many rows and columns does AB have?

13 The entries of AB are just the dot products of the rows of A with the columns of B. Which rows and columns do you use to obtain the entry in the third row and fourth column of AB?

* **14** For $T(x,y) = (3x - y, 2x)$ and $S(x,y) = (2x + y, 0)$ calculate $TS(x,y)$ and $ST(x,y)$ directly from the definition of transformation multiplication. Find the matrix of S, T, ST, and TS.

15 Suppose $\bar{w} = \frac{1}{3}(1,2,2)$, P is projection onto $\bar{w}$, and T is reflection in the line through $\bar{w}$. Let P_0 and T_0 denote the matrices of P and T, respectively.
a Find P_0 and T_0.
b Verify that $P_0^2 = P_0$ and $T_0^2 = I$.

16 Suppose $\bar{v} = \frac{1}{\sqrt{5}}(1,2)$ and $\bar{w} = \frac{1}{\sqrt{5}}(2,-1)$. Let P_0 and Q_0 denote the matrices of projection onto $\bar{v}$ and $\bar{w}$, respectively.
a Find P_0 and Q_0.
b Verify that $P_0^2 = P_0$, $Q_0^2 = Q_0$, $P_0Q_0 = Q_0P_0$, and $P_0 + Q_0 = I$.

□ **17** The concepts and results of this section extend to complex vector spaces.

a Find $\begin{bmatrix} 1 & 1+i \\ 2 & -i \end{bmatrix} \begin{bmatrix} 1-i & i \\ 1 & i \end{bmatrix}$ **b** Find $\begin{bmatrix} 1 & 1+i \\ 2 & -i \end{bmatrix}^2$

c Find the matrix of $S + T$, iT, and ST where
$S(x,y) = (ix, 0)$ and $T(x,y) = ((1 + i)y, ix)$

SECTION 5 Rules and Special Products

While it is *not* true in general that $ST = TS$ for transformations S and T (or for matrices), some useful rules of transformation (and hence matrix) multiplication are true. A summary of these rules follows:

1
a $R(S + T) = RS + RT$
b $(R + S)T = RT + ST$
c $R(ST) = (RS)T$
d $a(ST) = (aS)T = S(aT)$

The first two are sometimes called *distributive laws* and the latter two, *associative laws*. These rules, of course, assume that the products and sums are defined. The same rules are true automatically for matrix products as well. We shall derive only the third rule, the derivations of the other rules being similar. We shall therefore proceed to show that

$$R(ST) = (RS)T$$

We assume that after applying T we obtain a vector for which S is defined, and that after then applying S we obtain a vector for which R is defined. To establish this law it is necessary to show that

$$[R(ST)]\bar{u} = [(RS)T]\bar{u}$$

for each vector $\bar{u}$, for which T is defined. In order to do this we show that both sides are equal to $R[S(T\bar{u})]$: Apply the definition of product (*see* page 121) to obtain

$$[R(ST)]\bar{u} = R[(ST)\bar{u}]$$

Apply the definition again to replace $(ST)\bar{u}$ by $S(T\bar{u})$. Hence we have the equality $[R(ST)]\bar{u} = R[S(T\bar{u})]$. Similar arguments show that $[(RS)T]\bar{u} = R[S(T\bar{u})]$, thereby completing the proof of rule **1c**.

Special rules hold for products involving the zero transformation 0 and the identity transformation I, which were defined in Section 3. These are

2
a $S0 = 0 \qquad 0T = 0$
b $SI = S \qquad IT = T$

These rules assume that 0 and I denote the appropriate zero and identity transformations so that $S0$, $0T$, SI, and IT are defined.

For example, if 0 denotes the zero transformation from V into W and S is a linear transformation from W into U, then

$$(S0)\bar{u} = S(0\bar{u}) = S\bar{0} = \bar{0}$$

Therefore, $S0$ is the zero transformation from V into U. This establishes the first part of rule **2a**.

Suppose T is a linear transformation from V into W and that I is the identity transformation on W. Then for each $\bar{u}$ in V we have

$$(IT)\bar{u} = I(T\bar{u}) = T\bar{u}$$

since $T\bar{u}$ is in W and I leaves fixed any vector in W. This establishes the second part of rule **2b**. The proofs of the other parts of rule **2** are omitted.

EXAMPLE 1 Some care needs to be exercised in manipulating transformations and matrices because the commutative law is *not* in general true. For example, the identity

$$(a + b)(a - b) = a^2 - b^2$$

which holds for all real numbers a and b, uses the fact that $ab = ba$. For transformations S and T such that $S + T$, S^2, T^2, ST, and TS are defined, we can use rules **1** to obtain

$$\begin{aligned}(S + T)(S - T) &= S(S - T) + T(S - T)\\ &= SS - ST + TS - TT\\ &= S^2 - ST + TS - T^2\end{aligned}$$

Thus we can *only* conclude that

$$(S + T)(S - T) = S^2 - T^2$$

when we know that $ST = TS$. In fact, if this result were true for a given S and T, we must have

$$S^2 - T^2 = S^2 - ST + TS - T^2$$

Therefore, after subtracting S^2 and adding T^2 to both sides we must have $0 = -ST + TS$, which is the same as $ST = TS$. In other words,

3 $(S + T)(S - T) = S^2 - T^2$ *if and only if* $ST = TS$.

EXAMPLE 2 The expression $y'' - y$ can be written in operator form as $(D^2 - I)y$, where $Dy = y'$ and I is the identity, for we have

$$(D^2 - I)y = D^2y - Iy = y'' - y$$

Since $DI = ID$ (for the identity commutes with any operator) we can apply result **3** to obtain

$$D^2 - I = (D + I)(D - I)$$

We shall find such factorization particularly useful in our discussion of linear differential equations in Chapter 4.

EXAMPLE 3 *Matrix and Operator Polynomials.*

Polynomial notation can be used to simplify discussion of expressions such as $A^2 - I$ or $A^3 - 3A^2 + 3A - I$, where A represents a matrix (or transformation), and I is the identity matrix (or the identity operator). If $p(\lambda)$ is the polynomial

$$p(\lambda) = a_k\lambda^k + a_{k-1}\lambda^{k-1} + \cdots + a_1\lambda + a_0$$

where $a_k, a_{k-1}, \ldots, a_1, a_0$ are scalars, then for a square matrix A, the symbol $p(A)$ will be used to denote the matrix

$$p(A) = a_kA^k + a_{k-1}A^{k-1} + \cdots + a_1A + a_0I$$

If T is a linear transformation from V into V, we use the symbol $p(T)$ to denote the transformation

$$p(T) = a_kT^k + a_{k-1}T^{k-1} + \cdots + a_1T + a_0I$$

For example, suppose $A = \begin{bmatrix} 2 & 1 \\ -1 & 0 \end{bmatrix}$ and $p(\lambda) = 3\lambda^3 - 2\lambda^2 + 4$. Then

$$\begin{aligned} p(A) &= 3A^3 - 2A^2 + 4I \\ &= 3\begin{bmatrix} 4 & 3 \\ -3 & -2 \end{bmatrix} - 2\begin{bmatrix} 3 & 2 \\ -2 & -1 \end{bmatrix} + 4\begin{bmatrix} 1 & 0 \\ 0 & 1 \end{bmatrix} \\ &= \begin{bmatrix} 10 & 5 \\ -5 & 0 \end{bmatrix} \end{aligned}$$

We note that if $p(\lambda)$ and $q(\lambda)$ are polynomials, the matrices $p(A)$ and $q(A)$ *commute* (as do $p(T)$ and $q(T)$ for transformations T). For example, if $p(\lambda) = \lambda^2 - 3\lambda + 1$ and $q(\lambda) = 5\lambda^2 - \lambda - 2$, then

$$p(A) = A^2 - 3A + I \text{ and } q(A) = 5A^2 - A - 2I.$$

Therefore, $p(A)q(A) = (A^2 - 3A + I)(5A^2 - A - 2I)$. Using rules **1** and **2** we obtain $p(A)q(A) = 5A^4 - 16A^3 + 6A^2 + 5A - 2I$.

The same rules also yield

$$\begin{aligned} q(A)p(A) &= (5A^2 - A - 2I)(A^2 - 3A + I) \\ &= 5A^4 - 16A^3 + 6A^2 + 5A - 2I \end{aligned}$$

Therefore, we indeed have $p(A)q(A) = q(A)p(A)$.

In the discussion of linear differential operators in Chapter 4 we shall make use of the fact that polynomial factorization gives a corresponding matrix or operator factorization. For example, if $p(\lambda) = \lambda^2 - 1$, $q(\lambda) = \lambda - 1$, and $r(\lambda) = \lambda + 1$, then $p(\lambda) = q(\lambda)r(\lambda)$, and for any square matrix A we have $p(A) = q(A)r(A)$. Of course, this is exactly the relation used in Example 2, above.

The remaining examples of this chapter exhibit the use of these rules for matrices, as well as giving some further special rules.

EXAMPLE 4

a $$\begin{bmatrix} 0 & 0 \\ 0 & 0 \end{bmatrix} \begin{bmatrix} 2 & 1 & 3 \\ 4 & -1 & -7 \end{bmatrix} = \begin{bmatrix} 0 & 0 & 0 \\ 0 & 0 & 0 \end{bmatrix}$$

b $$\begin{bmatrix} 2 & 1 & 3 \\ 4 & -1 & -7 \end{bmatrix} \begin{bmatrix} 0 & 0 & 0 & 0 \\ 0 & 0 & 0 & 0 \\ 0 & 0 & 0 & 0 \end{bmatrix} = \begin{bmatrix} 0 & 0 & 0 & 0 \\ 0 & 0 & 0 & 0 \end{bmatrix}$$

c $$\begin{bmatrix} 1 & 0 \\ 0 & 1 \end{bmatrix} \begin{bmatrix} 2 & 1 & 3 \\ 4 & -1 & -7 \end{bmatrix} = \begin{bmatrix} 2 & 1 & 3 \\ 4 & -1 & -7 \end{bmatrix}$$

d $$\begin{bmatrix} 2 & 1 & 3 \\ 4 & -1 & -7 \end{bmatrix} \begin{bmatrix} 1 & 0 & 0 \\ 0 & 1 & 0 \\ 0 & 0 & 1 \end{bmatrix} = \begin{bmatrix} 2 & 1 & 3 \\ 4 & -1 & -7 \end{bmatrix}$$

Note that the zero and identity matrices have the appropriate sizes in order that the products are defined. For example,

$$\begin{bmatrix} 0 & 0 & 0 \\ 0 & 0 & 0 \end{bmatrix} \begin{bmatrix} 2 & 1 & 3 \\ 4 & -1 & -7 \end{bmatrix}$$

is *not* defined.

EXAMPLE 5 If A has a row of zeros, the same row of AB consists of zeros. For example,

a $$\begin{bmatrix} -2 & -3 & 1 \\ 0 & 0 & 0 \\ 1 & -1 & 0 \end{bmatrix} \begin{bmatrix} 6 & -2 & 1 \\ 3 & 1 & 2 \\ -1 & 1 & 1 \end{bmatrix} = \begin{bmatrix} -22 & 2 & -7 \\ 0 & 0 & 0 \\ 3 & -3 & -1 \end{bmatrix}$$

If B has a column of zeros, the same column of AB consists of zeros. For example,

b $$\begin{bmatrix} 4 & 1 & 0 \\ -1 & 2 & 3 \\ 1 & 0 & 1 \end{bmatrix} \begin{bmatrix} 1 & 0 & 1 \\ -2 & 0 & 1 \\ 1 & 0 & 1 \end{bmatrix} = \begin{bmatrix} 2 & 0 & 5 \\ -2 & 0 & 4 \\ 2 & 0 & 2 \end{bmatrix}$$

EXAMPLE 6 Suppose A is a **diagonal matrix**; that is, A has the same number of rows as columns and each entry *not* on the left-to-right downward diagonal is zero. Each row of AB is then just the product of the corresponding row of B with the corresponding diagonal entry of A. For example,

a $$\begin{bmatrix} 2 & 0 & 0 \\ 0 & -1 & 0 \\ 0 & 0 & 3 \end{bmatrix} \begin{bmatrix} 4 & 2 & 1 \\ -1 & 0 & 6 \\ 2 & 1 & -3 \end{bmatrix} = \begin{bmatrix} 8 & 4 & 2 \\ 1 & 0 & -6 \\ 6 & 3 & -9 \end{bmatrix}$$

b $$\begin{bmatrix} 4 & 0 & 0 & 0 \\ 0 & 0 & 0 & 0 \\ 0 & 0 & 3 & 0 \\ 0 & 0 & 0 & -2 \end{bmatrix} \begin{bmatrix} 3 & 0 & -1 & 2 \\ -1 & 1 & 0 & 1 \\ 4 & -1 & -2 & 1 \\ 0 & 1 & 3 & -4 \end{bmatrix} = \begin{bmatrix} 12 & 0 & -4 & 8 \\ 0 & 0 & 0 & 0 \\ 12 & -3 & -6 & 3 \\ 0 & -2 & -6 & 8 \end{bmatrix}$$

c $$\begin{bmatrix} 2 & 0 & 0 \\ 0 & -1 & 0 \\ 0 & 0 & 3 \end{bmatrix}^2 = \begin{bmatrix} 2 & 0 & 0 \\ 0 & -1 & 0 \\ 0 & 0 & 3 \end{bmatrix} \begin{bmatrix} 2 & 0 & 0 \\ 0 & -1 & 0 \\ 0 & 0 & 3 \end{bmatrix} = \begin{bmatrix} 4 & 0 & 0 \\ 0 & 1 & 0 \\ 0 & 0 & 9 \end{bmatrix}$$

Note in **c** how easy it is to take the powers of a diagonal matrix. Continuing with further powers we have

d $$\begin{bmatrix} 2 & 0 & 0 \\ 0 & -1 & 0 \\ 0 & 0 & 3 \end{bmatrix}^3 = \begin{bmatrix} 2 & 0 & 0 \\ 0 & -1 & 0 \\ 0 & 0 & 3 \end{bmatrix} \begin{bmatrix} 2 & 0 & 0 \\ 0 & -1 & 0 \\ 0 & 0 & 3 \end{bmatrix}^2 = \begin{bmatrix} 8 & 0 & 0 \\ 0 & -1 & 0 \\ 0 & 0 & 27 \end{bmatrix}$$

e $$\begin{bmatrix} 2 & 0 & 0 \\ 0 & -1 & 0 \\ 0 & 0 & 3 \end{bmatrix}^{10} = \begin{bmatrix} 2^{10} & 0 & 0 \\ 0 & 1 & 0 \\ 0 & 0 & 3^{10} \end{bmatrix}$$

EXAMPLE 7 If B is a diagonal matrix, each column of AB is just the product of the corresponding column of A with the corresponding diagonal entry of B.

a $$\begin{bmatrix} 4 & 2 & 1 \\ -1 & 0 & 6 \\ 2 & 1 & -3 \end{bmatrix} \begin{bmatrix} 2 & 0 & 0 \\ 0 & -1 & 0 \\ 0 & 0 & 3 \end{bmatrix} = \begin{bmatrix} 8 & -2 & 3 \\ -2 & 0 & 18 \\ 4 & -1 & -9 \end{bmatrix}$$

$$
\mathbf{b} \quad \begin{bmatrix} 3 & 0 & -1 & 2 \\ -1 & 1 & 0 & 1 \\ 4 & -1 & -2 & 1 \\ 0 & 1 & 3 & -4 \end{bmatrix} \begin{bmatrix} 4 & 0 & 0 & 0 \\ 0 & 0 & 0 & 0 \\ 0 & 0 & 3 & 0 \\ 0 & 0 & 0 & -2 \end{bmatrix} = \begin{bmatrix} 12 & 0 & -3 & -4 \\ -4 & 0 & 0 & -2 \\ 16 & 0 & -6 & -2 \\ 0 & 0 & 9 & 8 \end{bmatrix}
$$

EXAMPLE 8 If A and B are both diagonal matrices having n rows and n columns, they commute. In other words, $AB = BA$.

$$
\mathbf{a} \quad \begin{bmatrix} 2 & 0 & 0 \\ 0 & -1 & 0 \\ 0 & 0 & 3 \end{bmatrix} \begin{bmatrix} -2 & 0 & 0 \\ 0 & 4 & 0 \\ 0 & 0 & -6 \end{bmatrix} = \begin{bmatrix} -4 & 0 & 0 \\ 0 & -4 & 0 \\ 0 & 0 & -18 \end{bmatrix}
$$

$$
\mathbf{b} \quad \begin{bmatrix} -2 & 0 & 0 \\ 0 & 4 & 0 \\ 0 & 0 & -6 \end{bmatrix} \begin{bmatrix} 2 & 0 & 0 \\ 0 & -1 & 0 \\ 0 & 0 & 3 \end{bmatrix} = \begin{bmatrix} -4 & 0 & 0 \\ 0 & -4 & 0 \\ 0 & 0 & -18 \end{bmatrix}
$$

EXAMPLE 9 Much pathology can occur for matrix products. For example, each of the following can occur:

a We can have $AB \neq BA$.

$$
\begin{bmatrix} 2 & 1 \\ -1 & 0 \end{bmatrix} \begin{bmatrix} 1 & 0 \\ 3 & 1 \end{bmatrix} = \begin{bmatrix} 5 & 1 \\ -1 & 0 \end{bmatrix}
$$

$$
\begin{bmatrix} 1 & 0 \\ 3 & 1 \end{bmatrix} \begin{bmatrix} 2 & 1 \\ -1 & 0 \end{bmatrix} = \begin{bmatrix} 2 & 1 \\ 5 & 3 \end{bmatrix}
$$

b We can have $A \neq 0$, $B \neq 0$, and yet $AB = 0$.

$$
\begin{bmatrix} 0 & 1 \\ 0 & 0 \end{bmatrix} \begin{bmatrix} 0 & 4 \\ 0 & 0 \end{bmatrix} = \begin{bmatrix} 0 & 0 \\ 0 & 0 \end{bmatrix}
$$

$$
\begin{bmatrix} 1 & 1 \\ 1 & 1 \end{bmatrix} \begin{bmatrix} 1 & 1 \\ -1 & -1 \end{bmatrix} = \begin{bmatrix} 0 & 0 \\ 0 & 0 \end{bmatrix}
$$

c We can have $A \neq 0$ and $A^2 = 0$.

$$\begin{bmatrix} 0 & 1 \\ 0 & 0 \end{bmatrix}^2 = \begin{bmatrix} 0 & 0 \\ 0 & 0 \end{bmatrix}$$

$$\begin{bmatrix} 1 & -1 \\ 1 & -1 \end{bmatrix}^2 = \begin{bmatrix} 0 & 0 \\ 0 & 0 \end{bmatrix}$$

d We can have $A \neq 0$, $A^2 \neq 0$, $A^3 = 0$.

$$\begin{bmatrix} 0 & 1 & 1 \\ 0 & 0 & 1 \\ 0 & 0 & 0 \end{bmatrix}^2 = \begin{bmatrix} 0 & 1 & 1 \\ 0 & 0 & 1 \\ 0 & 0 & 0 \end{bmatrix} \begin{bmatrix} 0 & 1 & 1 \\ 0 & 0 & 1 \\ 0 & 0 & 0 \end{bmatrix} = \begin{bmatrix} 0 & 0 & 1 \\ 0 & 0 & 0 \\ 0 & 0 & 0 \end{bmatrix}$$

$$\begin{bmatrix} 0 & 1 & 1 \\ 0 & 0 & 1 \\ 0 & 0 & 0 \end{bmatrix}^3 = \begin{bmatrix} 0 & 1 & 1 \\ 0 & 0 & 1 \\ 0 & 0 & 0 \end{bmatrix} \begin{bmatrix} 0 & 0 & 1 \\ 0 & 0 & 0 \\ 0 & 0 & 0 \end{bmatrix} = \begin{bmatrix} 0 & 0 & 0 \\ 0 & 0 & 0 \\ 0 & 0 & 0 \end{bmatrix}$$

e We can have $A^2 = A$, with $A \neq 0$ and $A \neq I$.

$$\begin{bmatrix} \frac{1}{2} & \frac{1}{2} \\ \frac{1}{2} & \frac{1}{2} \end{bmatrix}^2 = \begin{bmatrix} \frac{1}{2} & \frac{1}{2} \\ \frac{1}{2} & \frac{1}{2} \end{bmatrix} \begin{bmatrix} \frac{1}{2} & \frac{1}{2} \\ \frac{1}{2} & \frac{1}{2} \end{bmatrix} = \begin{bmatrix} \frac{1}{2} & \frac{1}{2} \\ \frac{1}{2} & \frac{1}{2} \end{bmatrix}$$

This is the matrix of the projection onto the vector $\frac{1}{\sqrt{2}}(1,1)$.

f We can have $A^2 = I$ with $A \neq I$ and $A \neq -I$.

$$\begin{bmatrix} -1 & 0 \\ 0 & 1 \end{bmatrix}^2 = \begin{bmatrix} -1 & 0 \\ 0 & 1 \end{bmatrix} \begin{bmatrix} -1 & 0 \\ 0 & 1 \end{bmatrix} = \begin{bmatrix} 1 & 0 \\ 0 & 1 \end{bmatrix}$$

This is the matrix of reflection in the y-axis. Certainly reflecting twice returns us to our initial position.

EXAMPLE 10 Suppose E is obtained from I by interchanging two rows of I. Then EA simply interchanges the same two rows of A.

a $$\begin{bmatrix} 1 & 0 & 0 \\ 0 & 0 & 1 \\ 0 & 1 & 0 \end{bmatrix} \begin{bmatrix} 4 & 2 & 1 & -1 \\ 3 & 1 & 0 & 1 \\ -2 & 1 & 6 & -5 \end{bmatrix} = \begin{bmatrix} 4 & 2 & 1 & -1 \\ -2 & 1 & 6 & -5 \\ 3 & 1 & 0 & 1 \end{bmatrix}$$

Certainly $E^2 = I$, for example,

$$\mathbf{b} \quad \begin{bmatrix} 1 & 0 & 0 \\ 0 & 0 & 1 \\ 0 & 1 & 0 \end{bmatrix} \begin{bmatrix} 1 & 0 & 0 \\ 0 & 0 & 1 \\ 0 & 1 & 0 \end{bmatrix} = \begin{bmatrix} 1 & 0 & 0 \\ 0 & 1 & 0 \\ 0 & 0 & 1 \end{bmatrix}$$

Suppose F is obtained from I by multiplying one row of I by $a \neq 0$. Then FA just multiplies the same row of A by a.

$$\mathbf{c} \quad \begin{bmatrix} 1 & 0 & 0 \\ 0 & 1 & 0 \\ 0 & 0 & a \end{bmatrix} \begin{bmatrix} 4 & 2 & 1 & -1 \\ 3 & 1 & 0 & 1 \\ -2 & 1 & 6 & -5 \end{bmatrix} = \begin{bmatrix} 4 & 2 & 1 & -1 \\ 3 & 1 & 0 & 1 \\ -2a & a & 6a & -5a \end{bmatrix}$$

Given such an F, suppose F_1 is obtained from I by multiplying the same row by $1/a$. Then $F_1F = I$.

$$\mathbf{d} \quad \begin{bmatrix} 1 & 0 & 0 \\ 0 & 1 & 0 \\ 0 & 0 & 1/a \end{bmatrix} \begin{bmatrix} 1 & 0 & 0 \\ 0 & 1 & 0 \\ 0 & 0 & a \end{bmatrix} = \begin{bmatrix} 1 & 0 & 0 \\ 0 & 1 & 0 \\ 0 & 0 & 1 \end{bmatrix}$$

Suppose G is obtained from I by adding to one row, say row i, of I, b times another row, say row j, $j \neq i$. Then GA is found by adding to row i of A, b times row j of A.

$$\mathbf{e} \quad \begin{bmatrix} 1 & 0 & b \\ 0 & 1 & 0 \\ 0 & 0 & 1 \end{bmatrix} \begin{bmatrix} 4 & 2 & 1 & -1 \\ 3 & 1 & 0 & 1 \\ -2 & 1 & 6 & -5 \end{bmatrix} = \begin{bmatrix} 4-2b & 2+b & 1+6b & -1-5b \\ 3 & 1 & 0 & 1 \\ -2 & 1 & 6 & -5 \end{bmatrix}$$

Given such a G, suppose G_1 is obtained from I by adding to row i of I, $-b$ times row j of I. Then $G_1G = I$.

$$\mathbf{f} \quad \begin{bmatrix} 1 & 0 & -b \\ 0 & 1 & 0 \\ 0 & 0 & 1 \end{bmatrix} \begin{bmatrix} 1 & 0 & b \\ 0 & 1 & 0 \\ 0 & 0 & 1 \end{bmatrix} = \begin{bmatrix} 1 & 0 & 0 \\ 0 & 1 & 0 \\ 0 & 0 & 1 \end{bmatrix}$$

EXAMPLE 11 Example 10 shows that a row operation on a matrix A can be performed by multiplying on the left of A by a suitable matrix, such as the matrices E, F, or G given above. The effect of such an operation can be undone by a related row operation given by multiplying on the left by a suitable matrix, respectively E, F_1, and G_1.

This information can be used along with the associative law of multiplication (rule **1c**) to prove that the method of row reduction of Chapter 1 does in fact preserve the solutions of a system.

For example, suppose $A\bar{u} = \bar{0}$. Then for any matrix B for which the product BA is defined we have $(BA)\bar{u} = B(A\bar{u}) = B\bar{0} = \bar{0}$. We conclude that

4 *Every vector in the null space of A is* also *in the null space of BA.*

Suppose E, F, and G are matrices like the E, F, and G of Example 10. Then from property **4** we have:

5 *Every vector in the null space of A is also in the null space of each of the matrices EA, FA, and GA.*

Select E, F_1, and G_1 as in Example 10. We can use this result with A replaced respectively by EA, FA, and GA and B replaced by E, F_1, and G_1 respectively to conclude that each of the following statements is true.

6
- **a** *Every vector in the null space of EA is also in the null space of $E(EA)$.*
- **b** *Every vector in the null space of FA is also in the null space of $F_1(FA)$.*
- **c** *Every vector in the null space of GA is also in the null space of $G_1(GA)$.*

We showed in Example 10 that $EE = I$, $F_1F = I$, and $G_1G = I$. Thus the associative law gives

$$E(EA) = (EE)A = IA = A$$
$$F_1(FA) = (F_1F)A = IA = A$$
$$G_1(GA) = (G_1G)A = IA = A$$

We combine this information with that given in statements **5** and **6** to conclude that

7 *Each of the matrices A, EA, FA, and GA has the same null space.*

Since a row operation on A can be performed by multiplying on the left of A by a matrix such as E, F, or G, we have shown that row operations of the kind given in Chapter 1 *do not change* the solutions to $A\bar{u} = \bar{0}$.

A similar argument can be given to show that row operations applied to the augmented matrix do not change the solutions to $A\bar{u} = \bar{v}$.

EXERCISES

1 For the given matrices verify that $A(BC) = (AB)C$ and that $A(B + C) = AB + AC$

$$A = \begin{bmatrix} 2 & 1 \\ 0 & 1 \end{bmatrix}, \quad B = \begin{bmatrix} 3 & -1 \\ 1 & 1 \end{bmatrix}, \quad C = \begin{bmatrix} -1 & 1 \\ 1 & 1 \end{bmatrix}$$

2 Solve for B where $2A - 3B = AC$.

3 Show that $A^2 - 4I = (A + 2I)(A - 2I)$.

4 Is it always true that $(A + B)^2 = A^2 + 2AB + B^2$?

5 Suppose R is a counterclockwise rotation through the angle θ, T is a counterclockwise rotation through the angle φ, and S is a counterclockwise rotation through the angle ψ. Describe $R(ST)$, $(RS)T$, $R(S^2T^3)$, and $(RS^2)T^3$.

6 Find each of the following products.

a $\begin{bmatrix} 0 & 0 \\ 0 & 0 \end{bmatrix} \begin{bmatrix} 1 & 2 \\ 1 & 1 \end{bmatrix}$ **b** $\begin{bmatrix} 0 & 0 \\ 0 & 0 \end{bmatrix} \begin{bmatrix} 1 & 2 & 1 \\ 1 & 1 & 1 \end{bmatrix}$

c $\begin{bmatrix} 1 & 0 \\ 0 & 1 \end{bmatrix} \begin{bmatrix} 1 & 2 \\ 1 & 1 \end{bmatrix}$ **d** $\begin{bmatrix} 1 & 0 \\ 0 & 1 \end{bmatrix} \begin{bmatrix} 1 & 2 & 1 \\ 1 & 1 & 1 \end{bmatrix}$

e $\begin{bmatrix} 0 & 0 & 0 & 0 \\ 0 & 0 & 0 & 0 \end{bmatrix} \begin{bmatrix} 3 & 1 \\ 2 & -1 \\ 0 & 1 \\ 1 & 1 \end{bmatrix}$ **f** $\begin{bmatrix} 3 & 1 \\ 2 & -1 \\ 0 & 1 \\ 1 & 1 \end{bmatrix} \begin{bmatrix} 1 & 0 \\ 0 & 1 \end{bmatrix}$

g $\begin{bmatrix} 2 & 1 & 0 \\ 1 & 1 & 1 \end{bmatrix} \begin{bmatrix} 1 & 0 & 0 \\ 0 & 1 & 0 \\ 0 & 0 & 1 \end{bmatrix} \begin{bmatrix} 0 & 0 \\ 0 & 0 \\ 0 & 0 \end{bmatrix} \begin{bmatrix} 2 & 1 \\ 1 & 1 \\ 1 & 1 \end{bmatrix}$

7 Find each of the following products.

a $\begin{bmatrix} 2 & 1 \\ 0 & 0 \end{bmatrix} \begin{bmatrix} 3 & 2 \\ 1 & 1 \end{bmatrix}$ **b** $\begin{bmatrix} 3 & 2 \\ 1 & 1 \end{bmatrix} \begin{bmatrix} -1 & 0 \\ 1 & 0 \end{bmatrix}$

c $\begin{bmatrix} 4 & 1 & 2 \\ 0 & 0 & 0 \\ 0 & 0 & 0 \end{bmatrix} \begin{bmatrix} 0 & 3 & 1 & 6 \\ 0 & 1 & 2 & 1 \\ 0 & 0 & 0 & 0 \end{bmatrix}$ **d** $\begin{bmatrix} 3 & 1 & 0 \\ 0 & 0 & 0 \\ 1 & 2 & 0 \end{bmatrix}^2$

8 Find each of the following products.

a $\begin{bmatrix} 3 & 0 \\ 0 & -1 \end{bmatrix} \begin{bmatrix} 4 & 2 & 6 & \frac{1}{2} \\ -2 & 1 & 0 & -\frac{1}{2} \end{bmatrix}$

b $\begin{bmatrix} -4 & 0 & 0 & 0 \\ 0 & \frac{1}{2} & 0 & 0 \\ 0 & 0 & 3 & 0 \\ 0 & 0 & 0 & -\frac{1}{2} \end{bmatrix} \begin{bmatrix} 6 & 6 & 1 & 6 \\ -1 & 0 & 1 & 1 \\ 0 & 1 & 3 & 0 \\ 0 & 2 & -1 & 1 \end{bmatrix}$

c $\begin{bmatrix} 6 & 6 & 1 & 6 \\ -1 & 0 & 1 & 1 \\ 0 & 1 & 3 & 0 \\ 0 & 2 & -1 & 1 \end{bmatrix} \begin{bmatrix} -4 & 0 & 0 & 0 \\ 0 & \frac{1}{2} & 0 & 0 \\ 0 & 0 & 3 & 0 \\ 0 & 0 & 0 & -\frac{1}{2} \end{bmatrix}$

d $\begin{bmatrix} 2 & 1 \\ 1 & 0 \\ 1 & 1 \\ 1 & -1 \end{bmatrix} \begin{bmatrix} \frac{1}{2} & 0 \\ 0 & \frac{3}{2} \end{bmatrix}$

9 Find each of the following products.

a $\begin{bmatrix} 1 & 0 & 0 \\ 0 & 2 & 0 \\ 0 & 0 & 3 \end{bmatrix}^3$ **b** $\begin{bmatrix} 3 & 0 & 0 \\ 0 & 7 & 0 \\ 0 & 0 & -1 \end{bmatrix}^2 \begin{bmatrix} 1 & 0 & 0 \\ 0 & 0 & 0 \\ 0 & 0 & -2 \end{bmatrix}^3$

c $\begin{bmatrix} 1 & 0 & 0 \\ 0 & -1 & 0 \\ 0 & 0 & 1 \end{bmatrix}^{27}$ **d** $\begin{bmatrix} 0 & 0 & 0 & 0 \\ 0 & 1 & 0 & 0 \\ 0 & 0 & 3 & 0 \\ 0 & 0 & 0 & -1 \end{bmatrix}^3$

10 For each of the following matrices A find $p(A)$, $q(A)$, and $r(A)$, where $p(\lambda) = \lambda^3 - \lambda^2 + \lambda$, $q(\lambda) = \lambda - 3$, and $r(\lambda) = 2\lambda^2 - 4$. Note the simplicity of these calculations when A is diagonal.

a $\begin{bmatrix} 1 & 2 \\ 0 & -1 \end{bmatrix}$ **b** $\begin{bmatrix} 3 & 1 & 0 \\ 2 & -1 & 1 \\ 1 & 1 & 2 \end{bmatrix}$ **c** $\begin{bmatrix} 4 & 0 & 0 \\ 0 & -1 & 0 \\ 0 & 0 & 2 \end{bmatrix}$

11 Suppose

$$A = \begin{bmatrix} a & 0 & 0 \\ 0 & b & 0 \\ 0 & 0 & c \end{bmatrix}$$

and $p(\lambda)$ is a polynomial. What is $p(A)$? In particular what is $p(A)$ when $p(\lambda) = (\lambda - a)(\lambda - b)(\lambda - c)$?

12 Find a matrix B such that $B^3 = \begin{bmatrix} 8 & 0 & 0 \\ 0 & 27 & 0 \\ 0 & 0 & -8 \end{bmatrix}$

13 Compute $A^3 - 3A^2 + A - 2I$ for $A = \begin{bmatrix} 1 & 0 & 0 \\ 0 & 2 & 0 \\ 0 & 0 & 3 \end{bmatrix}$ and for $A = \begin{bmatrix} 2 & 1 \\ 1 & 3 \end{bmatrix}$

14 Suppose A has two rows and two columns, and $AB = BA$ for every diagonal matrix B with two rows and two columns. Show that A is a diagonal matrix.

15 Describe linear transformations S and T such that

a $ST \neq TS$ **b** $ST = TS$

c $S \neq 0$, $T \neq 0$, and $ST = 0$ **d** $T^2 = T$, $S^2 = S$, and $ST = 0$

16 **a** Find A such that $A^2 \neq A$ and $A^3 = A$.

b Find A such that $A \neq I$ and $A^3 = I$.

c Find A such that $A^3 \neq 0$ and $A^4 = 0$.

17 Suppose $P^2 = P$ and $Q^2 = Q$. Show that

a $(I - P)^2 = I - P$.

b If $PQ = QP$, then $(P + Q - QP)^2 = P + Q - QP$.

c Find matrices P and Q such that $P^2 = P$, $Q^2 = Q$, and $PQ \neq QP$.

18 Suppose $AC = I$ and $BD = I$. Show that $(AB)(DC) = I$.

19 Show that $A^3 - I = (A^2 + A + I)(A - I)$.

20 Use the techniques of Example 10 to find, by noting the form of the left matrix,

a $\begin{bmatrix} 0 & 1 & 0 \\ 1 & 0 & 0 \\ 0 & 0 & 1 \end{bmatrix} \begin{bmatrix} 3 & 2 & 1 \\ 1 & -1 & 1 \\ 2 & 1 & 1 \end{bmatrix}$ **b** $\begin{bmatrix} 1 & 0 & 0 \\ 0 & \frac{1}{2} & 0 \\ 0 & 0 & 1 \end{bmatrix} \begin{bmatrix} 3 & 2 & 1 \\ 1 & -1 & 1 \\ 2 & 1 & 1 \end{bmatrix}$

c $\begin{bmatrix} 1 & 0 & 0 \\ 3 & 1 & 0 \\ 0 & 0 & 1 \end{bmatrix} \begin{bmatrix} 3 & 2 & 1 \\ 1 & -1 & 1 \\ 2 & 1 & 1 \end{bmatrix}$ **d** $\begin{bmatrix} 1 & 0 & 0 \\ -3 & 1 & 0 \\ 0 & 0 & 1 \end{bmatrix} \begin{bmatrix} 3 & 2 & 1 \\ 1 & -1 & 1 \\ 2 & 1 & 1 \end{bmatrix}$

21 For each of the following matrices A find a matrix A_1 such that $A_1 A = I$ by using the techniques of Example 10.

a $A = \begin{bmatrix} 0 & 1 & 0 \\ 1 & 0 & 0 \\ 0 & 0 & 1 \end{bmatrix}$ **b** $A = \begin{bmatrix} 1 & 0 & 0 \\ 0 & \frac{1}{2} & 0 \\ 0 & 0 & 1 \end{bmatrix}$

c $A = \begin{bmatrix} 1 & 0 & 0 \\ 3 & 1 & 0 \\ 0 & 0 & 1 \end{bmatrix}$ **d** $A = \begin{bmatrix} 1 & 0 & 0 \\ -3 & 1 & 0 \\ 0 & 0 & 1 \end{bmatrix}$

22 Find $EDCBA$ for

$$A = \begin{bmatrix} 2 & 1 \\ 1 & 1 \end{bmatrix} \quad B = \begin{bmatrix} 0 & 1 \\ 1 & 0 \end{bmatrix} \quad C = \begin{bmatrix} 1 & 0 \\ -2 & 1 \end{bmatrix}$$

$$D = \begin{bmatrix} 1 & 0 \\ 0 & -1 \end{bmatrix} \quad E = \begin{bmatrix} 1 & -1 \\ 0 & 1 \end{bmatrix}$$

Can you find a matrix A' such that $A'A = I$?

23 Find matrices A and B such that the null space of BA is *not* the same as the null space of A.

□ **24** Calculate, using the tricks of this section,

a $\begin{bmatrix} 0 & 0 \\ 0 & 0 \end{bmatrix} \begin{bmatrix} i & 2i \\ 1+i & 3-i \end{bmatrix}$ **b** $\begin{bmatrix} 1 & 0 \\ 0 & 1 \end{bmatrix} \begin{bmatrix} i & 2i \\ 1+i & 3-i \end{bmatrix}$

c $\begin{bmatrix} 2 & 1 \\ 0 & 0 \end{bmatrix} \begin{bmatrix} i & 2i \\ 1+i & 3-i \end{bmatrix}$ **d** $\begin{bmatrix} i & 2i \\ 1+i & 3-i \end{bmatrix} \begin{bmatrix} 0 & i \\ 0 & 1 \end{bmatrix}$

e $\begin{bmatrix} i & 0 \\ 0 & 2i \end{bmatrix} \begin{bmatrix} i & 2i \\ 1+i & 3-i \end{bmatrix}$ **f** $\begin{bmatrix} i & 2i \\ 1+i & 3-i \end{bmatrix} \begin{bmatrix} i & 0 \\ 0 & 2i \end{bmatrix}$

g $\begin{bmatrix} i & 0 \\ 0 & -i \end{bmatrix}^4$

SECTION 6 The Inverse

If a, b, and c are numbers, and $a \neq 0$ we can solve the equation $ab = c$ for b by multiplying by $a^{-1} = 1/a$ to obtain $b = a^{-1}c$. The number a^{-1} has the property $a^{-1}a = 1$.

We shall discuss in this section a similar process for solving matrix equations by multiplying by the "inverse" of a matrix. The discussion will be confined to square matrices, that is, matrices with the same number of rows as columns.

We call B **an inverse** of A if

1 $$BA = I$$

We also say that A is **invertible** if A has an inverse. We wish to give conditions that guarantee that A is invertible. We shall also be able to show that a matrix has at most one inverse. A method for calculating this inverse will be given.

Suppose $BA = I$ and that $A\bar{u} = \bar{0}$. We then have $B(A\bar{u}) = (BA)\bar{u} = \bar{u}$. Since we also have $B(A\bar{u}) = B\bar{0} = \bar{0}$, we conclude that $\bar{u}$ must be zero. This shows that

2 *If A is invertible, then the equation $A\bar{u} = \bar{0}$ has only one solution, namely, $\bar{u} = \bar{0}$.*

Since the converse of this result is also true, we have

THEOREM 13 Suppose A is square; it is then invertible if and only if the equation $A\bar{u} = \bar{0}$ has a unique solution.

We give a proof of this result in Appendix 2, where we also establish the important result:

THEOREM 14 If A is square and $BA = I$, then $AB = I$.

We can use this theorem and a trick to show that an invertible matrix has exactly one inverse. Suppose that

$$BA = I \qquad \text{and} \qquad CA = I$$

Theorem 14 then tells us that $AB = I$. We thus have

$$C = CI = C(AB) = (CA)B = IB = B$$

which indeed shows that

3 *If A is invertible it has a unique inverse.*

Denoting this unique inverse by A^{-1}, we have

$$A^{-1}A = AA^{-1} = I$$

Theorem 13 gives a condition for A to be invertible. Other conditions will be discussed in Section 8. We shall now show how to construct the inverse of an invertible matrix A. For simplicity, suppose that A has two rows and two columns. Suppose

$$A^{-1} = \begin{bmatrix} B_{11} & B_{12} \\ B_{21} & B_{22} \end{bmatrix}$$

so that $$A^{-1}\begin{bmatrix} 1 \\ 0 \end{bmatrix} = \begin{bmatrix} B_{11} \\ B_{21} \end{bmatrix} \qquad \text{and} \qquad A^{-1}\begin{bmatrix} 0 \\ 1 \end{bmatrix} = \begin{bmatrix} B_{12} \\ B_{22} \end{bmatrix}$$

Multiplying each of these by A and using the fact that $AA^{-1} = I$, we have

$$\begin{bmatrix} 1 \\ 0 \end{bmatrix} = A\begin{bmatrix} B_{11} \\ B_{21} \end{bmatrix} \qquad \text{and} \qquad \begin{bmatrix} 0 \\ 1 \end{bmatrix} = A\begin{bmatrix} B_{12} \\ B_{22} \end{bmatrix}$$

Therefore,

4 *The columns of A^{-1} are the solutions to* $A\bar{u} = \begin{bmatrix} 1 \\ 0 \end{bmatrix}$ and $A\bar{u} = \begin{bmatrix} 0 \\ 1 \end{bmatrix}$

We can solve each of these equations by forming the augmented matrix of each and reducing. Since the same operations will be performed on each matrix, we can combine the procedures and proceed as follows: If

$$A = \begin{bmatrix} A_{11} & A_{12} \\ A_{21} & A_{22} \end{bmatrix}$$

we form the matrix

5 $$A_1 = \left[\begin{array}{cc:cc} A_{11} & A_{12} & 1 & 0 \\ A_{21} & A_{22} & 0 & 1 \end{array}\right]$$

We reduce this to

6 $$B_1 = \left[\begin{array}{cc:cc} 1 & 0 & B_{11} & B_{12} \\ 0 & 1 & B_{21} & B_{22} \end{array}\right]$$

Then

$$A^{-1} = \begin{bmatrix} B_{11} & B_{12} \\ B_{21} & B_{22} \end{bmatrix}$$

This is just a device for solving equations

$$A\bar{u} = \begin{bmatrix} 1 \\ 0 \end{bmatrix} \quad \text{and} \quad A\bar{u} = \begin{bmatrix} 0 \\ 1 \end{bmatrix}$$

at the same time.

This method clearly generalizes to give a procedure for finding A^{-1}. We form $A_1 = [A \,\vdots\, I]$ and reduce to $[I \,\vdots\, B]$. Then $A^{-1} = B$.

Some examples of the use of this method are given below. It is important that the student learn to find inverses quickly and correctly.

EXAMPLE 1 The matrix

$$A = \begin{bmatrix} 2 & 1 \\ -4 & -2 \end{bmatrix} \quad \text{reduces to} \quad \begin{bmatrix} 1 & \frac{1}{2} \\ 0 & 0 \end{bmatrix}$$

Therefore $A\bar{u} = \bar{0}$ has solutions $\bar{u} \neq \bar{0}$. Theorem 13 tells us that A is not invertible.

EXAMPLE 2 Since the matrix

$$A = \begin{bmatrix} 3 & 1 \\ -1 & 6 \end{bmatrix} \quad \text{reduces to} \quad \begin{bmatrix} 1 & 0 \\ 0 & 1 \end{bmatrix}$$

A is invertible. To find A^{-1} we form

$$\left[\begin{array}{cc:cc} 3 & 1 & 1 & 0 \\ -1 & 6 & 0 & 1 \end{array}\right] \quad \text{and reduce it to} \quad \left[\begin{array}{cc:cc} 1 & 0 & \frac{6}{19} & -\frac{1}{19} \\ 0 & 1 & \frac{1}{19} & \frac{3}{19} \end{array}\right]$$

We conclude that

$$A^{-1} = \begin{bmatrix} \frac{6}{19} & -\frac{1}{19} \\ \frac{1}{19} & \frac{3}{19} \end{bmatrix}$$

The student should check to see that indeed $A^{-1}A = I$ and $AA^{-1} = I$.

EXAMPLE 3 Since the matrix

$$\begin{bmatrix} 1 & -7 & -14 \\ 2 & 1 & -1 \\ 1 & 3 & 4 \end{bmatrix} \quad \text{reduces to} \quad \begin{bmatrix} 1 & 0 & -\frac{7}{5} \\ 0 & 1 & \frac{9}{5} \\ 0 & 0 & 0 \end{bmatrix}$$

it does *not* have an inverse.

The matrix

$$A = \begin{bmatrix} 3 & 1 & 0 \\ 1 & -1 & 2 \\ 1 & 1 & 1 \end{bmatrix} \quad \text{reduces to} \quad \begin{bmatrix} 1 & 0 & 0 \\ 0 & 1 & 0 \\ 0 & 0 & 1 \end{bmatrix}$$

Therefore A is invertible. Forming

$$\left[\begin{array}{ccc:ccc} 3 & 1 & 0 & 1 & 0 & 0 \\ 1 & -1 & 2 & 0 & 1 & 0 \\ 1 & 1 & 1 & 0 & 0 & 1 \end{array}\right]$$

and reducing it to

$$\left[\begin{array}{ccc:ccc} 1 & 0 & 0 & \frac{3}{8} & \frac{1}{8} & -\frac{2}{8} \\ 0 & 1 & 0 & -\frac{1}{8} & -\frac{3}{8} & \frac{6}{8} \\ 0 & 0 & 1 & -\frac{2}{8} & \frac{2}{8} & \frac{4}{8} \end{array}\right] \quad \text{we have} \quad A^{-1} = \begin{bmatrix} \frac{3}{8} & \frac{1}{8} & -\frac{2}{8} \\ -\frac{1}{8} & -\frac{3}{8} & \frac{6}{8} \\ -\frac{2}{8} & \frac{2}{8} & \frac{4}{8} \end{bmatrix}$$

The student should of course carry out these calculations and check his results by showing that $A^{-1}A = I$.

EXAMPLE 4 The matrix

$$A = \begin{bmatrix} 1 & 1 & 1 & 1 \\ 0 & 1 & 1 & 1 \\ 0 & 0 & 1 & 1 \\ 0 & 0 & 0 & 1 \end{bmatrix} \quad \text{clearly reduces to } I_4$$

To find its inverse we reduce

$$\left[\begin{array}{cccc:cccc} 1 & 1 & 1 & 1 & 1 & 0 & 0 & 0 \\ 0 & 1 & 1 & 1 & 0 & 1 & 0 & 0 \\ 0 & 0 & 1 & 1 & 0 & 0 & 1 & 0 \\ 0 & 0 & 0 & 1 & 0 & 0 & 0 & 1 \end{array}\right]$$

to

$$\left[\begin{array}{cccc:cccc} 1 & 0 & 0 & 0 & 1 & -1 & 0 & 0 \\ 0 & 1 & 0 & 0 & 0 & 1 & -1 & 0 \\ 0 & 0 & 1 & 0 & 0 & 0 & 1 & -1 \\ 0 & 0 & 0 & 1 & 0 & 0 & 0 & 1 \end{array}\right]$$

so that

$$A^{-1} = \begin{bmatrix} 1 & -1 & 0 & 0 \\ 0 & 1 & -1 & 0 \\ 0 & 0 & 1 & -1 \\ 0 & 0 & 0 & 1 \end{bmatrix}$$

EXAMPLE 5 Determining invertibility and finding inverses for diagonal matrices is particularly simple, for if one of the diagonal entries is zero, the matrix is not invertible. If all the diagonal entries are *not* zero, the inverse is then obtained by inverting these diagonal entries. For example,

$$\begin{bmatrix} 1 & 0 & 0 \\ 0 & 0 & 0 \\ 0 & 0 & 3 \end{bmatrix}$$

is not invertible, while

$$\begin{bmatrix} 1 & 0 & 0 \\ 0 & 2 & 0 \\ 0 & 0 & 3 \end{bmatrix}^{-1} = \begin{bmatrix} 1 & 0 & 0 \\ 0 & \frac{1}{2} & 0 \\ 0 & 0 & \frac{1}{3} \end{bmatrix}$$

and

$$\begin{bmatrix} 3 & 0 & 0 & 0 & 0 \\ 0 & -2 & 0 & 0 & 0 \\ 0 & 0 & \frac{1}{4} & 0 & 0 \\ 0 & 0 & 0 & 6 & 0 \\ 0 & 0 & 0 & 0 & -1 \end{bmatrix}^{-1} = \begin{bmatrix} \frac{1}{3} & 0 & 0 & 0 & 0 \\ 0 & -\frac{1}{2} & 0 & 0 & 0 \\ 0 & 0 & 4 & 0 & 0 \\ 0 & 0 & 0 & \frac{1}{6} & 0 \\ 0 & 0 & 0 & 0 & -1 \end{bmatrix}$$

EXAMPLE 6 Suppose A is **upper triangular**, that is, the entries below the diagonal are zeros. If one of the diagonal entries of A is zero, A is not invertible. For example,

$$A = \begin{bmatrix} 2 & 1 & 1 \\ 0 & 0 & 3 \\ 0 & 0 & 1 \end{bmatrix}$$

is not invertible.

If all the diagonal entries of A are *nonzero*, there is a method for calculating A^{-1} which is quicker than the method of forming matrix **5** and reducing to matrix **6**. For example, if

$$A = \begin{bmatrix} 1 & 2 & -1 \\ 0 & 3 & 1 \\ 0 & 0 & -4 \end{bmatrix}$$

A^{-1} must then be of the form

$$A^{-1} = \begin{bmatrix} 1 & a & b \\ 0 & \frac{1}{3} & c \\ 0 & 0 & -\frac{1}{4} \end{bmatrix}$$

and we can determine a, b, and c from the relation $AA^{-1} = I$. Since we have

$$AA^{-1} = \begin{bmatrix} 1 & a + \frac{2}{3} & b + 2c + \frac{1}{4} \\ 0 & 1 & 3c - \frac{1}{4} \\ 0 & 0 & 1 \end{bmatrix}$$

we must have $a + \frac{2}{3} = 0$, $b + 2c + \frac{1}{4} = 0$, and $3c - \frac{1}{4} = 0$. These are easily solved to give $a = -\frac{2}{3}$, $c = \frac{1}{12}$, and $b = -\frac{5}{12}$ so that

$$A^{-1} = \begin{bmatrix} 1 & -\frac{2}{3} & -\frac{5}{12} \\ 0 & \frac{1}{3} & \frac{1}{12} \\ 0 & 0 & -\frac{1}{4} \end{bmatrix}$$

In other words, for upper triangular matrices the diagonal entries of A^{-1} are the reciprocals of the diagonal entries of A, and the entries below the diagonal of A^{-1} are all zero. The entries above the diagonal can then be simply calculated from the relation $AA^{-1} = I$.

EXERCISES

1 Use Theorem 13 to show that each of the following matrices is not invertible.

a $\begin{bmatrix} 1 & 1 \\ 2 & 2 \end{bmatrix}$ **b** $\begin{bmatrix} 5 & 2 & 6 \\ 1 & 2 & 2 \\ -1 & 2 & 0 \end{bmatrix}$ **c** $\begin{bmatrix} 1 & 2 & 0 & 3 \\ -1 & 1 & 0 & 4 \\ 4 & 1 & 0 & 2 \\ 3 & 2 & 0 & 1 \end{bmatrix}$

2 Use the method of forming matrix **5** and reducing to matrix **6** to find the inverse of each of the following matrices. Check by showing that $A^{-1}A = AA^{-1} = I$.

a $\begin{bmatrix} 6 & 1 \\ 2 & 4 \end{bmatrix}$ **b** $\begin{bmatrix} -1 & -1 \\ 1 & -1 \end{bmatrix}$ **c** $\begin{bmatrix} 1 & 2 \\ 3 & 4 \end{bmatrix}$

d $\begin{bmatrix} 1 & 0 \\ 2 & 1 \end{bmatrix}$ **e** $\begin{bmatrix} 2 & 1 & 1 \\ 1 & 3 & 1 \\ -1 & 4 & 0 \end{bmatrix}$ **f** $\begin{bmatrix} 1 & 1 & 1 \\ 0 & 1 & 1 \\ 0 & 0 & 1 \end{bmatrix}$

g $\begin{bmatrix} 3 & 1 & 2 \\ 4 & 1 & -6 \\ 1 & 0 & 1 \end{bmatrix}$ **h** $\begin{bmatrix} 1 & 2 & 1 & 1 \\ 0 & 2 & 0 & 1 \\ 0 & 0 & -\frac{1}{2} & 1 \\ 0 & 0 & 0 & -1 \end{bmatrix}$ **i** $\begin{bmatrix} 1 & 1 & 1 & 1 \\ 1 & 1 & 1 & -1 \\ 1 & 1 & -1 & 1 \\ 1 & -1 & 1 & 1 \end{bmatrix}$

3 Find the inverse of each of the following.

a $\begin{bmatrix} 1 & 1 \\ 0 & 1 \end{bmatrix}$ **b** $\begin{bmatrix} 1 & 1 & 1 \\ 0 & 1 & 1 \\ 0 & 0 & 1 \end{bmatrix}$ **c** $\begin{bmatrix} 1 & 1 & 1 & 1 & 1 \\ 0 & 1 & 1 & 1 & 1 \\ 0 & 0 & 1 & 1 & 1 \\ 0 & 0 & 0 & 1 & 1 \\ 0 & 0 & 0 & 0 & 1 \end{bmatrix}$

4 Find the inverse of each of the following.

a $\begin{bmatrix} 2 & 0 \\ 0 & -2 \end{bmatrix}$ **b** $\begin{bmatrix} \frac{1}{4} & 0 & 0 \\ 0 & \frac{1}{2} & 0 \\ 0 & 0 & \frac{1}{3} \end{bmatrix}$ **c** $\begin{bmatrix} 1 & 0 & 0 & 0 & 0 \\ 0 & 4 & 0 & 0 & 0 \\ 0 & 0 & 2 & 0 & 0 \\ 0 & 0 & 0 & -1 & 0 \\ 0 & 0 & 0 & 0 & 3 \end{bmatrix}$

5 Which of the following matrices are invertible? Use the method of Example 6 to find the inverse if the matrix is invertible.

a $\begin{bmatrix} 2 & 0 & -1 \\ 0 & 1 & 3 \\ 0 & 0 & 0 \end{bmatrix}$ **b** $\begin{bmatrix} 3 & 2 & 1 \\ 0 & 2 & 2 \\ 0 & 0 & -1 \end{bmatrix}$ **c** $\begin{bmatrix} 3 & 1 & 1 & 2 \\ 0 & 1 & 1 & 3 \\ 0 & 0 & 2 & 1 \\ 0 & 0 & 0 & -1 \end{bmatrix}$

d $\begin{bmatrix} 2 & -1 & 1 & 2 \\ 0 & 0 & 1 & 3 \\ 0 & 0 & 2 & 1 \\ 0 & 0 & 0 & -3 \end{bmatrix}$ **e** $\begin{bmatrix} 2 & 0 & 0 & 0 \\ 1 & 3 & 0 & 0 \\ -1 & 1 & 2 & 0 \\ 1 & 2 & 1 & 1 \end{bmatrix}$

6 If $ad - bc \neq 0$, show that $\begin{bmatrix} a & b \\ c & d \end{bmatrix}^{-1} = \dfrac{1}{ad - bc}\begin{bmatrix} d & -b \\ -c & a \end{bmatrix}$

7 Suppose $A = \begin{bmatrix} 1 & 0 & 0 \\ 0 & 1 & 0 \end{bmatrix}$ and $B = \begin{bmatrix} 1 & 0 \\ 0 & 1 \\ 0 & 0 \end{bmatrix}$

Find AB and BA.
Why does this not contradict Theorem 14?

8 Show that if A has m rows and n columns, and B has n rows and m columns, and if $m > n$, then AB is not invertible. (Hint: Apply Theorem 5 to B to find $\bar{u} \neq \bar{0}$ such that $B\bar{u} = \bar{0}$. Then apply property 2 to AB.)

□ 9 The method of forming the matrix 5 and reducing extends to complex matrices. Find the inverse of

a $\begin{bmatrix} i & 1 \\ 2 & -i \end{bmatrix}$ **b** $\begin{bmatrix} 1+i & 0 \\ 0 & 1-i \end{bmatrix}$

SECTION 7 The Inverse (continued)

If we know that A is invertible we can solve the equation

1 $$AB = C$$

for B by multiplying by A^{-1}. We have $A^{-1}(AB) = A^{-1}C$, and therefore $B = A^{-1}C$, since $A^{-1}(AB) = (A^{-1}A)B = IB = B$. Care must be exercised to maintain the correct order. For example, we *cannot* in general write $B = CA^{-1}$ as the solution to equation 1, for we do not in general know that $A^{-1}C = CA^{-1}$.

We can "cancel" invertible matrices. For example, if A is invertible and $AB = AC$, we can multiply by A^{-1} to conclude that $B = C$.

The inverse method can be used to describe the solution to $A\bar{u} = \bar{v}$, for if A is invertible, we can multiply by A^{-1} to obtain $\bar{v} = A^{-1}\bar{u}$. This method is particularly useful in calculating coordinates with respect to a basis. Suppose, for example, that $\bar{u}_1, \bar{u}_2, \ldots, \bar{u}_n$ is a basis for R^n. Let A be the matrix whose columns are $\bar{u}_1, \bar{u}_2, \ldots, \bar{u}_n$. Then the equation

$$\bar{u} = c_1\bar{u}_1 + c_2\bar{u}_2 + \cdots + c_n\bar{u}_n$$

can be rewritten (in column form) as

$$\bar{u} = A\bar{c} \qquad \text{where} \qquad \bar{c} = \begin{bmatrix} c_1 \\ c_2 \\ \vdots \\ c_n \end{bmatrix}$$

Thus

2 *The coordinates of $\bar{u}$ with respect to $\bar{u}_1, \bar{u}_2, \ldots, \bar{u}_n$ are just the entries of $A^{-1}\bar{u}$.*

The concept of inverse can be extended to linear transformations. For example, suppose T is a linear transformation from R^n into R^n. We can then find a matrix A such that $T\bar{u} = A\bar{u}$. (*See* Theorem 12.) We say that T is **invertible** if A is invertible. If S is the transformation defined by $S\bar{u} = A^{-1}\bar{u}$, we call S **the inverse** of T and write $S = T^{-1}$. In this case we have $T^{-1}T = I$, the identity operator. We also have (*see* Theorem 14) $TT^{-1} = I$.

Note the following two results:

3 *A linear transformation T from R^n into R^n is invertible if and only if the null space of T has dimension zero; that is, $T\bar{u} = \bar{0}$ implies that $\bar{u} = \bar{0}$.*

4 *Suppose T is invertible. Then $T\bar{u} = \bar{v}$ if and only if $T^{-1}\bar{v} = \bar{u}$.*

Property **3** is just the transformation form of Theorem 13. The proof of property **4** is simple. If $T\bar{u} = \bar{v}$, then

$$T^{-1}\bar{v} = T^{-1}(T\bar{u}) = (T^{-1}T)\bar{u} = I\bar{u} = \bar{u}$$

and, conversely, if $T^{-1}\bar{v} = \bar{u}$, then

$$T\bar{u} = T(T^{-1}\bar{v}) = (TT^{-1})\bar{v} = I\bar{v} = \bar{v}$$

Property **4** tells us that operating with T^{-1} undoes the effect of operating with T. In fact this property gives a way to describe T^{-1} without using matrices. Suppose that S and T are linear transformations from R^n into R^n and

5 $$S\bar{v} = \bar{u} \quad \text{if and only if} \quad T\bar{u} = \bar{v}.$$

Then we have $ST\bar{u} = S(T\bar{u}) = S\bar{v} = \bar{u}$; thus $ST = I$. Therefore, if A and B are the matrices of T and S, respectively, we have $BA = I$, and consequently, $B = A^{-1}$. We conclude that if S satisfies property **5** then S must be T^{-1}.

For vector spaces other than coordinate spaces we use the following definition of invertibility: If T is a linear transformation from V into V, T is **invertible** if there is a linear transformation S from V into V such that

6 $$ST = TS = I, \text{ the identity operator on } V$$

We can then show that there is at most one such transformation S. (The proof of this is identical with the proof of property **3**, page 144, except for the use of different symbols.) We therefore call S **the inverse** of T and write $S = T^{-1}$. The proof that property **4** holds in this general setting carries over without significant change. A general form of statement **3** will be proved in Appendix 2.

The assumption that S is linear is redundant, for it is a consequence of property **6**. A proof of this is outlined in Exercise 16.

For square matrices (and hence for linear transformations defined on R^n) Theorem 14 asserts that the condition $AB = I$ is a consequence of the assumption that $BA = I$. This is also true for linear transformations defined on finite dimensional spaces (as shown in Appendix 2) but may not be true for spaces that are not finite dimensional. (*See* Example 9.)

EXAMPLE 1 As shown in Example 3 of the previous section, if

$$A = \begin{bmatrix} 3 & 1 & 0 \\ 1 & -1 & 2 \\ 1 & 1 & 1 \end{bmatrix} \quad \text{then} \quad A^{-1} = \begin{bmatrix} \frac{3}{8} & \frac{1}{8} & -\frac{2}{8} \\ -\frac{1}{8} & -\frac{3}{8} & \frac{6}{8} \\ -\frac{2}{8} & \frac{2}{8} & \frac{4}{8} \end{bmatrix}$$

Thus the equation

$$AB = \begin{bmatrix} 4 & 1 & 2 & 0 \\ 1 & -1 & 1 & 0 \\ 1 & 1 & 2 & 1 \end{bmatrix}$$

has the unique solution

$$B = A^{-1}\begin{bmatrix} 4 & 1 & 2 & 0 \\ 1 & -1 & 1 & 0 \\ 1 & 1 & 2 & 1 \end{bmatrix} = \begin{bmatrix} \frac{11}{8} & 0 & \frac{3}{8} & -\frac{2}{8} \\ -\frac{1}{8} & 1 & \frac{7}{8} & \frac{6}{8} \\ -\frac{2}{8} & 0 & \frac{6}{8} & \frac{4}{8} \end{bmatrix}$$

EXAMPLE 2 If A is invertible, $AB = 0$ has only one solution, namely $B = 0$.

If A is *not* invertible, the equation does not have a unique solution, and therefore "cancellation" with matrices that are not invertible is not allowable.

For example, if

$$A = \begin{bmatrix} 0 & 1 \\ 0 & 0 \end{bmatrix} \quad \text{and} \quad B = \begin{bmatrix} 0 & 2 \\ 0 & 0 \end{bmatrix}$$

then certainly $AB = 0$ and $B \neq 0$.

EXAMPLE 3 Suppose we wish to find the coordinates of (x,y,z) with respect to the basis $(1,1,-1)$, $(1,-1,1)$, $(1,1,1)$. In other words, we wish to solve $c_1(1,1,-1) + c_2(1,-1,1) + c_3(1,1,1) = (x,y,z)$ for c_1, c_2, and c_3 in terms of x, y, and z. In column form this equation becomes

$$\begin{bmatrix} 1 & 1 & 1 \\ 1 & -1 & 1 \\ -1 & 1 & 1 \end{bmatrix}\begin{bmatrix} c_1 \\ c_2 \\ c_3 \end{bmatrix} = \begin{bmatrix} x \\ y \\ z \end{bmatrix}$$

Using the methods of Section 6 we have

$$\begin{bmatrix} 1 & 1 & 1 \\ 1 & -1 & 1 \\ -1 & 1 & 1 \end{bmatrix}^{-1} = \begin{bmatrix} \frac{1}{2} & 0 & -\frac{1}{2} \\ \frac{1}{2} & -\frac{1}{2} & 0 \\ 0 & \frac{1}{2} & \frac{1}{2} \end{bmatrix}$$

so that

$$\begin{bmatrix} c_1 \\ c_2 \\ c_3 \end{bmatrix} = \begin{bmatrix} \frac{1}{2} & 0 & -\frac{1}{2} \\ \frac{1}{2} & -\frac{1}{2} & 0 \\ 0 & \frac{1}{2} & \frac{1}{2} \end{bmatrix}\begin{bmatrix} x \\ y \\ z \end{bmatrix}$$

which gives

$$\begin{aligned} c_1 &= \tfrac{1}{2}x \qquad\qquad - \tfrac{1}{2}z \\ c_2 &= \tfrac{1}{2}x - \tfrac{1}{2}y \\ c_3 &= \qquad\quad \tfrac{1}{2}y + \tfrac{1}{2}z \end{aligned}$$

EXAMPLE 4 If

$$T\bar{u} = \begin{bmatrix} 2 & 1 \\ -1 & 3 \end{bmatrix} \bar{u}$$

then since (the student should check this)

$$\begin{bmatrix} 2 & 1 \\ -1 & 3 \end{bmatrix}^{-1} = \begin{bmatrix} \frac{3}{7} & -\frac{1}{7} \\ \frac{1}{7} & \frac{2}{7} \end{bmatrix}$$

the inverse transformation T^{-1} is given by

$$T^{-1}\bar{u} = \begin{bmatrix} \frac{3}{7} & -\frac{1}{7} \\ \frac{1}{7} & \frac{2}{7} \end{bmatrix} \bar{u}$$

EXAMPLE 5 Suppose T is a counterclockwise rotation in R^2 through the angle θ. Certainly we have $T\bar{u} \neq \bar{0}$ if $\bar{u} \neq \bar{0}$, and therefore, property **3** implies that T is invertible. The inverse of T merely undoes the effect of T. Clearly, if S is a counterclockwise rotation through the angle $-\theta$ (that is, a clockwise rotation through θ), we must have $S\bar{v} = \bar{u}$ if and only if $\bar{u} = T\bar{v}$.

We see from property **4** that $S = T^{-1}$. The matrices of T and S are (*see* Example 3, page 109)

$$\begin{bmatrix} \cos\theta & -\sin\theta \\ \sin\theta & \cos\theta \end{bmatrix} \quad \text{and} \quad \begin{bmatrix} \cos(-\theta) & -\sin(-\theta) \\ \sin(-\theta) & \cos(-\theta) \end{bmatrix}$$

Since $ST = I$ tells us that

$$\begin{bmatrix} \cos\theta & -\sin\theta \\ \sin\theta & \cos\theta \end{bmatrix} \begin{bmatrix} \cos(-\theta) & -\sin(-\theta) \\ \sin(-\theta) & \cos(-\theta) \end{bmatrix} = \begin{bmatrix} 1 & 0 \\ 0 & 1 \end{bmatrix}$$

we conclude that $\cos\theta = \cos(-\theta)$ and $\sin\theta = -\sin(-\theta)$.

EXAMPLE 6 Suppose P is projection onto $\bar{v}$, where $\bar{v}$ is a nonzero vector in R. If $\bar{w}$ is orthogonal to $\bar{v}$, we must have $P\bar{w} = \bar{0}$. We conclude from property **3** that P is *not* invertible.

EXAMPLE 7 Suppose T is reflection in the line through $\bar{v}$, where $\bar{v}$ is a nonzero vector in R^2. Reflecting twice certainly returns us to our original position. We conclude that $T^2 = I$, and thus that $T = T^{-1}$. In other words, a reflection is its own inverse.

EXAMPLE 8 The inverse of A can often be found directly from the definition and from the fact that the inverse is unique. We recall that B is *the* inverse of A if B satisfies $BA = I$.

For example, the inverse of A^{-1} must be A, for A is a matrix such that $AA^{-1} = I$. If A is invertible, the inverse of A^2 must be $(A^{-1})^2$, for $(A^{-1})^2$ is a matrix such that $(A^{-1})^2A^2 = I$.

This method of finding inverses is useful in particular when A satisfies a polynomial relation. For example, if $A^2 - A + I = 0$, we have $A - A^2 = I$, and it follows that $(I - A)A = I$. We therefore must have $A^{-1} = I - A$, since $I - A$ is a matrix which satisfies $(I - A)A = I$.

EXAMPLE 9 In infinite-dimensional spaces the condition that $ST = I$ *does not* imply that $TS = I$. For example, suppose D is differentiation and T is integration, defined by

$$Df = f', \qquad \text{and} \qquad Tf(x) = \int_0^x f(t)\, dt$$

As shown in calculus, we have, for continuous functions f,

$$\frac{d}{dx}\int_0^x f(t)\, dt = f(x)$$

and for functions f such that f' is continuous,

$$\int_0^x f'(t)\, dt = f(x) - f(0)$$

These can be written in operator form as

7 $$(DT)f = f \qquad \text{and} \qquad (TD)f = f - f(0)$$

Thus, if V is the collection of all functions f such that f and all its derivatives are defined and continuous for $0 \leq x \leq 1$, then D and T are linear transformations from V into V. Formula 7 tells us that $DT = I$ and $TD \neq I$, where I is the identity operator on V. For example, $TD\,(\cos x) = T(-\sin x) = \cos x - 1 \neq \cos x$.

Let D_1 be the operator defined by $D_1 f = f' + f(0)$. Then

$$D_1 T(f) = D_1\left(\int_0^x f(t)\,dt\right) = f - \int_0^0 f(t)\,dt = f$$

This shows that it is possible in the infinite-dimensional case to have more than one operator S such that $ST = I$. (Compare this with property **3** of the previous section.)

EXERCISES

1 Solve each of the following equations for B.

a $\begin{bmatrix} 1 & 1 \\ 1 & -1 \end{bmatrix} B = \begin{bmatrix} 2 & 1 & 4 \\ 1 & 3 & 1 \end{bmatrix}$ **b** $\begin{bmatrix} 3 & 1 \\ 4 & 2 \end{bmatrix} B = \begin{bmatrix} -1 & 2 \\ 1 & 1 \end{bmatrix}$

c $\begin{bmatrix} 2 & 1 & 3 \\ 1 & -1 & 0 \\ 1 & 2 & 1 \end{bmatrix} B = \begin{bmatrix} 4 & -1 & 0 & 1 & 3 \\ 1 & 0 & 0 & 2 & -1 \\ 2 & 6 & 0 & 0 & 1 \end{bmatrix}$

2 Given $$A = \begin{bmatrix} 4 & 1 \\ 3 & 2 \end{bmatrix}$$

for each of the following vectors $\bar{v}$ solve $A\bar{u} = \bar{v}$ by first finding A^{-1}.

a $\begin{bmatrix} 1 \\ 1 \end{bmatrix}$ **b** $\begin{bmatrix} 1 \\ -1 \end{bmatrix}$ **c** $\begin{bmatrix} 3 \\ 2 \end{bmatrix}$ **d** $\begin{bmatrix} 0 \\ 0 \end{bmatrix}$

3 Suppose $B \neq 0$ and $AB = 0$. What can you say about the invertibility of A?

4 Suppose $A^2 = 0$. Is A invertible?

5 Suppose $P^2 = P$ and $P \neq I$. Show that P is not invertible. (Hint: $P(I - P) = 0$.)

6 Find a formula for the coordinates of (x,y,z) with respect to $(2,1,1)$, $(1,3,1)$, $(-1,4,0)$ by proceeding as in Example 3.

7 Suppose T is defined by $T\bar{u} = \begin{bmatrix} 1 & 2 & 1 \\ -1 & 1 & 3 \\ 0 & 1 & 1 \end{bmatrix} \bar{u}$. Find the matrix of T^{-1}.

8 Suppose T is a counterclockwise rotation through the angle θ.

a Describe T^{-1} if $\theta = \pi/4, -3\pi/2, \pi$.

b Describe the inverse of T^2.

c For what values of θ does $T^{-1} = T$?

d For what values of θ does $T^{-1} = T^3$?

9 Suppose $T(x,y) = (3x - y, x + 2y)$. Show that T is invertible and find a formula for T^{-1}. (Hint: Find the matrix of T.)

10 Suppose T is rotation followed by reflection. Describe T^{-1}.

11 Suppose $\bar{u}_1$ and $\bar{u}_2$ are a basis for R^2 and T is a linear transformation which satisfies $T\bar{u}_1 = 3\bar{u}_1$ and $T\bar{u}_2 = 2\bar{u}_1$. Show that T is *not* invertible. (Hint: Find $\bar{u} \neq \bar{0}$ such that $T\bar{u} = \bar{0}$.)

12 Suppose A is invertible. Find the inverse of each of the following: (*see* Example 8)
a A^3 **b** $3A$ **c** $-A^4$ **d** $(A^{-1})^2$

13 Find the inverse of A if $A^2 + 2A - 3I = 0$. If $A^6 - 5A^4 + 3A^2 + 2I = 0$. (*See* Example 8.)

14 State assumptions that allow you to solve for B; then solve for B.
a $AB + aB = D$ **b** $AB + 2C = DB$ **c** $AB = C + 3B$
d $BA + BC = C$ **e** $BA = CA$

15 Suppose V is the vector space $C[0,1]$ of functions that are defined and continuous for $0 \leq x \leq 1$. Suppose $Tf = gf$, where g is in $C[0,1]$ and $g(x) \neq 0$, $0 \leq x \leq 1$. What is T^{-1}? In particular, what is T^{-1} if $g = e^{ax}$?

16 Suppose S and T are transformations of V into V such that $ST = TS = I$, the identity operator on V.
a Show that $S\bar{v} = \bar{u}$ if and only if $T\bar{u} = \bar{v}$.
b Show that if T is linear S must also be linear. [Hint: Use part **a** to show that $S(\bar{v}_1 + \bar{v}_2) = S\bar{v}_1 + S\bar{v}_2$ by setting $\bar{u}_1 = S\bar{v}_1$, $\bar{u}_2 = S\bar{v}_2$, and finding $T(\bar{u}_1 + \bar{u}_2)$.]

□ **17** **a** Solve for B $\begin{bmatrix} i & 1-i \\ 0 & 2i \end{bmatrix} B = \begin{bmatrix} 3-i & i \\ 1 & 2i \end{bmatrix}$

b Proceed as in Example 3 to find a formula for the coordinates of (x,y) with respect to $(i, 1+2i)$ and $(1-i,0)$.

SECTION 8 Conditions for Invertibility

We have indicated one condition for the invertibility of a matrix A, namely, that the null space of A is the zero subspace (Theorem 13). Some other useful conditions for invertibility will be presented in this section. Unless stated otherwise, it is assumed throughout this section that the matrices are square.

We have given a number of equivalent formulations of the condition that the null space of A be the zero subspace. (*See* Theorems 5, 8, and 11.) Theorem 15 merely summarizes these results and their relation to invertibility.

THEOREM 15 If A has n rows and n columns, the following statements are equivalent:

- **a** A is invertible.
- **b** The only solution to $A\bar{u} = \bar{0}$ is $\bar{u} = \bar{0}$.
- **c** The columns of A are independent.
- **d** The columns of A are a basis for R^n.
- **e** The columns of A span R^n; that is, every vector in R^n is a linear combination of the columns of A.

The equivalence of **a** and **b** is stated in Theorem 13. The equivalence of **b**, **c**, **d**, and **e** follows from Theorem 10.

We shall now use a trick to change questions about columns into questions about rows to show that Theorem 15 remains true when the word "columns" is replaced by the word "rows."

The **transpose** of A, denoted by A^t, is the matrix obtained from A by interchanging the rows and columns of A. For example, if

$$A = \begin{bmatrix} 3 & 1 & 2 \\ 1 & 4 & 0 \end{bmatrix} \qquad \text{then} \qquad A^t = \begin{bmatrix} 3 & 1 \\ 1 & 4 \\ 2 & 0 \end{bmatrix}$$

We observe that

1 $$(AB)^t = B^t A^t$$

For example, if

$$A = \begin{bmatrix} A_{11} & A_{12} \\ A_{21} & A_{22} \end{bmatrix} \qquad B = \begin{bmatrix} B_{11} & B_{12} \\ B_{21} & B_{22} \end{bmatrix}$$

it follows that

$$AB = \begin{bmatrix} A_{11}B_{11} + A_{12}B_{21} & A_{11}B_{12} + A_{12}B_{22} \\ A_{21}B_{11} + A_{22}B_{21} & A_{21}B_{12} + A_{22}B_{22} \end{bmatrix}$$

and

$$A^t = \begin{bmatrix} A_{11} & A_{21} \\ A_{12} & A_{22} \end{bmatrix} \qquad B^t = \begin{bmatrix} B_{11} & B_{21} \\ B_{12} & B_{22} \end{bmatrix}$$

Thus

$$B^tA^t = \begin{bmatrix} B_{11}A_{11} + B_{21}A_{12} & B_{11}A_{21} + B_{21}A_{22} \\ B_{12}A_{11} + B_{22}A_{12} & B_{12}A_{21} + B_{22}A_{22} \end{bmatrix}$$

which is just the transpose of AB.

If I is the identity matrix, then

2 $$I^t = I$$

Clearly, interchanging rows and columns twice returns us to our original matrix. In other words,

3 $$(A^t)^t = A$$

We shall use these facts and Theorem 14 to establish

THEOREM 16 If A is square and invertible, A^t is also invertible, and the inverse of A^t is the transpose of A^{-1}. In other words,

$$(A^t)^{-1} = (A^{-1})^t$$

Conversely, if A is square and A^t is invertible, A is also invertible.

PROOF: Suppose A is square and invertible and B is the inverse of A; then $BA = I$. Theorem 14 tells us that $AB = I$. We now take the transpose of this and, using property **1**, we have

$$I^t = (AB)^t = B^tA^t$$

Property **2** therefore gives $B^tA^t = I$. Thus A^t is invertible, and its inverse is B^t. Since B^t is the transpose of the inverse of A, we indeed have the formula $(A^t)^{-1} = (A^{-1})^t$.

Conversely, suppose A is square and A^t is invertible. If C denotes the inverse of A^t, we have $CA^t = I$. Applying Theorem 14, we also have $A^tC = I$. We now take transposes and use properties **1** and **2** to obtain

$$I = I^t = (A^tC)^t = C^t(A^t)^t$$

Applying property **3** thus gives $C^tA = I$. A therefore must be invertible, and the proof of Theorem 16 is completed.

The rows of A are just the columns of A^t, so we can combine Theorem 16 with Theorem 15 to obtain the result:

4

If A has n rows and n columns the following are equivalent:

- **a** *A is invertible.*
- **b** *The rows of A are independent.*
- **c** *The rows of A are a basis for R^n.*
- **d** *The rows of A span R^n; that is, every vector in R^n is a linear combination of the rows of A.*

EXAMPLE 1 If $A = \begin{bmatrix} 2 & 1 \\ 0 & 3 \end{bmatrix}$ then $A^{-1} = \begin{bmatrix} \frac{1}{2} & -\frac{1}{6} \\ 0 & \frac{1}{3} \end{bmatrix}$

(We used the method of Example 6, page 148, to find A^{-1}.)

Since $A^t = \begin{bmatrix} 2 & 0 \\ 1 & 3 \end{bmatrix}$, Theorem 16 tells us that $(A^t)^{-1} = \begin{bmatrix} \frac{1}{2} & 0 \\ -\frac{1}{6} & \frac{1}{3} \end{bmatrix}$

EXAMPLE 2 The columns of

$$A = \begin{bmatrix} 2 & 0 & 1 \\ 1 & 0 & -1 \\ 2 & 0 & 3 \end{bmatrix}$$

are certainly dependent; therefore A is *not* invertible. We can conclude from statement **4** that the rows of A *are also dependent.* Therefore, since neither the columns nor the rows of A can span R^3 (from Theorem 10), we know that there must be vectors $\bar{v}_1$ and $\bar{v}_2$ such that neither $A\bar{u} = \bar{v}_1$ nor $A^t\bar{u} = \bar{v}_2$ has a solution.

EXAMPLE 3 A square matrix A is called an **orthogonal matrix** if the columns of A are orthonormal. (*See* Section 11, Chapter 1, for a discussion of orthonormal sets.) The inverse of an orthogonal matrix is particularly simple to find, for we have the fact

5 *If A is an orthogonal matrix, then $A^{-1} = A^t$.*

For example, suppose

$$A = \begin{bmatrix} A_{11} & A_{12} \\ A_{21} & A_{22} \end{bmatrix} \quad \text{so that} \quad A^t = \begin{bmatrix} A_{11} & A_{21} \\ A_{12} & A_{22} \end{bmatrix}$$

Thus

$$A^tA = \begin{bmatrix} A_{11}^2 + A_{21}^2 & A_{11}A_{12} + A_{21}A_{22} \\ A_{12}A_{11} + A_{22}A_{21} & A_{12}^2 + A_{22}^2 \end{bmatrix}$$

and it follows that $A^tA = I$ if and only if

6
$$\begin{aligned} A_{11}^2 + A_{21}^2 &= 1 \qquad A_{11}A_{12} + A_{21}A_{22} = 0 \\ A_{12}A_{11} + A_{22}A_{21} &= 0 \qquad A_{12}^2 + A_{22}^2 = 1 \end{aligned}$$

These are precisely the conditions that the columns of A be orthonormal. Thus, if A is orthogonal, properties **6** hold, and therefore, $A^tA = I$ and statement **5** is true. The converse of statement **5** is also true, for if $A^{-1} = A^t$, then $A^tA = I$. Calculating A^tA shows that properties **6** hold; thus

A is an orthogonal matrix. This proof generalizes for larger matrices. Suppose A is orthogonal and therefore $A^tA = I$. Theorem 14 then tells us that $AA^t = I$. Since $A = (A^t)^t$, we can rewrite this as $B^tB = I$, where $B = A^t$.

We conclude from the previous arguments that B is also an orthogonal matrix, and consequently its columns are orthonormal. This rather interesting result follows:

7 *If the columns of A are orthonormal, and A is square, the rows are also orthonormal.*

For square matrices the converse of this statement is also true; that is, if the rows of A are orthonormal, the columns of A are also orthonormal.

EXAMPLE 4 Suppose A and B are square and invertible. Then AB is also invertible. Furthermore

8
$$(AB)^{-1} = B^{-1}A^{-1}$$

Notice that, just as with the transpose, the inverse of a product is the product of the inverses, *in reverse order*. To establish equation **8**, we note that

$$\begin{aligned}(B^{-1}A^{-1})(AB) &= B^{-1}(A^{-1}A)B \\ &= B^{-1}IB \\ &= B^{-1}B = I\end{aligned}$$

so AB is indeed invertible. Since AB has a unique inverse, equation **8** must be true.

Suppose A and B are square and B is not invertible. Theorem 13 then tells us that there is a $\bar{u} \neq \bar{0}$ such that $B\bar{u} = \bar{0}$. Since $AB\bar{u}$ is also $\bar{0}$, we conclude, again from Theorem 13, that AB is not invertible. In summary:

9 *If A and B are square and B is not invertible, then AB is not invertible.*

Now suppose A and B are square and B is invertible, but A is *not* invertible. Then B^t must be invertible, and A^t cannot be invertible. Thus, applying statement **9** with A and B replaced by B^t and A^t, respectively, we conclude that B^tA^t is *not* invertible. Furthermore, since $B^tA^t = (AB)^t$, $(AB)^t$ is not invertible. Applying Theorem 16, we conclude that AB is not invertible. We can summarize as follows:

10 *If A and B are square, the product AB is invertible when and only when each factor is invertible.*

EXERCISES

1 By showing dependence or independence of the columns decide which of the following are invertible.

a $\begin{bmatrix} 2 & 1 & 1 \\ 0 & 0 & 0 \\ 3 & 1 & 2 \end{bmatrix}$ **b** $\begin{bmatrix} 1 & 1 & 1 \\ 0 & 1 & 1 \\ 0 & 0 & 1 \end{bmatrix}$

c $\begin{bmatrix} 4 & 1 & 2 \\ 1 & 2 & 6 \\ 1 & 1 & 0 \end{bmatrix}$ **d** $\begin{bmatrix} 1 & 1 & 1 \\ 2 & 2 & 2 \\ -1 & 4 & 3 \end{bmatrix}$

2 Decide the question of invertibility for each of the matrices of Exercise 1 by showing dependence or independence of the columns of the transpose matrix.

3 For $A = \begin{bmatrix} 2 & 1 \\ 3 & 0 \end{bmatrix}$ $B = \begin{bmatrix} -1 & 2 \\ 1 & 1 \end{bmatrix}$

calculate AB, $(AB)^t$, and B^tA^t and verify that formula **1** holds.

4 Find the inverse of $A = \begin{bmatrix} 2 & 1 \\ 3 & 0 \end{bmatrix}$

and of A^t and verify that Theorem 16 is true.

5 Calculate $\begin{bmatrix} 3 & 1 \\ 2 & 1 \\ 1 & 1 \end{bmatrix} \begin{bmatrix} 2 & 1 & 0 \\ 1 & -1 & 1 \end{bmatrix}$

and verify directly that the result is not invertible. Reverse the order of the product. Is the resulting product invertible?

6 Show that each of the following matrices is an orthogonal matrix and find its inverse. Verify that the rows are also orthonormal.

a $\begin{bmatrix} 1/\sqrt{2} & 1/\sqrt{2} \\ -1/\sqrt{2} & 1/\sqrt{2} \end{bmatrix}$ **b** $\begin{bmatrix} 0 & 1 \\ 1 & 0 \end{bmatrix}$

c $\begin{bmatrix} 1/\sqrt{3} & 1/\sqrt{3} & 1/\sqrt{3} \\ 1/\sqrt{2} & -1/\sqrt{2} & 0 \\ 1/\sqrt{6} & 1/\sqrt{6} & -2/\sqrt{6} \end{bmatrix}$

7 **a** Show that $(A\bar{u}) \cdot \bar{v} = \bar{u} \cdot A^t\bar{v}$ for $A = \begin{bmatrix} A_{11} & A_{12} \\ A_{21} & A_{22} \end{bmatrix}$

b Suppose A is an orthogonal matrix. Show that $A\bar{u} \cdot A\bar{v} = \bar{u} \cdot \bar{v}$.

8 For $$A = \begin{bmatrix} 2 & 1 \\ 3 & 0 \end{bmatrix} \qquad B = \begin{bmatrix} -1 & 2 \\ 1 & 1 \end{bmatrix}$$

calculate A^{-1}, B^{-1}, $(AB)^{-1}$, and $B^{-1}A^{-1}$ and verify that equation **8** is true.

9 Suppose A has two rows and two columns. Show that

a If A is invertible and $\bar{u}_1$ and $\bar{u}_2$ are independent $A\bar{u}_1$ and $A\bar{u}_2$ are then independent.

b If there is some basis $\bar{u}_1$, $\bar{u}_2$ so that $A\bar{u}_1$ and $A\bar{u}_2$ are a basis, then A is invertible. (Hint: Let B have $\bar{u}_1$ and $\bar{u}_2$ as columns and apply the results of Example 4.)

10 Show that if A and B are orthogonal matrices then AB is an orthogonal matrix. (Hint: Show that $(AB)^{-1} = (AB)^t$ by using formulas **1** and **8**.)

11 **a** Show that if A is the matrix of a rotation in R^2, then A is an orthogonal matrix. (*See* Example 3, page 109.)

b Show that the matrix of a reflection in R^2 is an orthogonal matrix. (Hint: First find the matrix of a reflection in the line through $\bar{v} = (a,b)$, where $a^2 + b^2 = 1$.)

c Show that the product of a matrix of a rotation and a matrix of a reflection is orthogonal. (Hint: *See* Exercise 10. We discuss the converse of this in Appendix 1.)

□ **12** A complex matrix A is called a *unitary matrix* if its columns are orthonormal with respect to the complex dot product. (*See* Exercise 17, page 89.) Show that a complex matrix A with two rows and two columns is orthogonal if and only if A^{-1} is the transpose conjugate of A. (*See* Exercise 11, page 224.)

SECTION 9 Determinants

A useful condition for a matrix to be invertible can be given using the determinant. We shall sketch some of the relevant properties of the determinant. A complete discussion of determinants can be found elsewhere (*see* Bibliography).

The second-order determinant is defined by

1 $$\det \begin{bmatrix} a & b \\ c & d \end{bmatrix} = ad - bc$$

Higher-order determinants are defined as follows: Suppose A is a matrix with n rows and n columns. Form the matrix obtained from A by omitting the first row and jth column of A. This matrix has $n - 1$ rows and $n - 1$

columns. Denote its determinant by a_j and denote the entry in the first row and jth column of A by A_{1j}. Then the determinant of A is defined by

2 $$\det A = A_{11}a_1 - A_{12}a_2 + A_{13}a_3 - \cdots - (-1)^{n+1}A_{1n}a_n$$

For example, the third-order determinant is defined by

3 $$\det \begin{bmatrix} A_{11} & A_{12} & A_{13} \\ A_{21} & A_{22} & A_{23} \\ A_{31} & A_{32} & A_{33} \end{bmatrix} = A_{11} \det \begin{bmatrix} A_{22} & A_{23} \\ A_{32} & A_{33} \end{bmatrix} - A_{12} \det \begin{bmatrix} A_{21} & A_{23} \\ A_{31} & A_{33} \end{bmatrix} + A_{13} \det \begin{bmatrix} A_{21} & A_{22} \\ A_{31} & A_{32} \end{bmatrix}$$

The fourth-order determinant is the sum of multiples of third-order determinants, and so forth.

EXAMPLE 1 **a** $$\det \begin{bmatrix} 3 & 1 \\ 2 & -4 \end{bmatrix} = 3 \cdot (-4) - 1 \cdot 2 = -14$$

b $$\det \begin{bmatrix} 3 & 1 & 2 \\ 4 & 1 & -6 \\ 1 & 0 & 1 \end{bmatrix} = 3 \det \begin{bmatrix} 1 & -6 \\ 0 & 1 \end{bmatrix} - 1 \det \begin{bmatrix} 4 & -6 \\ 1 & 1 \end{bmatrix} + 2 \det \begin{bmatrix} 4 & 1 \\ 1 & 0 \end{bmatrix}$$

$$= 3[1 \cdot 1 - 0 \cdot (-6)] - 1[4 \cdot 1 - 1 \cdot (-6)] + 2[4 \cdot 0 - 1 \cdot 1] = -9$$

c $$\det \begin{bmatrix} 4 & 1 & 2 & -1 \\ 3 & -1 & 2 & 1 \\ 6 & -1 & 0 & -1 \\ 2 & -1 & 1 & 0 \end{bmatrix} = 4 \det \begin{bmatrix} -1 & 2 & 1 \\ -1 & 0 & -1 \\ -1 & 1 & 0 \end{bmatrix} - 1 \det \begin{bmatrix} 3 & 2 & 1 \\ 6 & 0 & -1 \\ 2 & 1 & 0 \end{bmatrix} + 2 \det \begin{bmatrix} 3 & -1 & 1 \\ 6 & -1 & -1 \\ 2 & -1 & 0 \end{bmatrix} - (-1) \det \begin{bmatrix} 3 & -1 & 2 \\ 6 & -1 & 0 \\ 2 & -1 & 1 \end{bmatrix}$$

These four third-order determinants can each be reduced to a sum of multiples of three second-order determinants by using formula **3**. The result is a sum of multiples of twelve second-order determinants, each of which can be evaluated using formula **1**.

DISCUSSION Fortunately, there is an easier way to evaluate high-order determinants by judicious use of row reduction. The basic properties of the determinant used in this process are listed in statement **4**, below. These properties are easily established by direct calculation in the second-order case, and their general proofs are omitted.

4
- **a** *If we interchange two rows of A, the determinant changes by a factor of (-1).*
- **b** *If we add to one row of A a multiple of another row, the determinant is* not *changed.*
- **c** *If all entries below the diagonal of A are zero, the determinant of A is the product of the diagonal entries of A.*

Thus, to find the determinant of A, we apply row operations of the two types given above until we obtain a matrix B such that every entry below the diagonal of B is zero. Then

5 $$\det A = \pm \det B$$

where the sign is positive if we interchanged an even number of rows and negative otherwise. Furthermore,

6 *$\det B =$ the product of the diagonal entries of B*

EXAMPLE 2 To find det A where

$$A = \begin{bmatrix} 3 & 2 & 0 \\ 4 & 4 & 1 \\ 1 & -1 & 3 \end{bmatrix}$$

we apply the following row operations, and use rules **4a** and **b**:

1. Interchange rows one and three.
2. Add to row two -4 times row one, and add to row three -3 times row one.
3. Add to row three $-\frac{5}{8}$ times row two.

We now have the matrix

$$B = \begin{bmatrix} 1 & -1 & 3 \\ 0 & 8 & -11 \\ 0 & 0 & -\frac{17}{8} \end{bmatrix}$$

Using rule **4c** we have

$$\det B = 1 \cdot 8 \cdot (-17/8) = -17$$

Operation **1** multiplies the determinant by -1, while operations **2** and **3** do not change the value. So we have

$$\det A = -\det B = 17$$

DISCUSSION Suppose A has two identical rows. We can then interchange those two rows and the matrix will be unchanged, while, from rule **4a**, its determinant changes by a factor of -1. This can happen only if $\det A = 0$.

If A has a row of zeros, we can add another row to that row. This will not affect the value of the determinant (rule **4b**), and the new matrix will have two rows that are identical. We conclude from the above argument that $\det A$ must be zero. In summary, we have:

7 *If two rows of A are identical, or if A has a row of zeros,* $\det A = 0$.

It follows that if one row of A is a linear combination of the other rows of A, repeated application of rule **4b** to that row will result in a row of zeros. In other words,

8 *If the rows of A are dependent, then* $\det A = 0$.

The condition that the rows be dependent is, from result **4**, page 159, the same as the condition that A does not have an inverse, and thus, property **8** can be rephrased as:

9 *If A is* not *invertible, then* $\det A = 0$.

The converse of this result can be established by using a row-reduction argument. It is also a simple consequence of the following result:

10 $$\det AB = \det A \det B$$

This is a consequence of rules **4**. We omit its proof. We shall use it to prove that

11 *If A is invertible, then* $\det A \neq 0$.

To prove this, suppose that A is invertible. Then $A^{-1}A = I$. Hence from equation **10** we have

$$\det I = \det A^{-1}A = \det A^{-1} \det A$$

Since $\det I = 1$ (from rule **4c**), we cannot have $\det A = 0$. This proves statement **11**. In summary, we have the following useful result:

THEOREM 17 A has an inverse if and only if $\det A \neq 0$.

EXAMPLE 3

a
$$\det\begin{bmatrix} 2 & 1 & 1 \\ 0 & 0 & 0 \\ 4 & 3 & 1 \end{bmatrix} = 0 \qquad \text{(from property 7)}$$

b
$$\det\begin{bmatrix} 3 & 0 & 0 \\ 2 & 1 & 0 \\ 1 & 2 & 0 \end{bmatrix} = 0$$

This follows from the fact that the columns of this matrix are dependent (since a set of vectors which includes the zero vector must be dependent); the matrix, therefore, is not invertible.

c $\det\begin{bmatrix} 4 & 1 & 2 \\ 8 & 2 & 4 \\ 3 & 1 & 0 \end{bmatrix} = 0$, since the second row is a multiple of the first row.

d
$$\det\begin{bmatrix} 2 & 1 \\ 3 & 5 \end{bmatrix} = 10 - 3 = 7 \neq 0$$

Therefore, this matrix is invertible.

e To find the determinant of

$$A = \begin{bmatrix} 3 & 1 & 2 \\ 2 & 6 & 4 \\ -2 & 1 & 3 \end{bmatrix}$$

we need only eliminate in the first column and then use formula 3. Adding suitable multiples of the first row to the other two rows gives the matrix

$$\begin{bmatrix} 3 & 1 & 2 \\ 0 & \frac{16}{3} & \frac{8}{3} \\ 0 & \frac{5}{3} & \frac{13}{3} \end{bmatrix}$$

whose determinant is (using formula 3):

$$3\det\begin{bmatrix} \frac{16}{3} & \frac{8}{3} \\ \frac{5}{3} & \frac{13}{3} \end{bmatrix} - 1\det\begin{bmatrix} 0 & \frac{8}{3} \\ 0 & \frac{13}{3} \end{bmatrix} + 2\det\begin{bmatrix} 0 & \frac{16}{3} \\ 0 & \frac{5}{3} \end{bmatrix}$$

Since the last two determinants are zero (from Theorem 17), it follows that

$$\det A = 3\det\begin{bmatrix} \frac{16}{3} & \frac{8}{3} \\ \frac{5}{3} & \frac{13}{3} \end{bmatrix} = 3\left(\frac{16}{3}\cdot\frac{13}{3} - \frac{8}{3}\cdot\frac{5}{3}\right) = 56$$

We conclude, in particular, that A is invertible.

f To find

$$\det\begin{bmatrix} 2 & 4 & 2 & 2 \\ 3 & 1 & 0 & 1 \\ 2 & 1 & 0 & -1 \\ 4 & 2 & 1 & 1 \end{bmatrix}$$

we eliminate in the first column to obtain

$$\begin{bmatrix} 2 & 4 & 2 & 2 \\ 0 & -5 & -3 & -2 \\ 0 & -3 & -2 & -3 \\ 0 & -6 & -3 & -3 \end{bmatrix}$$

An argument similar to that given in **e** shows that our desired determinant is

$$2\det\begin{bmatrix} -5 & -3 & -2 \\ -3 & -2 & -3 \\ -6 & -3 & -3 \end{bmatrix}$$

We can now proceed to eliminate in the first column of this matrix.

EXAMPLE 4 We shall later wish to find $\det(\lambda I - A)$. For example, if

$$A = \begin{bmatrix} a & b \\ c & d \end{bmatrix} \qquad \text{then} \qquad \lambda I - A = \begin{bmatrix} \lambda - a & -b \\ -c & \lambda - d \end{bmatrix}$$

so that

$$\det(\lambda I - A) = (\lambda - a)(\lambda - d) - (-b)(-c) = \lambda^2 - (a + d)\lambda + ad - bc$$

Notice that this is a polynomial of degree 2. It can be shown, using induction and formula 2, that

12 *$\det(\lambda I - A)$ is a polynomial of degree n if A has n rows and n columns.*

For example,

$$\det\left\{\lambda\begin{bmatrix} 1 & 0 & 0 \\ 0 & 1 & 0 \\ 0 & 0 & 1 \end{bmatrix} - \begin{bmatrix} A_{11} & A_{12} & A_{13} \\ A_{21} & A_{22} & A_{23} \\ A_{31} & A_{32} & A_{33} \end{bmatrix}\right\} = \det\begin{bmatrix} \lambda - A_{11} & -A_{12} & -A_{13} \\ -A_{21} & \lambda - A_{22} & -A_{23} \\ -A_{31} & -A_{32} & \lambda - A_{33} \end{bmatrix}$$

$$= (\lambda - A_{11})\det\begin{bmatrix} \lambda - A_{22} & -A_{23} \\ -A_{32} & \lambda - A_{33} \end{bmatrix} - (-A_{12})\det\begin{bmatrix} -A_{21} & -A_{23} \\ -A_{31} & \lambda - A_{33} \end{bmatrix}$$

$$+ (-A_{13})\det\begin{bmatrix} -A_{21} & \lambda - A_{22} \\ -A_{31} & -A_{32} \end{bmatrix}$$

Since the first term has degree 3, while the degree of the last two terms cannot exceed degree 1, we conclude that det $(\lambda I - A)$ has degree 3.

EXAMPLE 5 □ *The Wronskian.*

The *Wronskian* of two functions at $x = x_0$ is defined by

$$w(f,g,x_0) = \det \begin{bmatrix} f(x_0) & g(x_0) \\ f'(x_0) & g'(x_0) \end{bmatrix}$$

If f and g are dependent, there are numbers c_1 and c_2 not both zero such that

$$c_1 f + c_2 g = 0$$

Differentiating this gives

$$c_1 f' + c_2 g' = 0$$

so that, in particular,

$$c_1 \begin{bmatrix} f(x_0) \\ f'(x_0) \end{bmatrix} + c_2 \begin{bmatrix} g(x_0) \\ g'(x_0) \end{bmatrix} = \begin{bmatrix} 0 \\ 0 \end{bmatrix}$$

Since c_1 and c_2 are not both zero, Theorem 17 gives the following result:

13 *If f and g are dependent, then for each x_0, $w(f,g,x_0) = 0$.*

In general, the converse of this is *not* true.

The Wronskian for more than two functions is defined analogously. For example,

$$w(f,g,h,x_0) = \det \begin{bmatrix} f(x_0) & g(x_0) & h(x_0) \\ f'(x_0) & g'(x_0) & h'(x_0) \\ f''(x_0) & g''(x_0) & h''(x_0) \end{bmatrix}$$

EXAMPLE 6 □ *Area and Volume.*

The second-order determinant has a natural interpretation in terms of area, while the third-order determinant is related to volume. For example, suppose $\bar{u} = a\bar{i} + b\bar{j}$ and $\bar{v} = c\bar{i} + d\bar{j}$. Then $\bar{u}$ and $\bar{v}$ determine a parallelogram, as shown in Figure 10.

As Figure 11 shows, the vector $\bar{w}$, which is the projection of $\bar{v}$ orthogonal to $\bar{u}$, has length equal to the altitude of this parallelogram. Thus the area

Figure 10

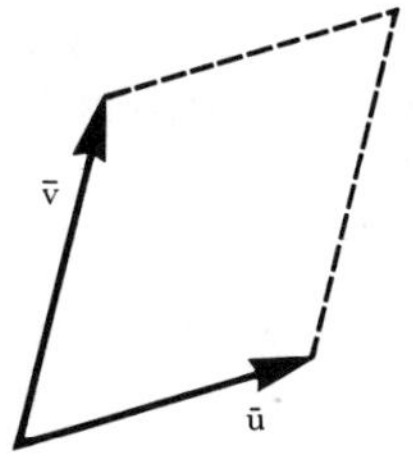

Figure 11

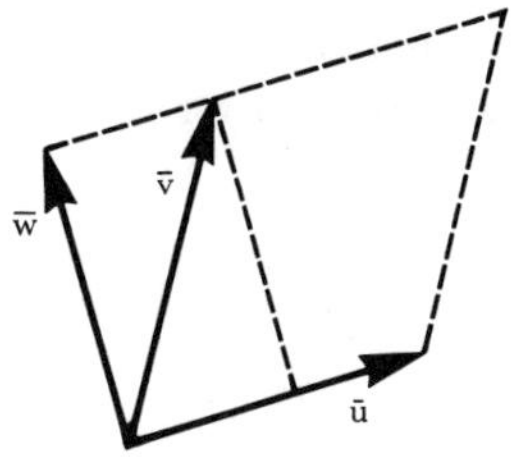

of the parallelogram is just $|\bar{u}|\,|\bar{w}|$. We recall that

$$\bar{w} = \bar{v} - \frac{(\bar{v}\cdot\bar{u})\bar{u}}{\bar{u}\cdot\bar{u}}$$

as established in formula **8**, page 82.

Since $\bar{w}$ is orthogonal to $\bar{u}$, we have

$$\begin{aligned}
\bar{w}\cdot\bar{w} &= \left(\bar{v} - \frac{\bar{v}\cdot\bar{u}}{\bar{u}\cdot\bar{u}}\bar{u}\right)\cdot\left(\bar{v} - \frac{\bar{v}\cdot\bar{u}}{\bar{u}\cdot\bar{u}}\bar{u}\right) \\
&= \bar{v}\cdot\bar{v} - \frac{\bar{v}\cdot\bar{u}}{\bar{u}\cdot\bar{u}}(\bar{u}\cdot\bar{v}) \\
&= \frac{(\bar{v}\cdot\bar{v})(\bar{u}\cdot\bar{u}) - (\bar{v}\cdot\bar{u})^2}{\bar{u}\cdot\bar{u}}
\end{aligned}$$

so that

$$|\bar{w}|^2|\bar{u}|^2 = |\bar{v}|^2|\bar{u}|^2 - (\bar{v}\cdot\bar{u})^2$$

is the square of the area of the parallelogram of Figure 10. With $\bar{u} = a\bar{i} + b\bar{j}$ and $\bar{v} = c\bar{i} + d\bar{j}$ we have

$$\begin{aligned}
|\bar{w}|^2|\bar{u}|^2 &= (c^2 + d^2)(a^2 + b^2) - (ac + bd)^2 \\
&= a^2d^2 + b^2c^2 - 2acbd \\
&= (ad - bc)^2
\end{aligned}$$

We conclude that

The area of the parallelogram determined by $\bar{u} = a\bar{i} + b\bar{j}$ *and* $\bar{v} = c\bar{i} + d\bar{j}$ *is the absolute value of* $\det\begin{bmatrix} a & b \\ c & d \end{bmatrix}$

A similar argument shows that

The volume of the parallelopiped determined by $a_1\bar{i} + b_1\bar{j} + c_1\bar{k}$, $a_2\bar{i} + b_2\bar{j} + c_2\bar{k}$, *and* $a_3\bar{i} + b_3\bar{j} + c_3\bar{k}$ *is* $\left|\det\begin{bmatrix} a_1 & b_1 & c_1 \\ a_2 & b_2 & c_2 \\ a_3 & b_3 & c_3 \end{bmatrix}\right|$

EXAMPLE 7 ☐ *The Determinant of the Transpose.*

Rules **4a** and **b** are also valid for column operations. This fact can be established directly for second-order determinants and then proved for higher-order determinants using formulas **2** and **3**. Thus properties **7** and **8** also hold for columns. We can use this information to prove directly that

14 $$\det A = \det A^t$$

We shall give an alternative proof of this which uses Theorem 17 and the results of Example 10, page 137. Suppose A^t is not invertible; from

Theorem 16 we know that A is also not invertible. Thus Theorem 17 implies that both sides of equation **14** are zero. To complete the proof, we need only establish equality when A^t is invertible. Suppose A^t is invertible. Then we can apply a sequence of row operations to reduce A^t to I. As shown in Example 10, each such row operation can be performed by multiplying on the left of A^t by a suitable matrix. Thus, we can find a sequence of matrices $E_1, E_2, \ldots, E_k$ of the types given in Example 10 such that

15 $$E_1 E_2 \cdots E_k A^t = I.$$

Applying formula **10** we conclude that

16 $$\det A^t = \frac{1}{\det E_1 \det E_2 \cdots \det E_k}$$

Suppose E_i is obtained from I by interchanging two rows of I. In this case $E_i^t = E_i$. For example, if

$$E_i = \begin{bmatrix} 1 & 0 & 0 \\ 0 & 0 & 1 \\ 0 & 1 & 0 \end{bmatrix} \quad \text{then} \quad E_i^t = \begin{bmatrix} 1 & 0 & 0 \\ 0 & 0 & 1 \\ 0 & 1 & 0 \end{bmatrix} \quad \text{also.}$$

Thus, in this case, $\det E_i^t = \det E_i$.

If E_i is obtained from I by multiplying one row of I by $a \neq 0$, we again have $E_i^t = E_i$. For example, if

$$E_i = \begin{bmatrix} 1 & 0 & 0 \\ 0 & a & 0 \\ 0 & 0 & 1 \end{bmatrix} \quad \text{then} \quad E_i^t = \begin{bmatrix} 1 & 0 & 0 \\ 0 & a & 0 \\ 0 & 0 & 1 \end{bmatrix}$$

Thus, again we have $\det E_i^t = \det E_i$.

Suppose E_i is obtained from I by adding to row s of I, b times row r. Then E_i^t is obtained from I by adding to row r of I, b times row s. For example, if

$$E_i = \begin{bmatrix} 1 & 0 & b \\ 0 & 1 & 0 \\ 0 & 0 & 1 \end{bmatrix} \quad \text{then} \quad E_i^t = \begin{bmatrix} 1 & 0 & 0 \\ 0 & 1 & 0 \\ b & 0 & 1 \end{bmatrix}$$

In this case since $\det E_i = 1$ and $\det E_i^t = 1$ (from rule **4b**) we again have $\det E_i = \det E_i^t$.

In summary, we have

17 $$\det E_1 \det E_2 \cdots \det E_k = \det E_1^t \det E_2^t \cdots \det E_k^t$$

Taking transposes of equation **15** and using formulas **1**, **2**, and **3** of the previous section, we conclude that

$$AE_k^t \cdots E_2^t E_1^t = I$$

Formula **10** therefore gives

$$\det A = \frac{1}{\det E_k^t \cdots \det E_2^t \det E_1^t}$$

Comparing this with equations **16** and **17** we conclude that equation **14** is true when A^t is invertible.

EXAMPLE 8 ☐ *The Classical Adjoint.*

Suppose B_{ij} is the determinant of the matrix obtained from A by omitting the ith row and jth column of A. Denote the entry in the ith row and jth column of A by A_{ij}. It can then be shown that, for each j, $1 \leq j \leq n$

18 $$\det A = (-1)^{1+j}A_{1j}B_{1j} + (-1)^{2+j}A_{2j}B_{2j} + \cdots + (-1)^{n+j}A_{nj}B_{nj}$$

Put

$$C = \begin{bmatrix} B_{11} & -B_{21} & B_{31} & \cdots & (-1)^{n+1}B_{n1} \\ -B_{12} & B_{22} & -B_{32} & \cdots & (-1)^{n+2}B_{n2} \\ \vdots & \vdots & \vdots & \cdots & \vdots \\ (-1)^{n+1}B_{1n} & (-1)^{n+2}B_{2n} & \vdots & \cdots & B_{nn} \end{bmatrix}$$

The use of formula **18** for $j = 1, 2, \ldots, n$ thus gives the formula

19 $$CA = (\det A)I$$

The matrix C is called the *classical adjoint* of A, while formula **18** is called the *Laplace expansion of the determinant of A along the* jth *column*. In the second-order case

$$C = \begin{bmatrix} d & -b \\ -c & a \end{bmatrix}$$

so equation **19** gives the formula (easily verified directly):

$$\begin{bmatrix} d & -b \\ -c & a \end{bmatrix} \begin{bmatrix} a & b \\ c & d \end{bmatrix} = [ad - bc] \begin{bmatrix} 1 & 0 \\ 0 & 1 \end{bmatrix}$$

Suppose

$$A = \begin{bmatrix} 3 & 1 & 2 \\ 0 & 1 & 1 \\ -1 & 1 & 0 \end{bmatrix}$$

Since

$$B_{11} = \det\begin{bmatrix} 1 & 1 \\ 1 & 0 \end{bmatrix} = -1,\ B_{12} = \det\begin{bmatrix} 0 & 1 \\ -1 & 0 \end{bmatrix} = 1,\ B_{13} = \det\begin{bmatrix} 0 & 1 \\ -1 & 1 \end{bmatrix} = 1$$

$$B_{21} = \det\begin{bmatrix} 1 & 2 \\ 1 & 0 \end{bmatrix} = -2,\ B_{22} = \det\begin{bmatrix} 3 & 2 \\ -1 & 0 \end{bmatrix} = 2,\ B_{23} = \det\begin{bmatrix} 3 & 1 \\ -1 & 1 \end{bmatrix} = 4$$

$$B_{31} = \det\begin{bmatrix} 1 & 2 \\ 1 & 1 \end{bmatrix} = -1,\ B_{32} = \det\begin{bmatrix} 3 & 2 \\ 0 & 1 \end{bmatrix} = 3,\ B_{33} = \det\begin{bmatrix} 3 & 1 \\ 0 & 1 \end{bmatrix} = 3$$

the classical adjoint is

$$C = \begin{bmatrix} -1 & 2 & -1 \\ -1 & 2 & -3 \\ 1 & -4 & 3 \end{bmatrix}$$

The student can check that $CA = (\det A)I$.

EXAMPLE 9 ☐ *Cramer's Rule.*

Formula **19** gives us a way to calculate A^{-1}, for if $\det A \neq 0$, it follows that $\left(\frac{1}{\det A}\right) CA = I$ where C is the classical adjoint. Therefore

$$A^{-1} = \left(\frac{1}{\det A}\right) C$$

In this case, $A\bar{u} = \bar{v}$ has the unique solution

$$\bar{u} = A^{-1}\bar{v} = \left(\frac{1}{\det A}\right) C\bar{v}$$

Suppose $\bar{v} = (y_1, y_2, \ldots, y_n)$. The formula for C then gives

$$\textbf{20}\quad C\bar{v} = \begin{bmatrix} B_{11}y_1 & - & B_{21}y_2 & + B_{31}y_3 - \cdots + (-1)^{n+1}B_{n1}y_n \\ -B_{12}y_1 & + & B_{22}y_2 & - B_{32}y_3 - \cdots + (-1)^{n+2}B_{n2}y_n \\ \vdots & & \vdots & \vdots \qquad\qquad \vdots \\ (-1)^{n+1}B_{1n}y_1 & + & (-1)^{n+2}B_{2n}y_n & \cdots + \cdots + \quad B_{nn}y_n \end{bmatrix}$$

The first row is just equal to (from formula **18**)

$$\det\begin{bmatrix} y_1 & A_{12} & A_{13} & \cdots & A_{1n} \\ y_2 & A_{22} & A_{23} & \cdots & A_{2n} \\ \vdots & \vdots & \vdots & \cdots & \vdots \\ y_n & A_{n2} & A_{n3} & \cdots & A_{nn} \end{bmatrix}$$

In general, each row of matrix **20** is just the determinant of the matrix that is obtained by replacing the corresponding column of A by $\bar{v}$. This gives the following procedure when $\det A \neq 0$, known as *Cramer's rule*, for solving $A\bar{u} = \bar{v}$:

> *Each coordinate of* $\bar{u}$ *is* $(1/\det A)$ *times the determinant of the matrix obtained by replacing the corresponding column of* A *by* $\bar{v}$.

This method of solution is quite useful in the second-order case, but requires more calculation than the elimination method in high-order cases.

Consider the equation

$$\begin{bmatrix} 3 & 1 \\ 2 & 4 \end{bmatrix} \begin{bmatrix} x \\ y \end{bmatrix} = \begin{bmatrix} -1 \\ 6 \end{bmatrix}$$

Cramer's rule gives

$$x = \frac{\det \begin{bmatrix} -1 & 1 \\ 6 & 4 \end{bmatrix}}{\det \begin{bmatrix} 3 & 1 \\ 2 & 4 \end{bmatrix}} = \frac{-10}{10} = -1 \qquad y = \frac{\det \begin{bmatrix} 3 & -1 \\ 2 & 6 \end{bmatrix}}{\det \begin{bmatrix} 3 & 1 \\ 2 & 4 \end{bmatrix}} = \frac{20}{10} = 2$$

EXERCISES

1 Use formula **2** to find the determinant of

$$\begin{bmatrix} 1 & 2 & 3 & 1 \\ 1 & -1 & 1 & 4 \\ 2 & 1 & 0 & 1 \\ 1 & 1 & 2 & 4 \end{bmatrix}$$

2 Find the determinant of the matrix of Exercise 1 by using rules **4** as in Example 2.

3 Find the determinants of each of the following matrices. (Hint: First see whether property **7**, **8**, or **9** is true.)

a $\begin{bmatrix} 2 & 1 \\ 1 & 2 \end{bmatrix}$ **b** $\begin{bmatrix} 2 & 1 \\ 4 & 2 \end{bmatrix}$ **c** $\begin{bmatrix} 1 & 0 \\ 3 & 0 \end{bmatrix}$

d $\begin{bmatrix} 3 & 1 & 2 \\ 1 & 0 & 6 \\ -1 & 1 & 1 \end{bmatrix}$ **e** $\begin{bmatrix} -1 & 1 & 3 \\ 2 & 1 & 1 \\ 4 & 2 & 2 \end{bmatrix}$ **f** $\begin{bmatrix} 1 & 1 & 2 \\ 4 & 3 & 6 \\ 1 & -1 & -2 \end{bmatrix}$

g $\begin{bmatrix} 1 & 1 & 2 & 1 \\ -1 & 1 & 0 & 1 \\ 2 & 1 & 1 & 0 \\ 1 & 3 & 1 & 0 \end{bmatrix}$ **h** $\begin{bmatrix} 4 & 1 & 2 & 6 \\ 0 & -1 & -2 & 1 \\ 1 & 2 & 4 & 1 \\ 0 & 6 & 12 & 0 \end{bmatrix}$ **i** $\begin{bmatrix} 3 & 1 & 0 & 6 & 1 \\ 1 & 2 & 1 & 3 & 1 \\ -1 & 1 & 1 & 1 & 1 \\ 1 & -1 & 1 & 1 & 1 \\ 0 & 0 & 1 & 1 & 1 \end{bmatrix}$

4 Which of the matrices of Exercise 3 are invertible? (Hint: Use Theorem 17.)

5 For $A = \begin{bmatrix} 1 & 2 \\ 4 & 1 \end{bmatrix}$ verify that $\det \begin{bmatrix} 4 & 1 \\ 1 & 2 \end{bmatrix} = -\det A$

and that $\det \begin{bmatrix} 1 + 3 \cdot 4 & 2 + 3 \cdot 1 \\ 4 & 1 \end{bmatrix} = \det A$

6 For $A = \begin{bmatrix} 1 & 2 \\ 4 & 1 \end{bmatrix}$ $B = \begin{bmatrix} -1 & 3 \\ 1 & 0 \end{bmatrix}$

find AB, det A, det B, det AB and verify equation **10**.

7 Show that if A is invertible, then $\det A^{-1} = 1/(\det A)$.

8 Show that $\det (PAP^{-1}) = \det A$.

9 For each of the following matrices A find $\det (\lambda I - A)$.

a $\begin{bmatrix} 3 & 1 \\ -1 & 2 \end{bmatrix}$ **b** $\begin{bmatrix} 2 & 1 & 0 \\ 1 & -1 & 1 \\ 1 & 2 & 1 \end{bmatrix}$

10 Derive the following formulas:

a If $A = \begin{bmatrix} a & b \\ c & d \end{bmatrix}$ then $\det (\lambda I - A) = \lambda^2 - (a + d)\lambda + ad - bc$.

b If $A = \begin{bmatrix} A_{11} & A_{12} & A_{13} \\ A_{21} & A_{22} & A_{23} \\ A_{31} & A_{32} & A_{33} \end{bmatrix}$ then

$$\det (\lambda I - A) = \lambda^3 - (A_{11} + A_{22} + A_{33})\lambda^2$$

$$+ \left\{ \det \begin{bmatrix} A_{11} & A_{12} \\ A_{21} & A_{22} \end{bmatrix} + \det \begin{bmatrix} A_{11} & A_{13} \\ A_{31} & A_{33} \end{bmatrix} + \det \begin{bmatrix} A_{22} & A_{23} \\ A_{32} & A_{33} \end{bmatrix} \right\} \lambda - \det A$$

Notice that the coefficient of λ^2 is the negative of the sum of the determinants obtained by successively omitting two rows and the corresponding two columns, while the coefficient of λ is the sum of the determinants obtained by successively omitting one row and its corresponding column.

11 Use the information of Exercise 10**b** to make a guess about a formula for det $(\lambda I - A)$, where A has four rows. Prove your conjecture.

☐ **12** Find det A where $A = \begin{bmatrix} i & 1 \\ 2+i & -i \end{bmatrix}$ Is A invertible?

☐ **13** Find the Wronskian of e^x, e^{2x}, and e^{3x} at $x = 0$.

☐ **14** **a** Find the Wronskian of 1, cos $2x$, and $\sin^2 x$ at $x = 0$. Are these functions dependent?

b Find the Wronskian of sin x and sin $2x$ at $x = 0$. Are these functions dependent?

☐ **15** For $A = \begin{bmatrix} a & b \\ c & d \end{bmatrix}$ verify that det A = det A^t.

☐ **16** For $A = \begin{bmatrix} 2 & 1 \\ 1 & 1 \end{bmatrix}$, $E_4 = \begin{bmatrix} 0 & 1 \\ 1 & 0 \end{bmatrix}$, $E_3 = \begin{bmatrix} 1 & 0 \\ -2 & 1 \end{bmatrix}$,

$$E_2 = \begin{bmatrix} 1 & 0 \\ 0 & -1 \end{bmatrix}, \quad E_1 = \begin{bmatrix} 1 & -1 \\ 0 & 1 \end{bmatrix}$$

verify that $E_1E_2E_3E_4A = I$, and that therefore the row operations given by these matrices reduce A to I. Show that for each i, det E_i = det E_i^t. Show that $A^tE_4^tE_3^tE_2^tE_1^t = I$. Show also that

$$\det A = \frac{1}{\det E_1 \det E_2 \det E_3 \det E_4} = \det A^t$$

☐ **17** Find the classical adjoint of $\begin{bmatrix} 1 & 1 & 2 \\ 4 & 3 & 6 \\ 1 & -1 & -2 \end{bmatrix}$ and verify equation **19** in this case.

☐ **18** Solve each of the following by using Cramer's rule.

a $\begin{bmatrix} 2 & 1 \\ 1 & 2 \end{bmatrix} \begin{bmatrix} x \\ y \end{bmatrix} = \begin{bmatrix} 1 \\ -3 \end{bmatrix}$

b $\begin{bmatrix} -3 & 0 \\ 1 & 4 \end{bmatrix} \begin{bmatrix} x \\ y \end{bmatrix} = \begin{bmatrix} 6 \\ 0 \end{bmatrix}$

c $\begin{bmatrix} 1 & 1 & 2 \\ 4 & 3 & 6 \\ 1 & -1 & 2 \end{bmatrix} \begin{bmatrix} x \\ y \\ z \end{bmatrix} = \begin{bmatrix} -1 \\ 2 \\ -1 \end{bmatrix}$

d
$$\begin{aligned} 3x - y + z &= 1 \\ x - 2y + z &= 2 \\ 2x + y + 3z &= 0 \end{aligned}$$

CHAPTER 3

REPRESENTATIONS OF LINEAR TRANSFORMATIONS

We have shown in the previous chapter that the operation of multiplication by a matrix is a linear operation and that every linear transformation defined for coordinate spaces can be represented as such an operation. We used the rather obvious definitions of matrix sum and multiple to show how to define sums and multiples of transformations. We then reversed this procedure, first giving a definition of transformation multiplication and then showing how this gave rise to a matrix product. This interplay between matrices and linear transformations was continued in the discussion of inverses.

Our discussion of this interrelationship between linear transformations and matrices has thus far been restricted to linear transformations of coordinate spaces. We proceed in Section 1 to remove this limitation by showing that in any finite-dimensional vector space a linear transformation can be represented as multiplication by a matrix. This new representation is given in terms of coordinates with respect to a basis for the space. This representation depends upon the basis chosen. We do, however, give a formula which describes a matrix relationship, known as similarity, which holds when different bases are used. In Section 2 we analyze further this matrix relationship of similarity.

This extended representation gives rise to new possibilities for treating linear transformations and matrices. In particular, we may be able to choose a basis so that a given linear transformation is represented by some "nice" matrix, such as a diagonal matrix, often resulting in simplification of calculations. Sections 3, 4, and 5 provide some of the machinery for discussing the problem of finding diagonal representations. Applications to geometry and differential equations are discussed in Section 6.

SECTION 1 The Matrix of a Linear Transformation with Respect to a Basis

We now wish to show how we can represent a linear transformation on a finite-dimensional vector space V by a matrix, relative to a given basis. To keep our discussion as simple as possible, we suppose that V is two-dimensional. To guide us in constructing this representation we first reexamine our matrix representation described in Section 2 of Chapter 2. Recall that if T is a linear transformation from R^2 into R^2, we can find a unique matrix A such that

$$T\bar{u} = A\bar{u} \qquad \text{for all } \bar{u} \text{ in } R^2$$

(This is just Theorem 12.) We have

$$A = \begin{bmatrix} A_{11} & A_{12} \\ A_{21} & A_{22} \end{bmatrix} \quad \text{where} \quad T\begin{bmatrix} 1 \\ 0 \end{bmatrix} = \begin{bmatrix} A_{11} \\ A_{21} \end{bmatrix}, \quad T\begin{bmatrix} 0 \\ 1 \end{bmatrix} = \begin{bmatrix} A_{12} \\ A_{22} \end{bmatrix}$$

We also recall that the numbers x and y are just the coordinates of the pair (x,y) with respect to the standard basis (1,0), (0,1). (*See* Example 1, page 67.) In other words, the columns of A consist of the coordinates of

$$T\begin{bmatrix} 1 \\ 0 \end{bmatrix} \quad \text{and} \quad T\begin{bmatrix} 0 \\ 1 \end{bmatrix} \quad \text{with respect to the basis} \quad \begin{bmatrix} 1 \\ 0 \end{bmatrix} \quad \text{and} \quad \begin{bmatrix} 0 \\ 1 \end{bmatrix}$$

We recall that if $\bar{u}_1$ and $\bar{u}_2$ are a basis for V the coordinates of $\bar{u}$ relative to $\bar{u}_1$ and $\bar{u}_2$ are the unique numbers c_1 and c_2 where $\bar{u} = c_1\bar{u}_1 + c_2\bar{u}_2$. (*See* Section 8 of Chapter 1.) This concept can be used to obtain a matrix representation of linear operations in V. Suppose T is a linear transformation from V into V. The **matrix of T relative to the basis $\bar{u}_1$ and $\bar{u}_2$** is the matrix B, whose columns are the coordinates of $T\bar{u}_1$ and $T\bar{u}_2$ relative to the basis $\bar{u}_1$, $\bar{u}_2$. In other words

1 $$B = \begin{bmatrix} B_{11} & B_{12} \\ B_{21} & B_{22} \end{bmatrix} \quad \text{where} \quad \begin{aligned} T\bar{u}_1 &= B_{11}\bar{u}_1 + B_{21}\bar{u}_2 \\ T\bar{u}_2 &= B_{12}\bar{u}_1 + B_{22}\bar{u}_2 \end{aligned}$$

It follows that

2 *If the coordinates of $\bar{u}$ relative to $\bar{u}_1$ and $\bar{u}_2$ are c_1 and c_2, the coordinates of $T\bar{u}$ relative to this basis are the entries of* $B\begin{bmatrix} c_1 \\ c_2 \end{bmatrix}$

Thus, the effect of applying T can, relative to coordinates with respect to $\bar{u}_1$ and $\bar{u}_2$, be described as multiplication by the matrix of T. To see that property **2** holds we merely use formula **1** and the fact that T is linear; for if $\bar{u} = c_1\bar{u}_1 + c_2\bar{u}_2$, then

$$T\bar{u} = T(c_1\bar{u}_1) + T(c_2\bar{u}_2) = c_1T\bar{u}_1 + c_2T\bar{u}_2$$

Therefore, if we substitute from relations **1**, we obtain

$$T\bar{u} = c_1(B_{11}\bar{u}_1 + B_{21}\bar{u}_2) + c_2(B_{12}\bar{u}_1 + B_{22}\bar{u}_2)$$

which can be rewritten as

$$T\bar{u} = (B_{11}c_1 + B_{12}c_2)\bar{u}_1 + (B_{21}c_1 + B_{22}c_2)\bar{u}_2$$

Thus the coordinates of $T\bar{u}$ relative to $\bar{u}_1$ and $\bar{u}_2$ are just the entries of

$$\begin{bmatrix} B_{11}c_1 + B_{12}c_2 \\ B_{21}c_1 + B_{22}c_2 \end{bmatrix} \quad \text{which is} \quad \begin{bmatrix} B_{11} & B_{12} \\ B_{21} & B_{22} \end{bmatrix} \begin{bmatrix} c_1 \\ c_2 \end{bmatrix}$$

so that property **2** is indeed true.

The matrix B is uniquely determined by property **2**. To see that this is so, suppose the coordinates of $T\bar{u}$ relative to $\bar{u}_1$ and $\bar{u}_2$ are given by

$$B_1 \begin{bmatrix} c_1 \\ c_2 \end{bmatrix}$$

where c_1 and c_2 are the coordinates $\bar{u}$ relative to $\bar{u}_1$, $\bar{u}_2$. We then observe that $\bar{u}_1 = 1 \cdot \bar{u}_1 + 0 \cdot \bar{u}_2$ and $\bar{u}_2 = 0 \cdot \bar{u}_1 + 1 \cdot \bar{u}_2$. Therefore, the coordinates of $\bar{u}_1$ and of $\bar{u}_2$ (written as column matrices) relative to $\bar{u}_1$ and $\bar{u}_2$ are, respectively,

$$\begin{bmatrix} 1 \\ 0 \end{bmatrix} \quad \text{and} \quad \begin{bmatrix} 0 \\ 1 \end{bmatrix}$$

The assumptions about B_1 tell us that the coordinates of $T\bar{u}_1$ and $T\bar{u}_2$ relative to $\bar{u}_1$ and $\bar{u}_2$ are, respectively,

$$B_1 \begin{bmatrix} 1 \\ 0 \end{bmatrix} \quad \text{and} \quad B_1 \begin{bmatrix} 0 \\ 1 \end{bmatrix}$$

These are just the first and second columns of B_1. Furthermore, if B is the matrix of T relative to $\bar{u}_1$ and $\bar{u}_2$ then, by definition of this matrix, the first and second columns of B are the coordinates of $T\bar{u}_1$ and $T\bar{u}_2$ relative to $\bar{u}_1$ and $\bar{u}_2$. We therefore know that B_1 and B have the same columns and thus must be equal.

We have shown that every linear transformation of V into V can be represented by a unique matrix relative to a given basis. In terms of coordinates relative to this basis, the representation is given by property **2**. The converse of this is also true; namely, if $\bar{u}_1$ and $\bar{u}_2$ are a basis for V and

$$B = \begin{bmatrix} B_{11} & B_{12} \\ B_{21} & B_{22} \end{bmatrix}$$

there is then a *unique* linear transformation T from V into V whose matrix is B, relative to $\bar{u}_1$, $\bar{u}_2$. This transformation T is defined by

$$T\bar{u} = (B_{11}c_1 + B_{12}c_2)\bar{u}_1 + (B_{21}c_1 + B_{22}c_2)\bar{u}_2$$

if $\bar{u} = c_1\bar{u}_1 + c_2\bar{u}_2$. We omit the proof that this does indeed define a linear transformation and that this is the only linear transformation from V into V whose matrix, relative to $\bar{u}_1$ and $\bar{u}_2$, is B. (*See* Exercise 17, Appendix 2.)

Our new representation also preserves our relationship between sums, scalar multiples, products, and inverses, in the sense that

3 *If A and B are the matrices of S and T relative to $\bar{u}_1$ and $\bar{u}_2$, then $A + B$, aB, and AB are the respective matrices of $S + T$, aT, and ST relative to $\bar{u}_1$ and $\bar{u}_2$. Furthermore, T is invertible if and only if B is invertible, and the matrix of T^{-1} relative to $\bar{u}_1$ and $\bar{u}_2$ is B^{-1}.*

We omit the proofs of these results (which are straightforward but somewhat tedious). These definitions and results extend easily to higher dimensions. Some examples follow.

EXAMPLE 1 Suppose V is the vector space of polynomials of degree not exceeding 2. (*See* Example 4, page 74.) The polynomials $\bar{u}_1 = 1$, $\bar{u}_2 = x$, and $\bar{u}_3 = x^2$ are a basis for V. We shall find the matrix of D, the differentiation operator, relative to this basis. Since $D1 = 0$, $Dx = 1$, and $Dx^2 = 2x$, we have

$$\begin{aligned} D\bar{u}_1 &= 0 \cdot \bar{u}_1 + 0 \cdot \bar{u}_2 + 0 \cdot \bar{u}_3 \\ D\bar{u}_2 &= 1 \cdot \bar{u}_1 + 0 \cdot \bar{u}_2 + 0 \cdot \bar{u}_3 \\ D\bar{u}_3 &= 0 \cdot \bar{u}_1 + 2 \cdot \bar{u}_2 + 0 \cdot \bar{u}_3 \end{aligned}$$

The matrix D_0 of D relative to $\bar{u}_1$, $\bar{u}_2$, and $\bar{u}_3$ has as its columns the coordinates of $D\bar{u}_1$, $D\bar{u}_2$, and $D\bar{u}_3$ with respect to $\bar{u}_1$, $\bar{u}_2$, and $\bar{u}_3$. Thus we have

$$D_0 = \begin{bmatrix} 0 & 1 & 0 \\ 0 & 0 & 2 \\ 0 & 0 & 0 \end{bmatrix}$$

We note that

$$D_0^{\,2} = \begin{bmatrix} 0 & 0 & 2 \\ 0 & 0 & 0 \\ 0 & 0 & 0 \end{bmatrix} \quad \text{and} \quad D_0^{\,3} = \begin{bmatrix} 0 & 0 & 0 \\ 0 & 0 & 0 \\ 0 & 0 & 0 \end{bmatrix}$$

which are, respectively, the matrices of D^2 and D^3 relative to $\bar{u}_1$, $\bar{u}_2$, and

$\bar{u}_3$ (from property 3). We can verify this directly, for we have

$$D^2\bar{u}_1 = 0 = 0 \cdot \bar{u}_1 + 0 \cdot \bar{u}_2 + 0 \cdot \bar{u}_3$$
$$D^2\bar{u}_2 = 0 = 0 \cdot \bar{u}_1 + 0 \cdot \bar{u}_2 + 0 \cdot \bar{u}_3$$
$$D^2\bar{u}_3 = 2 = 2 \cdot \bar{u}_1 + 0 \cdot \bar{u}_2 + 0 \cdot \bar{u}_3$$

and

$$D^3\bar{u}_1 = D^3\bar{u}_2 = D^3\bar{u}_3 = 0$$

We note that D is *not* invertible, for the columns of D_0 are dependent.

EXAMPLE 2 Suppose that V and D are as in Example 1. Recall that

$$f_1 = \frac{(x-1)(x-2)}{2}, \qquad f_2 = \frac{x(x-2)}{-1}, \qquad f_3 = \frac{x(x-1)}{2}$$

are also a basis for V and that for any f in V we have (*see* the Lagrange interpolation formula, page 74)

4 $$f = f(0)f_1 + f(1)f_2 + f(2)f_3$$

We shall find the matrix of D relative to f_1, f_2, and f_3. We have

$$f_1 = x^2/2 - 3x/2 + 1, \qquad f_2 = -x^2 + 2x, \qquad f_3 = x^2/2 - x/2$$

so that

5 $$Df_1 = x - \tfrac{3}{2}, \qquad Df_2 = -2x + 2, \qquad Df_3 = x - \tfrac{1}{2}$$

To find the matrix of D relative to f_1, f_2, and f_3 we need to find the coordinates of Df_1, Df_2, and Df_3 relative to f_1, f_2, and f_3. Formula 4 tells us that the coordinates of any f, relative to f_1, f_2, and f_3, are $f(0)$, $f(1)$, and $f(2)$. Therefore, setting $x = 0$, 1, and 2 in each expression in 5 we find that

$$(-\tfrac{3}{2}, -\tfrac{1}{2}, \tfrac{1}{2}), \ (2, 0, -2), \text{ and } (-\tfrac{1}{2}, \tfrac{1}{2}, \tfrac{3}{2})$$

are the respective coordinates of Df_1, Df_2, and Df_3 relative to f_1, f_2, and f_3. The matrix D_1 of D relative to this basis has these as its columns:

$$D_1 = \begin{bmatrix} -\tfrac{3}{2} & 2 & -\tfrac{1}{2} \\ -\tfrac{1}{2} & 0 & \tfrac{1}{2} \\ \tfrac{1}{2} & -2 & \tfrac{3}{2} \end{bmatrix}$$

We shall show below how this matrix is related to the matrix of Example 1.

EXAMPLE 3 Suppose T is defined for $\bar{u}$ in R^2 by

$$T\bar{u} = A\bar{u} \text{ where } A = \begin{bmatrix} 3 & -1 \\ 2 & 0 \end{bmatrix}$$

The vectors

$$\bar{u}_1 = \begin{bmatrix} 1 \\ 1 \end{bmatrix}, \qquad \bar{u}_2 = \begin{bmatrix} 2 \\ 4 \end{bmatrix}$$

are independent (the student should verify that this is so), so from Theorem 10 they are a basis for R^2. We shall find the matrix of T relative to this basis. We have

$$T\bar{u}_1 = A\bar{u}_1 = \begin{bmatrix} 2 \\ 2 \end{bmatrix}, \qquad T\bar{u}_2 = A\bar{u}_2 = \begin{bmatrix} 2 \\ 4 \end{bmatrix}$$

so that

$$T\bar{u}_1 = 2\bar{u}_1 + 0 \cdot \bar{u}_2, \qquad T\bar{u}_2 = 0 \cdot \bar{u}_1 + 1 \cdot \bar{u}_2$$

The matrix B of T relative to $\bar{u}_1$ and $\bar{u}_2$ has these coordinates as its columns, so we have

$$B = \begin{bmatrix} 2 & 0 \\ 0 & 1 \end{bmatrix}$$

Note that B is a diagonal matrix. Property 3 tells us that the matrix of T^{10}, relative to $\bar{u}_1$ and $\bar{u}_2$, must be

$$B^{10} = \begin{bmatrix} 2^{10} & 0 \\ 0 & 1 \end{bmatrix} = \begin{bmatrix} 1024 & 0 \\ 0 & 1 \end{bmatrix}$$

Observe that this description of T in terms of $\bar{u}_1$ and $\bar{u}_2$ results in a considerable simplification in calculations involving T. For example, the matrix of T^{10} relative to the standard basis is A^{10}. A long, arduous calculation gives

$$A^{10} = \begin{bmatrix} 2047 & -1023 \\ 2046 & -1022 \end{bmatrix}$$

Fortunately, we shall later describe a means of calculating A^{10} that takes advantage of the fact that A and B are the matrices of T relative to different bases.

DISCUSSION The matrices D_0 and D_1 of Examples 1 and 2 are related by the fact that each is the matrix of the differentiation operator D, relative to different bases. The matrices A and B of Example 3 are also related by the fact that each is the matrix of T, again relative to different bases. We now establish a general formula that gives a precise form of this relationship.

To keep the notation from becoming excessive we first suppose that T is a linear transformation from R^2 into R^2, defined for $\bar{u}$ in R^2 by

6 $$T\bar{u} = A\bar{u} \qquad \text{where } A = \begin{bmatrix} A_{11} & A_{12} \\ A_{21} & A_{22} \end{bmatrix}$$

We suppose that $\bar{u}_1$ and $\bar{u}_2$ are another basis for R^2 and that B is the matrix of T relative to $\bar{u}_1$ and $\bar{u}_2$, so that if

7 $$B = \begin{bmatrix} B_{11} & B_{12} \\ B_{21} & B_{22} \end{bmatrix} \qquad \text{then} \qquad \begin{aligned} T\bar{u}_1 &= B_{11}\bar{u}_1 + B_{21}\bar{u}_2 \\ T\bar{u}_2 &= B_{12}\bar{u}_1 + B_{22}\bar{u}_2 \end{aligned}$$

We shall show that *if P is the matrix whose columns are $\bar{u}_1$ and $\bar{u}_2$ then P is invertible and*

8 $$B = P^{-1}AP$$

This is the fundamental formula that relates B and A. In the next section we shall study this formula in some detail. To establish the formula we first note that P is certainly invertible (for its columns are independent, and we can therefore apply Theorem 15).

We know that $P\begin{bmatrix} 1 \\ 0 \end{bmatrix}$ is the first column of P, so $P\begin{bmatrix} 1 \\ 0 \end{bmatrix} = \bar{u}_1$. Thus

$$P^{-1}AP\begin{bmatrix} 1 \\ 0 \end{bmatrix} = P^{-1}A\bar{u}_1$$

We also know that (*see* formulas **6** and **7**) $A\bar{u}_1 = T\bar{u}_1$ and $T\bar{u}_1 = B_{11}\bar{u}_1 + B_{21}\bar{u}_2$ so

$$\begin{aligned} P^{-1}AP\begin{bmatrix} 1 \\ 0 \end{bmatrix} &= P^{-1}T\bar{u}_1 = P^{-1}(B_{11}\bar{u}_1 + B_{21}\bar{u}_2) \\ &= B_{11}P^{-1}\bar{u}_1 + B_{21}P^{-1}\bar{u}_2 \end{aligned}$$

Since

$$P\begin{bmatrix} 1 \\ 0 \end{bmatrix} = \bar{u}_1 \qquad \text{and} \qquad P\begin{bmatrix} 0 \\ 1 \end{bmatrix} = \bar{u}_2$$

we can multiply by P^{-1} to obtain

$$P^{-1}\bar{u}_1 = \begin{bmatrix} 1 \\ 0 \end{bmatrix} \quad \text{and} \quad P^{-1}\bar{u}_2 = \begin{bmatrix} 0 \\ 1 \end{bmatrix}$$

Substitution of these gives

$$\begin{aligned} P^{-1}AP\begin{bmatrix} 1 \\ 0 \end{bmatrix} &= B_{11}P^{-1}\bar{u}_1 + B_{21}P^{-1}\bar{u}_2 \\ &= B_{11}\begin{bmatrix} 1 \\ 0 \end{bmatrix} + B_{21}\begin{bmatrix} 0 \\ 1 \end{bmatrix} \\ &= \begin{bmatrix} B_{11} \\ B_{21} \end{bmatrix} \end{aligned}$$

This shows that the first column of $P^{-1}AP$ has the same entries as the first column of B. A similar calculation of

$$P^{-1}AP\begin{bmatrix} 0 \\ 1 \end{bmatrix}$$

establishes that the second columns also have the same entries and completes the proof of formula **8**.

We state a general version of this result, the proof of which is omitted:

9 *Suppose* $\bar{u}_1, \bar{u}_2, \ldots, \bar{u}_n$ *is a basis for* V *and that* $\bar{v}_1, \bar{v}_2, \ldots, \bar{v}_n$ *is also a basis for* V. *Suppose* T *is a linear transformation from* V *into* V *whose matrices with respect to these bases are, respectively,* A *and* B. *Let* P *be the matrix whose columns consist of the coordinates of each of the vectors* $\bar{v}_1, \bar{v}_2, \ldots, \bar{v}_n$ *with respect to* $\bar{u}_1, \bar{u}_2, \ldots, \bar{u}_n$. *Let* Q *be the matrix whose columns are the coordinates of each of the vectors* $\bar{u}_1, \bar{u}_2, \ldots, \bar{u}_n$ *with respect to* $\bar{v}_1, \bar{v}_2, \ldots, \bar{v}_n$. *Then*

$$QP = PQ = I, \text{ so that } Q = P^{-1} \text{ and } P = Q^{-1}$$

Furthermore,

$$B = P^{-1}AP \text{ and } A = Q^{-1}BQ$$

EXAMPLE 4 We shall verify formula **8** for the operator T of Example 3. We have

$$A = \begin{bmatrix} 3 & -1 \\ 2 & 0 \end{bmatrix}, \quad B = \begin{bmatrix} 2 & 0 \\ 0 & 1 \end{bmatrix}, \quad \bar{u}_1 = \begin{bmatrix} 1 \\ 1 \end{bmatrix}, \quad \bar{u}_2 = \begin{bmatrix} 2 \\ 4 \end{bmatrix}$$

If we set

$$P = \begin{bmatrix} 1 & 2 \\ 1 & 4 \end{bmatrix} \qquad \text{we find that} \qquad P^{-1} = \begin{bmatrix} 2 & -1 \\ -\frac{1}{2} & \frac{1}{2} \end{bmatrix}$$

We then have

$$\begin{aligned} P^{-1}AP &= P^{-1}\begin{bmatrix} 3 & -1 \\ 2 & 0 \end{bmatrix}\begin{bmatrix} 1 & 2 \\ 1 & 4 \end{bmatrix} = P^{-1}\begin{bmatrix} 2 & 2 \\ 2 & 4 \end{bmatrix} \\ &= \begin{bmatrix} 2 & -1 \\ -\frac{1}{2} & \frac{1}{2} \end{bmatrix}\begin{bmatrix} 2 & 2 \\ 2 & 4 \end{bmatrix} \\ &= \begin{bmatrix} 2 & 0 \\ 0 & 1 \end{bmatrix} \\ &= B \end{aligned}$$

EXAMPLE 5 We shall verify that statement **9** is true for the differentiation operator D and the two bases of Examples 1 and 2. We put

$$\bar{u}_1 = 1, \qquad \bar{u}_2 = x, \qquad \bar{u}_3 = x^2$$

$$\bar{v}_1 = \frac{(x-1)(x-2)}{2}, \qquad \bar{v}_2 = \frac{x(x-2)}{-1}, \qquad \bar{v}_3 = \frac{x(x-1)}{2}$$

so that relative to $\bar{u}_1$, $\bar{u}_2$, and $\bar{u}_3$ and $\bar{v}_1$, $\bar{v}_2$, and $\bar{v}_3$ the respective matrices of D are

$$D_0 = \begin{bmatrix} 0 & 1 & 0 \\ 0 & 0 & 2 \\ 0 & 0 & 0 \end{bmatrix} \qquad \text{and} \qquad D_1 = \begin{bmatrix} -\frac{3}{2} & 2 & -\frac{1}{2} \\ -\frac{1}{2} & 0 & \frac{1}{2} \\ \frac{1}{2} & -2 & \frac{3}{2} \end{bmatrix}$$

We have

$$\begin{aligned} \bar{v}_1 &= x^2/2 - 3x/2 + 1 = 1 \cdot \bar{u}_1 - \tfrac{3}{2}\bar{u}_2 + \tfrac{1}{2}\bar{u}_3 \\ \bar{v}_2 &= -x^2 + 2x \qquad\quad\;\; = 0 \cdot \bar{u}_1 + 2 \cdot \bar{u}_2 - \bar{u}_3 \\ \bar{v}_3 &= x^2/2 - x/2 \qquad\quad = 0 \cdot \bar{u}_1 - \tfrac{1}{2}\bar{u}_2 + \tfrac{1}{2}\bar{u}_3 \end{aligned}$$

and (using formula **4** for each of 1, x, and x^2)

$$\begin{aligned} \bar{u}_1 &= 1 \cdot \bar{v}_1 + 1 \cdot \bar{v}_2 + 1 \cdot \bar{v}_3 \\ \bar{u}_2 &= 0 \cdot \bar{v}_1 + 1 \cdot \bar{v}_2 + 2 \cdot \bar{v}_3 \\ \bar{u}_3 &= 0 \cdot \bar{v}_1 + 1 \cdot \bar{v}_2 + 4 \cdot \bar{v}_3 \end{aligned}$$

Thus with P and Q as in statement **9** we have

$$P = \begin{bmatrix} 1 & 0 & 0 \\ -\frac{3}{2} & 2 & -\frac{1}{2} \\ \frac{1}{2} & -1 & \frac{1}{2} \end{bmatrix} \qquad Q = \begin{bmatrix} 1 & 0 & 0 \\ 1 & 1 & 1 \\ 1 & 2 & 4 \end{bmatrix}$$

The student can then verify that $QP = PQ = I$, $D_1 = P^{-1}D_0P$, and $D_0 = Q^{-1}D_1Q$.

REMARK The results of this section can be extended to cover the case of linear transformations defined for vectors in one vector space V with values in a second vector space W. In this case a matrix description can be given relative to selection of a basis for V and a basis for W. Because the more interesting and useful theory occurs when V and W are the same, we have confined our discussion to this case.

EXERCISES

1 Suppose V is the vector space of polynomials of degree not exceeding 3. Find the matrix of the differentiation operator D with respect to the basis $1, x, x^2$, and x^3.

2 For V and D as in Exercise 1 find the matrix of D^2, D^3, and D^4 with respect to $1, x, x^2$, and x^3.

□ 3 For V and D as in Exercise 1, find the matrix of D relative to the basis

$$\bar{v}_1 = \frac{(x-1)(x-2)(x-3)}{-6}, \bar{v}_2 = \frac{x(x-2)(x-3)}{2}, \bar{v}_3 = \frac{x(x-1)(x-3)}{-2},$$

and

$$\bar{v}_4 = \frac{x(x-1)(x-2)}{6}.$$

(*See* Exercise 11 on page 77.)

4 What is the matrix of the identity operator I relative to the basis $\bar{u}_1, \bar{u}_2, \ldots, \bar{u}_n$ for V? What is the matrix of the zero operator relative to this basis? The matrix of aI?

5 For each of the following matrices A suppose T is defined by $T\bar{u} = A\bar{u}$ for $\bar{u}$ in R^2. Proceed as in Example 3 to find the matrix B of T relative to $\bar{u}_1 = (3,1)$ and $\bar{u}_2 = (5,2)$.

a $A = \begin{bmatrix} 28 & -75 \\ 10 & -27 \end{bmatrix}$ **b** $A = \begin{bmatrix} -2 & 9 \\ -1 & 4 \end{bmatrix}$

6 For each of the operators T of Exercise 5 find the matrix of each of the following, relative to (3,1) and (5,2), by using property **3**.

a T^3 **b** $T + I$

c $T^6 - T^4 + T^2$ **d** T^{-1}

7 Suppose T is defined for $\bar{u}$ in R^3 by $T\bar{u} = A\bar{u}$, where $A = \begin{bmatrix} 8 & 9 & 9 \\ 3 & 2 & 3 \\ -9 & -9 & -10 \end{bmatrix}$

a Find the matrix B of T relative to $(-1,1,0)$, $(-1,0,1)$, and $(-3,-1,3)$.
b What is the matrix of T^6 relative to this basis?

8 What is the relation between the matrix of T relative to $\bar{u}_1, \bar{u}_2$ and the matrix of T relative to $\bar{u}_2, \bar{u}_1$?

9 a For A and B as in Exercise 5**a** find an invertible matrix P such that $B = P^{-1}AP$. (*See* Example 4.)
b For A and B as in Exercise 7 find an invertible matrix P such that $B = P^{-1}AP$.

10 Suppose V is as in Example 1 and that T is the operator defined by

$$Tf = \frac{1}{x}\int_0^x f(t)\,dt \qquad \text{for} \qquad f \text{ in } V.$$

a Find $T(x^2 + 1)$.
b Find $T(1 - x)$.
c Find the matrix A of T relative to 1, x, and x^2.
d Find the inverse of the matrix of part **c** and use it to describe $T^{-1}1$, $T^{-1}x$, and $T^{-1}x^2$.

11 For V and T as in Exercise 10 find the matrix B of T relative to the basis of Example 2.

12 Suppose A, B, and P each have two rows and two columns and that $B = P^{-1}AP$. Show that there is a linear transformation T from R^2 into R^2 such that A and B are each the matrix of T with respect to a basis. (Hint: Let $T\bar{u} = A\bar{u}$ for $\bar{u}$ in R^2 and show that B is the matrix of T with respect to the columns of P.)

☐ 13 For the matrices A and B of Exercises 10 and 11, proceed as in Example 5 to find P and Q such that $QP = PQ = I$, $B = P^{-1}AP$, and $A = Q^{-1}BQ$.

☐ 14 The results of this section hold for complex vector spaces. Suppose T is defined for $\bar{u}$ in C^2 by

$$T\bar{u} = A\bar{u}, \text{ where } A = \begin{bmatrix} 7 + 4i & -12 + 24i \\ -1 + 2i & -7 - 3i \end{bmatrix}$$

a Find the matrix B of T relative to the basis $(4i,-1)$ and $(-3,-i)$.
b Find an invertible matrix P such that $B = P^{-1}AP$.

SECTION 2 Calculations with Similar Matrices

We say that the matrix B is **similar** to the matrix A if there is an invertible matrix P such that

1 $$B = P^{-1}AP$$

Suppose T is the linear transformation defined by $T\bar{u} = A\bar{u}$ for $\bar{u}$ in R^n, so that A is the matrix of T with respect to the standard basis. If B is the matrix of T with respect to another basis, then formula **8** of Section 1 tells us that B is similar to A. We also noted that if B is similar to A, then B is the matrix of T with respect to some other basis for R^n. (*See* Exercise 12, page 187.)

Our purpose in this section is to gain facility in calculating with formula **1**. We first note that

2 *If B is similar to A, then A is similar to B.*

If P is invertible and $B = P^{-1}AP$, we can solve for A by suitably multiplying by P and P^{-1}. We have

$$\begin{aligned} PBP^{-1} &= P(P^{-1}AP)P^{-1} \\ &= (PP^{-1})A(PP^{-1}) \\ &= A \end{aligned}$$

If we put $Q = P^{-1}$, so that $Q^{-1} = P$, we can then write

3 $$A = Q^{-1}BQ$$

and thus establish statement **2**.

The above procedure indicates a basic trick for calculating with formula **1**, namely, the cancellation effect of multiplying P by P^{-1} or P^{-1} by P. As another example, suppose $B = P^{-1}AP$. Then

$$\begin{aligned} B^2 &= (P^{-1}AP)(P^{-1}AP) \\ &= (P^{-1}A)(PP^{-1})(AP) \\ &= (P^{-1}A)I(AP) \\ &= P^{-1}AAP \\ &= P^{-1}A^2P \end{aligned}$$

Notice that the six factors of $(P^{-1}AP)(P^{-1}AP)$ collapse to the four factors of $P^{-1}A^2P$ because of the cancellation of $P^{-1}P$. This cancellation appears again in the calculation of other powers of B. For example,

$$\begin{aligned} B^3 &= (P^{-1}AP)(P^{-1}AP)(P^{-1}AP) \\ &= (P^{-1}A)(PP^{-1})A(PP^{-1})(AP) \\ &= P^{-1}A^3P \end{aligned}$$

In general, we have, for any positive integer k:

4 $$B^k = P^{-1}A^kP \qquad \text{if} \qquad B = P^{-1}AP$$

From this it follows that

5 *If B is similar to A, then B^k is similar to A^k.*

EXAMPLE 1 Suppose

$$A = \begin{bmatrix} 1 & 1 \\ 0 & 1 \end{bmatrix} \qquad \text{and} \qquad P = \begin{bmatrix} 1 & 1 \\ 1 & -1 \end{bmatrix}$$

Then (the student should verify these calculations)

$$P^{-1} = \begin{bmatrix} \frac{1}{2} & \frac{1}{2} \\ \frac{1}{2} & -\frac{1}{2} \end{bmatrix} \qquad \text{and} \qquad P^{-1}\,AP = \begin{bmatrix} \frac{3}{2} & -\frac{1}{2} \\ \frac{1}{2} & \frac{1}{2} \end{bmatrix}$$

Therefore if we put

$$B = \begin{bmatrix} \frac{3}{2} & -\frac{1}{2} \\ \frac{1}{2} & \frac{1}{2} \end{bmatrix}$$

then B is similar to A.

We shall verify directly that A is also similar to B. If

$$Q = \begin{bmatrix} \frac{1}{2} & \frac{1}{2} \\ \frac{1}{2} & -\frac{1}{2} \end{bmatrix} \qquad \text{so that } Q^{-1} = \begin{bmatrix} 1 & 1 \\ 1 & -1 \end{bmatrix}$$

it follows that

$$\begin{aligned} Q^{-1}BQ &= Q^{-1}\begin{bmatrix} \frac{3}{2} & -\frac{1}{2} \\ \frac{1}{2} & \frac{1}{2} \end{bmatrix}\begin{bmatrix} \frac{1}{2} & \frac{1}{2} \\ \frac{1}{2} & -\frac{1}{2} \end{bmatrix} = Q^{-1}\begin{bmatrix} \frac{1}{2} & 1 \\ \frac{1}{2} & 0 \end{bmatrix} \\ &= \begin{bmatrix} 1 & 1 \\ 1 & -1 \end{bmatrix}\begin{bmatrix} \frac{1}{2} & 1 \\ \frac{1}{2} & 0 \end{bmatrix} \\ &= \begin{bmatrix} 1 & 1 \\ 0 & 1 \end{bmatrix} \\ &= A \end{aligned}$$

To verify formula 4 for $k = 2$, we note that

$$B^2 = \begin{bmatrix} 2 & -1 \\ 1 & 0 \end{bmatrix} \quad \text{and} \quad A^2 = \begin{bmatrix} 1 & 2 \\ 0 & 1 \end{bmatrix}$$

Then,

$$\begin{aligned} P^{-1}A^2P &= P^{-1}\begin{bmatrix} 1 & 2 \\ 0 & 1 \end{bmatrix}\begin{bmatrix} 1 & 1 \\ 1 & -1 \end{bmatrix} = P^{-1}\begin{bmatrix} 3 & -1 \\ 1 & -1 \end{bmatrix} \\ &= \begin{bmatrix} \frac{1}{2} & \frac{1}{2} \\ \frac{1}{2} & -\frac{1}{2} \end{bmatrix}\begin{bmatrix} 3 & -1 \\ 1 & -1 \end{bmatrix} \\ &= \begin{bmatrix} 2 & -1 \\ 1 & 0 \end{bmatrix} \end{aligned}$$

The powers of A are easy to find. Direct calculation gives

$$A^3 = \begin{bmatrix} 1 & 3 \\ 0 & 1 \end{bmatrix}, \qquad A^4 = \begin{bmatrix} 1 & 4 \\ 0 & 1 \end{bmatrix}$$

In general, we obtain the formula

$$A^k = \begin{bmatrix} 1 & k \\ 0 & 1 \end{bmatrix}$$

We can now use formula 4 to find B^k, for we have

$$\begin{aligned} B^k = P^{-1}A^kP &= P^{-1}\begin{bmatrix} 1 & k \\ 0 & 1 \end{bmatrix}\begin{bmatrix} 1 & 1 \\ 1 & -1 \end{bmatrix} = P^{-1}\begin{bmatrix} 1+k & 1-k \\ 1 & -1 \end{bmatrix} \\ &= \begin{bmatrix} \frac{1}{2} & \frac{1}{2} \\ \frac{1}{2} & -\frac{1}{2} \end{bmatrix}\begin{bmatrix} 1+k & 1-k \\ 1 & -1 \end{bmatrix} \\ &= \begin{bmatrix} 1+k/2 & -k/2 \\ k/2 & 1-k/2 \end{bmatrix} \end{aligned}$$

EXAMPLE 2 If B is similar to A, and A is a diagonal matrix, the use of formula 4 often simplifies calculation of large powers of B. For example, suppose

$$A = \begin{bmatrix} 2 & 0 \\ 0 & 1 \end{bmatrix} \quad \text{and} \quad P = \begin{bmatrix} 2 & -1 \\ -1 & 1 \end{bmatrix}$$

Then

$$P^{-1} = \begin{bmatrix} 1 & 1 \\ 1 & 2 \end{bmatrix} \quad \text{and} \quad P^{-1}AP = \begin{bmatrix} 3 & -1 \\ 2 & 0 \end{bmatrix}$$

Therefore, if $B = P^{-1}AP$, we know from formula **4** that $B^k = P^{-1}A^kP$. For example,

$$A^6 = \begin{bmatrix} 64 & 0 \\ 0 & 1 \end{bmatrix}$$

so that

$$\begin{aligned} B^6 &= P^{-1}A^6P \\ &= \begin{bmatrix} 1 & 1 \\ 1 & 2 \end{bmatrix} \begin{bmatrix} 64 & 0 \\ 0 & 1 \end{bmatrix} \begin{bmatrix} 2 & -1 \\ -1 & 1 \end{bmatrix} \\ &= \begin{bmatrix} 127 & -63 \\ 126 & -62 \end{bmatrix} \end{aligned}$$

This method of calculating B^6 is certainly easier than direct calculation.

DISCUSSION Some further consequences of the similarity relationship follow. Suppose B is similar to A and A is invertible. We then have $B = P^{-1}AP$, and it follows that

$$\begin{aligned} (P^{-1}A^{-1}P)B &= (P^{-1}A^{-1}P)(P^{-1}AP) \\ &= (P^{-1}A^{-1})(PP^{-1})(AP) \\ &= (P^{-1}A^{-1})(AP) \\ &= P^{-1}(A^{-1}A)P \\ &= P^{-1}P = I \end{aligned}$$

Thus $P^{-1}A^{-1}P$ *must* be the inverse of B, and this fact shows that

6 $$B^{-1} = P^{-1}A^{-1}P$$

We recall (*See* Example 3, page 133.) that if $q(\lambda)$ is the polynomial

$$q(\lambda) = a_k\lambda^k + a_{k-1}\lambda^{k-1} + \cdots + a_1\lambda + a_0$$

then

$$q(A) = a_kA^k + a_{k-1}A^{k-1} + \cdots + a_1A + a_0I$$

Suppose B is similar to A, and we can thus write $B = P^{-1}AP$. Then

$$q(B) = a_kB^k + a_{k-1}B^{k-1} + \cdots + a_1B + a_0I$$

We then substitute, using formula **4** and the fact that $I = P^{-1}IP$ to write this as

$$q(B) = a_kP^{-1}A^kP + a_{k-1}P^{-1}A^{k-1}P + \cdots + a_1P^{-1}AP + a_0P^{-1}IP$$

It is now possible to factor out P^{-1} and P to obtain

$$q(B) = P^{-1}(a_kA^k + a_{k-1}A^{k-1} + \cdots + a_1A + a_0I)P$$

In other words,

7 $$q(B) = P^{-1}q(A)P \qquad \text{if } B = P^{-1}AP.$$

so that, in particular,

8 *If B is similar to A, then $q(B)$ is similar to $q(A)$ for any polynomial $q(\lambda)$.*

EXAMPLE 3 We shall verify formula **6** for the matrices of Example 1. We have

$$A = \begin{bmatrix} 1 & 1 \\ 0 & 1 \end{bmatrix} \qquad P = \begin{bmatrix} 1 & 1 \\ 1 & -1 \end{bmatrix} \qquad P^{-1} = \begin{bmatrix} \frac{1}{2} & \frac{1}{2} \\ \frac{1}{2} & -\frac{1}{2} \end{bmatrix}$$

and

$$B = P^{-1}AP = \begin{bmatrix} \frac{3}{2} & -\frac{1}{2} \\ \frac{1}{2} & \frac{1}{2} \end{bmatrix}$$

Simple calculation shows that

$$A^{-1} = \begin{bmatrix} 1 & -1 \\ 0 & 1 \end{bmatrix} \qquad \text{and} \qquad B^{-1} = \begin{bmatrix} \frac{1}{2} & \frac{1}{2} \\ -\frac{1}{2} & \frac{3}{2} \end{bmatrix}$$

We have

$$P^{-1}A^{-1}P = P^{-1}\begin{bmatrix} 1 & -1 \\ 0 & 1 \end{bmatrix}\begin{bmatrix} 1 & 1 \\ 1 & -1 \end{bmatrix} = P^{-1}\begin{bmatrix} 0 & 2 \\ 1 & -1 \end{bmatrix}$$

$$= \begin{bmatrix} \frac{1}{2} & \frac{1}{2} \\ \frac{1}{2} & -\frac{1}{2} \end{bmatrix}\begin{bmatrix} 0 & 2 \\ 1 & -1 \end{bmatrix}$$

$$= \begin{bmatrix} \frac{1}{2} & \frac{1}{2} \\ -\frac{1}{2} & \frac{3}{2} \end{bmatrix} = B^{-1}$$

EXAMPLE 4 If A is diagonal and q is a polynomial, $q(A)$ is simple to calculate. For example, if $A = \begin{bmatrix} 2 & 0 \\ 0 & 1 \end{bmatrix}$ and $q(\lambda) = \lambda^5 - 3\lambda^2 - 2$, then

$$\begin{aligned} q(A) &= A^5 - 3A^2 - 2I \\ &= \begin{bmatrix} 32 & 0 \\ 0 & 1 \end{bmatrix} - 3\begin{bmatrix} 4 & 0 \\ 0 & 1 \end{bmatrix} - 2\begin{bmatrix} 1 & 0 \\ 0 & 1 \end{bmatrix} \\ &= \begin{bmatrix} 18 & 0 \\ 0 & -4 \end{bmatrix} \end{aligned}$$

We note that $18 = q(2)$ and $-4 = q(1)$; therefore we can write

$$q(A) = \begin{bmatrix} q(2) & 0 \\ 0 & q(1) \end{bmatrix}$$

If B is similar to A, we can then use formula 7 to find $q(B)$. For example, suppose

$$P = \begin{bmatrix} 2 & -1 \\ -1 & 1 \end{bmatrix} \qquad \text{so that} \qquad P^{-1} = \begin{bmatrix} 1 & 1 \\ 1 & 2 \end{bmatrix}$$

Denoting $P^{-1}AP$ by B, we have (*see* Example 2)

$$B = \begin{bmatrix} 3 & -1 \\ 2 & 0 \end{bmatrix}$$

Thus, formula 7 gives

$$\begin{aligned} q(B) &= P^{-1}q(A)P \\ &= \begin{bmatrix} 1 & -1 \\ 1 & 2 \end{bmatrix} \begin{bmatrix} 18 & 0 \\ 0 & -4 \end{bmatrix} \begin{bmatrix} 2 & -1 \\ -1 & 1 \end{bmatrix} \\ &= \begin{bmatrix} 32 & -14 \\ 44 & -26 \end{bmatrix} \end{aligned}$$

EXAMPLE 5 *Finding Roots of a Matrix.*

We can sometimes use the similarity relationship to find roots. For example, suppose we want to find $B^{1/2}$. In other words, we are looking for a matrix C such that $C^2 = B$. Suppose

$$B = \begin{bmatrix} 3 & -1 \\ 2 & 0 \end{bmatrix}$$

We could, of course, put

$$C = \begin{bmatrix} a & b \\ c & d \end{bmatrix}$$

and determine a, b, c, and d from the equation $C^2 = B$. The resulting equations will be nonlinear and rather difficult to solve. Recall that, from Example 2, $B = P^{-1}AP$, where

$$A = \begin{bmatrix} 2 & 0 \\ 0 & 1 \end{bmatrix} \quad \text{and} \quad P = \begin{bmatrix} 2 & -1 \\ -1 & 1 \end{bmatrix}$$

We can then obtain solutions to $C^2 = B$ by obtaining solutions to $D^2 = A$ and using the similarity relationship. For example, if we put

$$D = \begin{bmatrix} \sqrt{2} & 0 \\ 0 & 1 \end{bmatrix}$$

then certainly $D^2 = A$. Thus, if we put $C = P^{-1}DP$ the cancellation effect gives

$$\begin{aligned} C^2 &= (P^{-1}DP)(P^{-1}DP) \\ &= (P^{-1}D)(P^{-1}P)(DP) \\ &= (P^{-1}D)(DP) \\ &= P^{-1}D^2P = P^{-1}AP \\ &= B \end{aligned}$$

We have

$$C = P^{-1}DP = \begin{bmatrix} 2\sqrt{2} - 1 & -\sqrt{2} + 1 \\ 2\sqrt{2} - 2 & -\sqrt{2} + 2 \end{bmatrix}$$

Therefore we have found a matrix C such that $C^2 = B$.

There are, of course, at least three other such matrices, obtained by using this process with each of the following:

$$\begin{bmatrix} -\sqrt{2} & 0 \\ 0 & 1 \end{bmatrix}, \quad \begin{bmatrix} \sqrt{2} & 0 \\ 0 & -1 \end{bmatrix}, \quad \begin{bmatrix} -\sqrt{2} & 0 \\ 0 & -1 \end{bmatrix}$$

EXAMPLE 6 *The Determinant of a Linear Transformation.*

We can use the properties of the determinant to show that similar matrices have the same determinant, for if $B = P^{-1}AP$, we then have $\det B = \det(P^{-1}AP)$. Using the facts that the determinant of a product is the product of the determinants, and that scalars commute, we have

$$\begin{aligned} \det B &= \det P^{-1} \det A \det P \\ &= \det A \det P^{-1} \det P \end{aligned}$$

Since we also know that $\det P^{-1} \det P = \det P^{-1}P = \det I = 1$ we must have $\det B = \det A$.

Suppose T is a linear transformation from V into V and that A is the matrix of T with respect to some basis for V. We then define $\det T$ by

$$\det T = \det A$$

The matrix A depends upon the choice of basis for V, but the number $\det T$ does not depend upon this basis choice, for if B is the matrix of T with respect to some other basis, we know that B is similar to A. (*See* statement **9**, page 184.) Thus the above shows that $\det B = \det A$.

EXERCISES

1 Suppose $B = P^{-1}AP$. Why is it that P^{-1} and P do not necessarily cancel each other in this formula?

2 Suppose $A = \begin{bmatrix} 1 & 1 & 0 \\ 0 & 1 & 1 \\ 0 & 0 & 1 \end{bmatrix}$ and $P = \begin{bmatrix} 1 & 1 & 1 \\ 2 & 3 & 3 \\ 1 & 0 & 1 \end{bmatrix}$

a Find P^{-1}.
b Find $B = P^{-1}AP$.
c Verify that $B^2 = P^{-1}A^2P$.
d For $Q = P^{-1}$ verify that $A = Q^{-1}BQ$.
e Verify that $B^{-1} = P^{-1}A^{-1}P$.
f For $q(\lambda) = \lambda^3 - 3\lambda + 4$ verify that $q(B) = P^{-1}q(A)P$.

3 Suppose $B = \begin{bmatrix} 8 & 9 & 9 \\ 3 & 2 & 3 \\ -9 & -9 & -10 \end{bmatrix}$ and $Q = \begin{bmatrix} -1 & -1 & -3 \\ 1 & 0 & -1 \\ 0 & 1 & 3 \end{bmatrix}$

a Find Q^{-1}.
b Find $A = Q^{-1}BQ$.
c Put $P = Q^{-1}$ and verify that $B = P^{-1}AP$.
d Verify that $B^2 = P^{-1}A^2P$.
e Find B^6 by using formula **4**.
f For $q(\lambda) = 3\lambda^4 - \lambda^2 + 2\lambda$ find $q(A)$ and then use formula **7** to find $q(B)$.

4 Suppose $B = \begin{bmatrix} 19 & -12 \\ 24 & -15 \end{bmatrix}$ and $Q = \begin{bmatrix} 3 & 2 \\ 4 & 3 \end{bmatrix}$

a Show that $Q^{-1}BQ = \begin{bmatrix} 3 & 0 \\ 0 & 1 \end{bmatrix}$

b Use the technique of Example 5 to find a matrix C such that $C^2 = B$.
c Find a matrix C_1 such that $C_1^3 = B$.

5 Suppose $A = \begin{bmatrix} a & 0 & 0 \\ 0 & b & 0 \\ 0 & 0 & c \end{bmatrix}$ and that B is similar to A. What is det B?

6 Suppose A is similar to I. What is A?

7 Suppose $q(\lambda)$ is a polynomial such that $q(A) = 0$. If B is similar to A, what is $q(B)$?

8 If $A = \begin{bmatrix} 0 & 1 & 1 \\ 0 & 0 & 1 \\ 0 & 0 & 0 \end{bmatrix}$ and B is similar to A,

a What is B^3?
b Show that $(I + B)^{-1} = I - B + B^2$.

9 Suppose $A = \begin{bmatrix} a & 0 & 0 \\ 0 & b & 0 \\ 0 & 0 & c \end{bmatrix}$

a If $q(\lambda) = a_3\lambda^3 + a_2\lambda^2 + a_1\lambda + a_0$, show that

$$q(A) = \begin{bmatrix} q(a) & 0 & 0 \\ 0 & q(b) & 0 \\ 0 & 0 & q(c) \end{bmatrix}$$

b If $q(\lambda) = (\lambda - a)(\lambda - b)(\lambda - c)$ use the information of part **a** to find $q(A)$.
c If $q(\lambda) = (\lambda - a)(\lambda - b)(\lambda - c)$ and B is similar to A, what is $q(B)$?

10 Suppose D is the differentiation operator on the vector space of polynomials of degree not exceeding two. By finding the matrix of D with respect to a basis, show that det $D = 0$.

11 **a** Show that A is similar to A.
b Show that if A is similar to B and B is similar to C, then A is similar to C.

12 Suppose $B = P^{-1}AP$ and $C = P^{-1}DP$.
a Show that BC is similar to AD.
b Show that if $BC = CB$, then $AD = DA$.

13 Suppose A is similar to B. Show that the transpose matrix A^t is similar to B^t.

14 Suppose A is invertible. Show that AB is similar to BA. Give an example which shows that AB might not be similar to BA if A is not invertible.

□ 15 The *trace* of A is the sum of the diagonal entries of A. Establish each of the following for matrices with two rows and two columns.
a Trace AB = trace BA.
b Similar matrices have the same trace.
c There do not exist matrices A and B such that $AB - BA = I$.

d For a linear transformation T, the trace of T is the trace of the matrix of T relative to a basis. Does this depend upon the basis?

□ **16** Suppose $A = \begin{bmatrix} 1+i & 0 \\ 0 & -1 \end{bmatrix}$ and $P = \begin{bmatrix} -i & 3 \\ 1 & 4i \end{bmatrix}$

a Find P^{-1} and $B = P^{-1}AP$.

b Use the similarity relationship to find B^8.

SECTION 3 Characteristic Vectors

If V is a finite-dimensional vector space and T is a linear transformation from V into V, then, as was shown in Section 1, T can be represented in terms of coordinates with respect to a given basis, as multiplication by a matrix A. The choice of a different basis results in a different matrix B, which is similar to A. In the next two sections, we shall discuss the problem of finding, if possible, a basis such that the matrix B is diagonal. In this section we present a concept that will be useful in later discussions.

We say that a vector $\bar{v}$ is a **characteristic vector** for T and that λ is a **characteristic value** of T if

$$T\bar{v} = \lambda\bar{v} \text{ and } \bar{v} \neq \bar{0}$$

In other words, a nonzero vector $\bar{v}$ is a characteristic vector if $T\bar{v}$ is a *multiple* of $\bar{v}$.

This concept gives a useful formulation of the problem of finding a diagonal matrix representation for T, for

1 *Suppose T is a linear transformation from V into V and that the matrix B of T with respect to the basis $\bar{u}_1, \bar{u}_2, \ldots, \bar{u}_n$ is diagonal. Then each $\bar{u}_i$ is a characteristic vector for T, and the diagonal entries of B are the corresponding characteristic values.*

To simplify the proof of this result we assume that $n = 2$. The columns of the matrix B are the coordinates of $T\bar{u}_1$ and $T\bar{u}_2$ with respect to the basis $\bar{u}_1, \bar{u}_2$. (*See* formula **1**, page 178.) Therefore

$$B = \begin{bmatrix} B_{11} & B_{12} \\ B_{21} & B_{22} \end{bmatrix} \quad \text{where} \quad \begin{aligned} T\bar{u}_1 &= B_{11}\bar{u}_1 + B_{21}\bar{u}_2 \\ T\bar{u}_2 &= B_{12}\bar{u}_1 + B_{22}\bar{u}_2 \end{aligned}$$

Thus, if B is diagonal, then $B_{12} = B_{21} = 0$, and therefore

2 $$T\bar{u}_1 = B_{11}\bar{u}_1 \quad \text{and} \quad T\bar{u}_2 = B_{22}\bar{u}_2$$

The vectors $\bar{u}_1$ and $\bar{u}_2$ are independent and hence nonzero. We therefore conclude that $\bar{u}_1$ and $\bar{u}_2$ are characteristic vectors, with corresponding characteristic values B_{11} and B_{22}, the diagonal entries of B.

The converse of statement **1** is also true, because

3 *If V has a basis $\bar{u}_1, \bar{u}_2, \ldots, \bar{u}_n$ consisting of characteristic vectors for T, the matrix of T with respect to this basis is diagonal.*

To simplify our proof, we again assume that $n = 2$. Suppose $\bar{u}_1$ and $\bar{u}_2$ are a basis for V consisting of characteristic vectors for T. We therefore know that $T\bar{u}_1$ is a multiple of $\bar{u}_1$ and that $T\bar{u}_2$ is a multiple of $\bar{u}_2$, so we can write

$$T\bar{u}_1 = a\bar{u}_1 \qquad \text{and} \qquad T\bar{u}_2 = b\bar{u}_2$$

We can rewrite this in the form

$$T\bar{u}_1 = a\bar{u}_1 + 0\bar{u}_2 \qquad \text{and} \qquad T\bar{u}_2 = 0\bar{u}_1 + b\bar{u}_2$$

from which we see that the matrix of T with respect to $\bar{u}_1$ and $\bar{u}_2$ is the diagonal matrix

$$\begin{bmatrix} a & 0 \\ 0 & b \end{bmatrix}$$

Some examples will now be given to illustrate these concepts, after which a method for finding characteristic vectors and characteristic values will be provided.

EXAMPLE 1 Geometric means can be used to find characteristic vectors and characteristic values for rotations, reflections, and projections. We make use of the fact that a nonzero vector $\bar{v}$ is a characteristic vector for T if and only if $T\bar{v}$ is a multiple of $\bar{v}$.

Suppose T is a counterclockwise rotation in R^2 through the angle θ and that θ is *not* a multiple of π. If $\bar{v} \neq \bar{0}$, $T\bar{v}$ cannot be a multiple of $\bar{v}$, as shown in Figure 1.

Figure 1

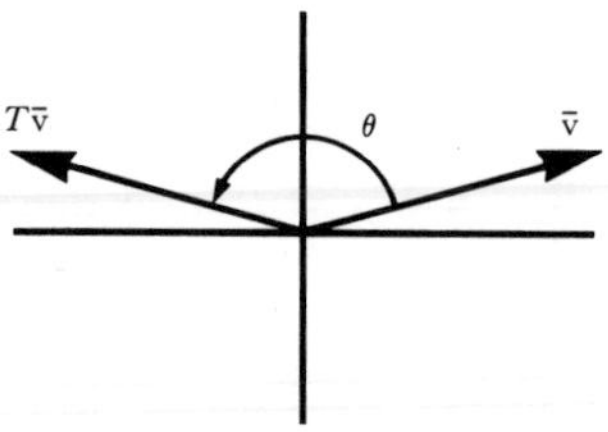

Figure 2

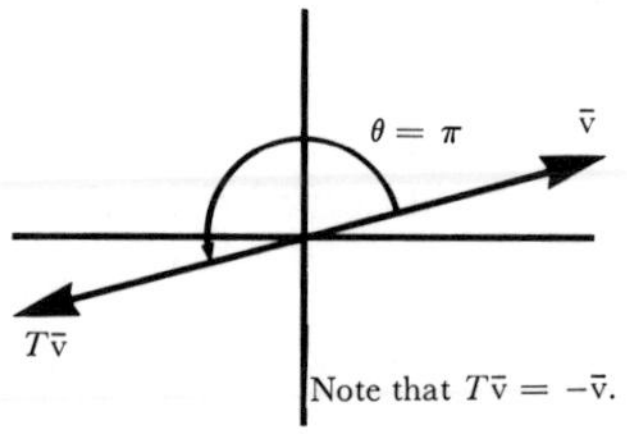

This fact establishes that

A rotation through θ has no characteristic vectors, if θ is not a multiple of π.

Suppose $\theta = \pi$. Then, as Figure 2 indicates, for *every* nonzero vector $\bar{v}$ we have $T\bar{v} = -\bar{v}$. Since this is also true if θ is any odd multiple of π, we know that

If θ is an odd multiple of π, then every nonzero vector is a characteristic vector belonging to the characteristic value $\lambda = -1$.

If θ is an even multiple of π, then T is just the identity operator. Thus for every nonzero vector $\bar{v}$ we have $T\bar{v} = \bar{v}$. In other words,

If θ is an even multiple of π then every nonzero vector is a characteristic vector belonging to the characteristic value $\lambda = 1$.

EXAMPLE 2 Suppose T is the projection in R^2 onto the nonzero vector $\bar{w}$. A vector parallel to $\bar{w}$ is left fixed by T; that is, if $\bar{v}$ is a multiple of $\bar{w}$, $T\bar{v} = \bar{v}$. This shows that every nonzero multiple of $\bar{w}$ is a characteristic vector belonging to the characteristic value $\lambda = 1$.

If $\bar{v}$ is orthogonal to $\bar{w}$, then $T\bar{v} = \bar{0}$. Since $\bar{0} = 0\bar{v}$, this statement shows that every nonzero vector $\bar{v}$ which is orthogonal to $\bar{w}$ is a characteristic vector belonging to the characteristic value $\lambda = 0$.

If $\bar{v}$ is neither parallel nor orthogonal to $\bar{w}$, then, as Figure 3 indicates, $T\bar{v}$ is *not* parallel to $\bar{v}$, and such a vector $\bar{v}$ cannot be a characteristic vector.

In summary we have shown that

The projection T onto $\bar{w}$ has the characteristic values $\lambda = 0$ and $\lambda = 1$. The nonzero multiples of $\bar{w}$ are the characteristic vectors belonging to $\lambda = 1$, and the nonzero vectors orthogonal to $\bar{w}$ are the characteristic vectors belonging to $\lambda = 0$.

Figure 3

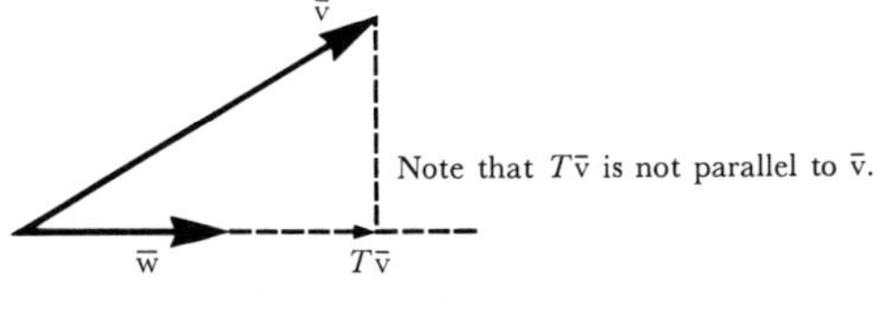

DISCUSSION We extend our terminology to matrices by saying that a vector $\bar{v}$ (written as a column matrix) is a **characteristic vector** for A belonging to the **characteristic value** λ if

$$A\bar{v} = \lambda\bar{v} \text{ and } \bar{v} \neq \bar{0}$$

Since $I\bar{v} = \bar{v}$, we can rewrite the equation $A\bar{v} = \lambda\bar{v}$ as

$$(\lambda I - A)\bar{v} = \bar{0}$$

Therefore, if $\bar{v}$ is a characteristic vector for A belonging to λ, it follows that $\bar{v}$ is a nonzero solution to $(\lambda I - A)\bar{u} = \bar{0}$; that is, $\bar{v}$ is a nonzero vector in the null space of $\lambda I - A$. Such a $\bar{v}$ can exist only if $\lambda I - A$ is not invertible (Theorem 13). We therefore have established that

4 *If $\bar{v}$ is a characteristic vector for A belonging to λ, $\lambda I - A$ is not invertible.*

If $\lambda I - A$ is not invertible and $\bar{v}$ is a nonzero vector such that $(\lambda I - A)\bar{v} = \bar{0}$, we can then rewrite this equation to conclude that $A\bar{v} = \lambda\bar{v}$ and $\bar{v} \neq \bar{0}$. This shows that

5 *If $\lambda I - A$ is not invertible, any nonzero vector $\bar{v}$ in the null space of $\lambda I - A$ is a characteristic vector belonging to the characteristic value λ.*

We know from Theorem 17 that $\lambda I - A$ is not invertible if and only if $\det(\lambda I - A) = 0$. The function

$$f(\lambda) = \det(\lambda I - A)$$

is called the **characteristic polynomial** of A. In summary:

THEOREM 18 The characteristic values of A are the roots of the characteristic polynomial $f(\lambda) = \det(\lambda I - A)$. If λ is a root of this polynomial, then any nonzero vector in the null space of $\lambda I - A$ is a characteristic vector belonging to λ.

We have previously noted that f is indeed a polynomial whose degree is the size of A. (*See* Example 4, page 168.)

EXAMPLE 3 Suppose

$$A = \begin{bmatrix} 2 & -6 \\ -2 & 1 \end{bmatrix}, \quad \bar{v}_1 = \begin{bmatrix} 3 \\ -1 \end{bmatrix}, \quad \bar{v}_2 = \begin{bmatrix} -2 \\ 1 \end{bmatrix}, \quad \bar{v}_3 = \begin{bmatrix} 3 \\ 2 \end{bmatrix}$$

We then have

$$A\bar{v}_1 = \begin{bmatrix} 12 \\ -7 \end{bmatrix}, \quad A\bar{v}_2 = \begin{bmatrix} -10 \\ 5 \end{bmatrix}, \quad A\bar{v}_3 = \begin{bmatrix} -6 \\ -4 \end{bmatrix}$$

We see that $A\bar{v}_1$ is not a multiple of $\bar{v}_1$, while $A\bar{v}_2 = 5\bar{v}_2$ and $A\bar{v}_3 = -2\bar{v}_3$. Thus $\bar{v}_2$ and $\bar{v}_3$ are characteristic vectors for A that belong to the respective characteristic values $\lambda = 5$ and $\lambda = -2$. We observe that

$$5I - A = 5\begin{bmatrix} 1 & 0 \\ 0 & 1 \end{bmatrix} - \begin{bmatrix} 2 & -6 \\ -2 & 1 \end{bmatrix} = \begin{bmatrix} 3 & 6 \\ 2 & 4 \end{bmatrix}$$

and

$$-2I - A = -2\begin{bmatrix} 1 & 0 \\ 0 & 1 \end{bmatrix} - \begin{bmatrix} 2 & -6 \\ -2 & 1 \end{bmatrix} = \begin{bmatrix} -4 & 6 \\ 2 & -3 \end{bmatrix}$$

These reduce respectively to

$$\begin{bmatrix} 1 & 2 \\ 0 & 0 \end{bmatrix} \quad \text{and} \quad \begin{bmatrix} 1 & -\frac{3}{2} \\ 0 & 0 \end{bmatrix}$$

from which we see that $\bar{v}_2$ is a basis for the null space of $5I - A$, and $\bar{v}_3$ is a basis for the null space of $-2I - A$.

Since the characteristic vectors belonging to the characteristic value λ are the nonzero vectors in the null space of $\lambda I - A$ we have shown that

The characteristic vectors of A belonging to $\lambda = 5$ are the nonzero multiples of $\bar{v}_2$, and belonging to $\lambda = -2$ are the nonzero multiples of $\bar{v}_3$.

We shall indicate in the next section how this information can be used to show that A is similar to

$$\begin{bmatrix} 5 & 0 \\ 0 & -2 \end{bmatrix}$$

EXAMPLE 4 Theorem 18 provides a method for finding the characteristic values and corresponding characteristic vectors for a matrix. For example, suppose

$$A = \begin{bmatrix} 3 & -1 \\ 2 & 0 \end{bmatrix}$$

We form the matrix

$$\lambda I - A = \lambda\begin{bmatrix} 1 & 0 \\ 0 & 1 \end{bmatrix} - \begin{bmatrix} 3 & -1 \\ 2 & 0 \end{bmatrix} = \begin{bmatrix} \lambda - 3 & 1 \\ -2 & \lambda \end{bmatrix}$$

and take its determinant to obtain the characteristic polynomial of A:

$$\begin{aligned} f(\lambda) &= \det(\lambda I - A) \\ &= (\lambda - 3)\lambda + 2 \\ &= \lambda^2 - 3\lambda + 2 \\ &= (\lambda - 2)(\lambda - 1). \end{aligned}$$

Since the roots of $f(\lambda)$ are $\lambda = 2$ and $\lambda = 1$, Theorem 18 tells us that these are the characteristic values of A. We then find the corresponding characteristic vectors by finding the nonzero vectors in the null spaces of $2I - A$ and $1I - A$. We have

$$2I - A = 2\begin{bmatrix} 1 & 0 \\ 0 & 1 \end{bmatrix} - \begin{bmatrix} 3 & -1 \\ 2 & 0 \end{bmatrix} = \begin{bmatrix} -1 & 1 \\ -2 & 2 \end{bmatrix}$$

$$1I - A = 1\begin{bmatrix} 1 & 0 \\ 0 & 1 \end{bmatrix} - \begin{bmatrix} 3 & -1 \\ 2 & 0 \end{bmatrix} = \begin{bmatrix} -2 & 1 \\ -2 & 1 \end{bmatrix}$$

which reduce, respectively, to

$$\begin{bmatrix} 1 & -1 \\ 0 & 0 \end{bmatrix} \quad \text{and} \quad \begin{bmatrix} 1 & -\frac{1}{2} \\ 0 & 0 \end{bmatrix}$$

We see that

$$\bar{v}_1 = \begin{bmatrix} 1 \\ 1 \end{bmatrix} \quad \text{and} \quad \bar{v}_2 = \begin{bmatrix} 1 \\ 2 \end{bmatrix}$$

are respective bases for the null spaces of $2I - A$ and $1I - A$. Therefore, we know that

> *The characteristic values of A are $\lambda = 2$ and $\lambda = 1$. The nonzero multiples of $\bar{v}_1$ are the characteristic vectors belonging to $\lambda = 2$, while the nonzero multiples of $\bar{v}_2$ are the characteristic vectors belonging to $\lambda = 1$.*

We shall use this information in the next section to show that A is similar to

$$\begin{bmatrix} 2 & 0 \\ 0 & 1 \end{bmatrix}$$

EXAMPLE 5 In using Theorem 18 it is necessary to calculate $\det(\lambda I - A)$. This can be done using the definition of determinant. (*See* formula 2, page 164.) The formulas of Exercise 10, page 175, are, however, worth remembering:

6 If $A = \begin{bmatrix} a & b \\ c & d \end{bmatrix}$ then $\det(\lambda I - A) = \lambda^2 - (a + d)\lambda + ad - bc$.

If $A = \begin{bmatrix} A_{11} & A_{12} & A_{13} \\ A_{21} & A_{22} & A_{23} \\ A_{31} & A_{32} & A_{33} \end{bmatrix}$ then

7

$$\det(\lambda I - A) = \lambda^3 - (A_{11} + A_{22} + A_{33})\lambda^2 + \left\{\det\begin{bmatrix} A_{11} & A_{12} \\ A_{21} & A_{22} \end{bmatrix} + \det\begin{bmatrix} A_{11} & A_{13} \\ A_{31} & A_{33} \end{bmatrix} + \det\begin{bmatrix} A_{22} & A_{23} \\ A_{32} & A_{33} \end{bmatrix}\right\}\lambda - \det A$$

We shall use formula 7 to find the characteristic values of

$$A = \begin{bmatrix} 8 & 9 & 9 \\ 3 & 2 & 3 \\ -9 & -9 & -10 \end{bmatrix}$$

Formula 7 gives

$$\det(\lambda I - A) = \lambda^3 - (8 + 2 - 10)\lambda^2 + \left\{\det\begin{bmatrix} 8 & 9 \\ 3 & 2 \end{bmatrix} + \det\begin{bmatrix} 8 & 9 \\ -9 & -10 \end{bmatrix} + \det\begin{bmatrix} 2 & 3 \\ -9 & -10 \end{bmatrix}\right\}\lambda - \det A$$

It follows that

$$\det(\lambda I - A) = \lambda^3 - 3\lambda - 2 = (\lambda + 1)^2(\lambda - 2)$$

Theorem 18 then tells us that the characteristic values of A are $\lambda = -1$ and $\lambda = 2$. Corresponding characteristic vectors are found by finding the nonzero vectors in the null spaces of $-1I - A$ and $2I - A$.

EXAMPLE 6 The characteristic values of an upper (or lower) triangular matrix are easy to find. For example, if

$$A = \begin{bmatrix} 2 & 0 & 1 & 2 \\ 0 & 2 & -1 & 3 \\ 0 & 0 & -3 & 1 \\ 0 & 0 & 0 & 4 \end{bmatrix}$$

then

$$f(\lambda) = \det(\lambda I - A) = \det\begin{bmatrix} \lambda - 2 & 0 & -1 & -2 \\ 0 & \lambda - 2 & 1 & -3 \\ 0 & 0 & \lambda + 3 & -1 \\ 0 & 0 & 0 & \lambda - 4 \end{bmatrix}$$

The determinant of an upper triangular matrix is the product of the diagonal entries. (*See* property **4c**, page 165.) Therefore

$$f(\lambda) = (\lambda - 2)(\lambda - 2)(\lambda + 3)(\lambda - 4)$$

so that the characteristic values are 2, −3, and 4.

In general,

8 *The characteristic values of an upper (or lower) triangular matrix are the diagonal entries of the matrix.*

EXERCISES

1 For each of the following operators T describe the characteristic values and vectors. Figures may be helpful.

- **a** T is reflection in R^2 through the line through $\overline{w}$.
- **b** T is projection in R^2 *orthogonal* to $\overline{w}$.
- **c** T is reflection in R^3 through the line through $\overline{w}$.
- **d** T is projection in R^3 onto $\overline{w}$.
- **e** T is projection in R^3 orthogonal to $\overline{w}$.
- **f** T is counterclockwise rotation in R^2 through $\pi/4$ followed by reflection in the x-axis.

2 Suppose $Df = f'$. Show that every real number is a characteristic value of D. (Hint: Calculate $D(e^{ax})$.)

3 Show that $\begin{bmatrix} 1 \\ 1 \end{bmatrix}$ and $\begin{bmatrix} 1 \\ -1 \end{bmatrix}$ are characteristic vectors for $A = \begin{bmatrix} 2 & 1 \\ 1 & 2 \end{bmatrix}$.

What are the corresponding characteristic values?

4 Use Theorem 18 and formulas **6**, **7**, or **8** to find the characteristic polynomial and the characteristic values for each of the following matrices.

a $\begin{bmatrix} \frac{1}{2} & \frac{1}{2} \\ \frac{1}{2} & \frac{1}{2} \end{bmatrix}$ **b** $\begin{bmatrix} 3 & 1 \\ 1 & 3 \end{bmatrix}$ **c** $\begin{bmatrix} 3 & 1 & 0 \\ 1 & 3 & 0 \\ 0 & 0 & 2 \end{bmatrix}$

d $\begin{bmatrix} 5 & 1 & 1 \\ -3 & 1 & -3 \\ -2 & -2 & 2 \end{bmatrix}$ **e** $\begin{bmatrix} 1 & 2 & 1 \\ 0 & 2 & 1 \\ 0 & 0 & 3 \end{bmatrix}$ **f** $\begin{bmatrix} 0 & 1 & 2 & 1 \\ 0 & 0 & 1 & 3 \\ 0 & 0 & 0 & 1 \\ 0 & 0 & 0 & 0 \end{bmatrix}$

e **5** For each of the matrices of Exercise 4 find at least one characteristic vector for each characteristic value.

6 Show that $\begin{bmatrix} 1 & -2 \\ 1 & -1 \end{bmatrix}$ has no real characteristic values. (See also Exercise 11.)

7 a Show that if $A\bar{v} = \lambda\bar{v}$, then $A^2\bar{v} = \lambda^2\bar{v}$.

b Suppose $\lambda_1, \lambda_2, \ldots, \lambda_k$ are the characteristic values of A. What are the characteristic values of A^2?

c Suppose
$$A = \begin{bmatrix} 1 & 2 & 1 \\ 0 & -1 & 0 \\ 0 & 0 & 3 \end{bmatrix}$$
What are the characteristic values of A^2? of A^3?

8 a Show that if $A\bar{v} = \lambda\bar{v}$, then
$$(A^3 - 3A^2 + A - 2I)\bar{v} = (\lambda^3 - 3\lambda^2 + \lambda - 2)\bar{v}$$

b Suppose $q(\lambda)$ is a polynomial and $\lambda_1, \lambda_2, \ldots, \lambda_k$ are the characteristic values of A. What are the characteristic values of $q(A)$? (Hint: *See* part **a**.)

9 a Show that similar matrices have the same characteristic polynomial. (Hint: $\lambda I - P^{-1}AP = P^{-1}(\lambda I - A)P$.)

b How would you define the characteristic polynomial of a linear transformation T from V into V? Does your definition depend upon the choice of basis for V?

10 Suppose A is similar to
$$\begin{bmatrix} 2 & 0 & 0 \\ 0 & -1 & 0 \\ 0 & 0 & 3 \end{bmatrix}$$
What are the characteristic values of A? (Hint: *See* Exercise 9**a**.)

☐ 11 Show that
$$\begin{bmatrix} 2 \\ 1 - i \end{bmatrix} \quad \text{and} \quad \begin{bmatrix} 2 \\ 1 + i \end{bmatrix}$$
are complex characteristic vectors for
$$\begin{bmatrix} 1 & -2 \\ 1 & -1 \end{bmatrix}$$
What are the corresponding characteristic values? Compare this with Exercise 6.

☐ 12 Find the characteristic polynomial, the complex characteristic values, and at least one corresponding characteristic vector for each of the following.

a $\begin{bmatrix} 2 - i & 2 \\ 1 + 3i & -1 + 3i \end{bmatrix}$ **b** $\begin{bmatrix} 0 & -1 \\ 1 & 0 \end{bmatrix}$

☐ 13 An important theorem, known as the Cayley-Hamilton Theorem, asserts that if $f(\lambda)$ is the characteristic polynomial of A, $f(A)$ is the zero matrix. Verify that this is so for

NB

$$A = \begin{bmatrix} 2 & -1 \\ 1 & 3 \end{bmatrix}$$

SECTION 4 Matrices Similar to Diagonal Matrices

We now turn to the problem of finding, for a given matrix A, an invertible matrix P such that $B = P^{-1}AP$ is a diagonal matrix. If T is a linear transformation from V into V such that A is the matrix of T with respect to some basis, the problem is simply to find another basis for which the matrix of T is diagonal. (*See* statement **9**, page 184.) We have seen that this is just the same as the problem of finding a basis for V consisting of characteristic vectors for T. (*See* statements **1** and **3** of the previous section.) For matrices this translates to:

1 *A matrix A with n rows and n columns is similar to a diagonal matrix if and only if R^n has a basis consisting of characteristic vectors for A.*

If R^n has such a basis, and we let P be the matrix with these basis vectors as columns, P is invertible (Theorem 15) and $P^{-1}AP$ is a diagonal matrix whose diagonal entries are the corresponding characteristic values of A. (This assertion is just the matrix version of statements **1** and **3** of the previous section, using statement **8** and Exercise 12 of Section 1.)

Not every matrix is similar to a diagonal matrix (*see* Example 2, below), and hence not every linear transformation has a diagonal representation. Knowledge of the roots of the characteristic polynomial is not enough to guarantee that a given matrix is similar to a diagonal matrix. If these roots are real and distinct, however, the matrix can be diagonalized, as the following theorem implies. The proof can be found in Appendix 2.

THEOREM 19 Suppose A has n rows and n columns and its characteristic polynomial has n *distinct*, real roots $a_1, a_2, \ldots, a_n$. If $\bar{v}_1, \bar{v}_2, \ldots, \bar{v}_n$ are corresponding characteristic vectors, these vectors are independent and hence are a basis for R^n.

If A satisfies the conditions of Theorem 19, we can let P be the matrix with $\bar{v}_1, \bar{v}_2, \ldots, \bar{v}_n$ as columns and then $P^{-1}AP$ will be the diagonal matrix with diagonal entries $a_1, a_2, \ldots, a_n$.

We now give some examples which indicate a procedure for diagonalizing a matrix or a transformation.

EXAMPLE 1 We shall show how to find an invertible matrix P such that $B = P^{-1}AP$ is diagonal, where

$$A = \begin{bmatrix} 22 & 20 \\ -25 & -23 \end{bmatrix}$$

First we find the characteristic polynomial (using formula **6**, page 202):

$$f(\lambda) = \det(\lambda I - A) = \lambda^2 - (22 - 23)\lambda + \det A$$
$$= \lambda^2 + \lambda - 6 = (\lambda - 2)(\lambda + 3)$$

This gives the characteristic values $\lambda = 2$ and $\lambda = -3$. We then find one characteristic vector for each characteristic value by finding a nonzero vector in the null spaces of $2I - A$ and $-3I - A$. We have

$$2I - A = \begin{bmatrix} -20 & -20 \\ 25 & 25 \end{bmatrix} \quad \text{and} \quad -3I - A = \begin{bmatrix} -25 & -20 \\ 25 & 20 \end{bmatrix}$$

which reduce, respectively, to

$$\begin{bmatrix} 1 & 1 \\ 0 & 0 \end{bmatrix} \quad \text{and} \quad \begin{bmatrix} 1 & \frac{4}{5} \\ 0 & 0 \end{bmatrix}$$

Thus

$$\bar{v}_1 = \begin{bmatrix} 1 \\ -1 \end{bmatrix} \quad \text{and} \quad \bar{v}_2 = \begin{bmatrix} -4 \\ 5 \end{bmatrix}$$

are, respectively, nonzero vectors in the null space of $2I - A$ and $-3I - A$, and consequently,

2 $$A\bar{v}_1 = 2\bar{v}_1 \quad \text{and} \quad A\bar{v}_2 = -3\bar{v}_2$$

The vectors $\bar{v}_1$ and $\bar{v}_2$ are easily seen to be independent (we can apply Theorem 19 to reach the same conclusion) and hence, from Theorem 10, are a basis for R^2 consisting of characteristic vectors for A. If we let P be the matrix whose columns are $\bar{v}_1$ and $\bar{v}_2$, P is invertible (from Theorem 15). We have

$$P = \begin{bmatrix} 1 & -4 \\ -1 & 5 \end{bmatrix} \quad \text{and we calculate to find} \quad P^{-1} = \begin{bmatrix} 5 & 4 \\ 1 & 1 \end{bmatrix}$$

Since the columns of P are $\bar{v}_1$ and $\bar{v}_2$, relations **2** tell us that the columns of AP are $2\bar{v}_1$ and $-3\bar{v}_2$. We know that

$$P^{-1}\bar{v}_1 = \begin{bmatrix} 1 \\ 0 \end{bmatrix} \quad \text{and} \quad P^{-1}\bar{v}_2 = \begin{bmatrix} 0 \\ 1 \end{bmatrix}$$

Therefore,

$$P^{-1}(2\bar{v}_1) = \begin{bmatrix} 2 \\ 0 \end{bmatrix} \quad \text{and} \quad P^{-1}(-3\bar{v}_2) = \begin{bmatrix} 0 \\ -3 \end{bmatrix}$$

In other words,

$$P^{-1}AP = \begin{bmatrix} 2 & 0 \\ 0 & -3 \end{bmatrix}$$

Note that the diagonal entries of $P^{-1}AP$ are the characteristic values corresponding to $\bar{v}_1$ and $\bar{v}_2$.

Interchanging the columns of P will interchange the diagonal entries. For example, if we put

$$P = \begin{bmatrix} -4 & 1 \\ 5 & -1 \end{bmatrix}$$

we have (the student should verify this)

$$P^{-1}AP = \begin{bmatrix} -3 & 0 \\ 0 & 2 \end{bmatrix}$$

EXAMPLE 2 We may not be able to find enough characteristic vectors for A to form a basis. This may occur for two reasons: the characteristic polynomial may have complex roots, or there may be an insufficient number of independent characteristic vectors (which *may* occur when the characteristic polynomial has repeated roots). For example, if

$$A = \begin{bmatrix} 1 & -2 \\ 1 & -1 \end{bmatrix}$$

the characteristic polynomial is $f(\lambda) = \det(\lambda I - A) = \lambda^2 - (1 - 1)\lambda + \det A = \lambda^2 + 1$, which has no real roots. Hence there are no characteristic vectors in R^2. Thus, from property 1, there does not exist a *real* invertible matrix P such that $P^{-1}AP$ is diagonal. We can, however, find a complex invertible matrix P such that $P^{-1}AP$ is diagonal by proceeding, as in Example 1, using complex matrices. (*See* Exercise 11.)

Suppose

$$A_1 = \begin{bmatrix} 1 & 1 \\ 0 & 1 \end{bmatrix}$$

Since its characteristic polynomial is $f(\lambda) = \det(\lambda I - A_1) = (\lambda - 1)^2$, $\lambda = 1$ is the only characteristic value for A_1. We have

$$1I - A_1 = \begin{bmatrix} 0 & -1 \\ 0 & 0 \end{bmatrix} \quad \text{which reduces to} \quad \begin{bmatrix} 0 & 1 \\ 0 & 0 \end{bmatrix}$$

Thus, the nonzero vectors in the null space of $1I - A_1$ are the nonzero multiples of

$$\bar{v} = \begin{bmatrix} 1 \\ 0 \end{bmatrix}$$

We have shown that

The only characteristic vectors for A_1 *are the nonzero multiples of* $\bar{v} = \begin{bmatrix} 1 \\ 0 \end{bmatrix}$.

Since $\begin{bmatrix} 1 \\ 0 \end{bmatrix}$ is not a basis for R^2, statement **1** tells us that

$$A_1 = \begin{bmatrix} 1 & 1 \\ 0 & 1 \end{bmatrix}$$

is not similar to a diagonal matrix.

EXAMPLE 3 Suppose

$$A = \begin{bmatrix} 1 & 0 & 1 \\ 0 & 2 & 3 \\ 0 & 0 & -1 \end{bmatrix}$$

The characteristic values of A are the diagonal entries $\lambda = 1, 2, -1$, since A is upper triangular. (*See* statement **8**, page 204.) From Theorem 19 we deduce that A is similar to

$$B = \begin{bmatrix} 1 & 0 & 0 \\ 0 & 2 & 0 \\ 0 & 0 & -1 \end{bmatrix}$$

To find an invertible matrix P such that $B = P^{-1}AP$ we need only find one nonzero vector in each of the null spaces of $I - A$, $2I - A$, and $-I - A$. We have

$$I - A = \begin{bmatrix} 0 & 0 & -1 \\ 0 & -1 & -3 \\ 0 & 0 & 2 \end{bmatrix}, \quad 2I - A = \begin{bmatrix} 1 & 0 & -1 \\ 0 & 0 & -3 \\ 0 & 0 & 3 \end{bmatrix},$$

$$-I - A = \begin{bmatrix} -2 & 0 & -1 \\ 0 & -3 & -3 \\ 0 & 0 & 0 \end{bmatrix}$$

which reduce, respectively, to

$$\begin{bmatrix} 0 & 1 & 0 \\ 0 & 0 & 1 \\ 0 & 0 & 0 \end{bmatrix}, \quad \begin{bmatrix} 1 & 0 & 0 \\ 0 & 0 & 1 \\ 0 & 0 & 0 \end{bmatrix}, \quad \begin{bmatrix} 1 & 0 & \frac{1}{2} \\ 0 & 1 & 1 \\ 0 & 0 & 0 \end{bmatrix}$$

These have the respective nonzero solutions

$$\begin{bmatrix} 1 \\ 0 \\ 0 \end{bmatrix}, \quad \begin{bmatrix} 0 \\ 1 \\ 0 \end{bmatrix}, \quad \begin{bmatrix} -1 \\ -2 \\ 2 \end{bmatrix}$$

Therefore, if we put

$$P = \begin{bmatrix} 1 & 0 & -1 \\ 0 & 1 & -2 \\ 0 & 0 & 2 \end{bmatrix} \quad \text{then} \quad P^{-1} = \begin{bmatrix} 1 & 0 & \frac{1}{2} \\ 0 & 1 & 1 \\ 0 & 0 & \frac{1}{2} \end{bmatrix}$$

and $B = P^{-1}AP$. (The student should, of course, verify that these calculations are correct.)

EXAMPLE 4 Theorem 19 applies only if the roots of the characteristic polynomial are real and distinct. If some of the roots are complex, as in Example 2, the matrix is not similar to a real diagonal matrix. If some roots are repeated, the matrix may or may not be similar to a diagonal matrix. For example, the matrices

$$\begin{bmatrix} 1 & 1 \\ 0 & 1 \end{bmatrix} \quad \text{and} \quad \begin{bmatrix} 1 & 0 \\ 0 & 1 \end{bmatrix}$$

have the same characteristic polynomial, $(\lambda - 1)^2$. The latter matrix is diagonal, while the former is not similar to a diagonal matrix. (*See* Example 2.)

In general a matrix is similar to a diagonal matrix if for each root of the characteristic polynomial of multiplicity k we can find k independent characteristic vectors. (The proof of this fact is omitted.) For example, consider the matrix

$$A = \begin{bmatrix} 8 & 9 & 9 \\ 3 & 2 & 3 \\ -9 & -9 & -10 \end{bmatrix}$$

We saw in Example 5, page 202, that its characteristic polynomial is $(\lambda + 1)^2(\lambda - 2)$; thus the characteristic roots are $\lambda = -1$ and $\lambda = 2$. We have

$$-I - A = \begin{bmatrix} -9 & -9 & -9 \\ -3 & -3 & -3 \\ 9 & 9 & 9 \end{bmatrix} \quad \text{which reduces to} \quad \begin{bmatrix} 1 & 1 & 1 \\ 0 & 0 & 0 \\ 0 & 0 & 0 \end{bmatrix}$$

Thus, the vectors

$$\bar{v}_1 = \begin{bmatrix} -1 \\ 1 \\ 0 \end{bmatrix} \quad \text{and} \quad \bar{v}_2 = \begin{bmatrix} -1 \\ 0 \\ 1 \end{bmatrix}$$

are a basis for the null space of $-I - A$ and are therefore independent characteristic vectors belonging to $\lambda = -1$.

By reducing the matrix $2I - A$ we find the characteristic vector (belonging to $\lambda = 2$)

$$\bar{v}_3 = \begin{bmatrix} -3 \\ -1 \\ 3 \end{bmatrix}$$

The student can show that $\bar{v}_1$, $\bar{v}_2$, and $\bar{v}_3$ are independent. Therefore, if we put

$$P = \begin{bmatrix} -1 & -1 & -3 \\ 1 & 0 & -1 \\ 0 & 1 & 3 \end{bmatrix} \quad \text{then } P^{-1}AP = \begin{bmatrix} -1 & 0 & 0 \\ 0 & -1 & 0 \\ 0 & 0 & 2 \end{bmatrix}$$

EXAMPLE 5 To find a diagonal matrix representation for a linear transformation T we can proceed directly by some means to find a basis consisting of characteristic vectors; or we can first select a basis, then find the matrix A of T with respect to this basis, and, finally, apply the above methods, as shown in Example 6, below.

For example, if T is a counterclockwise rotation in R^2 through the angle θ, then, as we saw in Example 1 of the previous section, T has *no* characteristic values if θ is not a multiple of π. Therefore, unless θ is a multiple of π, T has *no* diagonal matrix representation. If θ is an even multiple of π, $T = I$, and its matrix, with respect to *any* basis, is the identity matrix (which is certainly diagonal). If θ is an odd multiple of π, then $T = -I$, and consequently the matrix of T with respect to any basis is $-I$.

Suppose T is projection in R^2 onto the nonzero vector $\overline{w}$. Let $\overline{w}_1$ be a nonzero vector orthogonal to $\overline{w}$. We then know that $T\overline{w} = \overline{w}$, $T\overline{w}_1 = \overline{0}$, and that $\overline{w}$ and $\overline{w}_1$ are independent. Thus $\overline{w}$ and $\overline{w}_1$ form a basis for R^2 (from Theorem 10). The matrix of T with respect to $\overline{w}$ and $\overline{w}_1$ is

$$\begin{bmatrix} 1 & 0 \\ 0 & 0 \end{bmatrix}$$

EXAMPLE 6 Suppose V is the vector space of polynomials of degree not exceeding two and D is the differentiation operator on V. The matrix of D with respect to the basis $1, x, x^2$ is (*see* Example 1 of page 180)

$$D_0 = \begin{bmatrix} 0 & 1 & 0 \\ 0 & 0 & 2 \\ 0 & 0 & 0 \end{bmatrix}$$

This matrix has only one characteristic root, namely $\lambda = 0$ (*see* property **8**, page 204), and $0I - D_0$ reduces to

$$\begin{bmatrix} 0 & 1 & 0 \\ 0 & 0 & 1 \\ 0 & 0 & 0 \end{bmatrix}$$

so that every characteristic vector of D_0 is a nonzero multiple of

$$\begin{bmatrix} 1 \\ 0 \\ 0 \end{bmatrix}$$

Since this is not a basis for R^3, we conclude that D_0 is *not* similar to a diagonal matrix. Therefore, the differentiation operator D on V has *no* diagonal matrix representation.

EXERCISES

1 For each of the following matrices A find an invertible matrix P such that $P^{-1}AP$ is a diagonal matrix B.

a $\begin{bmatrix} \frac{1}{2} & \frac{1}{2} \\ \frac{1}{2} & \frac{1}{2} \end{bmatrix}$ **b** $\begin{bmatrix} 3 & 1 \\ 1 & 3 \end{bmatrix}$ **c** $\begin{bmatrix} 3 & 1 & 0 \\ 1 & 3 & 0 \\ 0 & 0 & 2 \end{bmatrix}$

d $\begin{bmatrix} 1 & 2 & 1 \\ 0 & 2 & 1 \\ 0 & 0 & 3 \end{bmatrix}$ **e** $\begin{bmatrix} 5 & 1 & 1 \\ -3 & 1 & -3 \\ -2 & -2 & 2 \end{bmatrix}$ **f** $\begin{bmatrix} 3 & 11 & 3 \\ 0 & -4 & -3 \\ 2 & 6 & 1 \end{bmatrix}$

2 For each of the matrices A of Examples 3 and 4 of Section 3 find an invertible matrix P such that $P^{-1}AP$ is diagonal.

3 Show that $\begin{bmatrix} 0 & 1 & 1 \\ 0 & 0 & 2 \\ 0 & 0 & 1 \end{bmatrix}$ *is not* similar to a diagonal matrix.

4 Show that
$$A = \begin{bmatrix} a & d & e \\ 0 & b & f \\ 0 & 0 & c \end{bmatrix}$$
is similar to a diagonal matrix if $(a - b)(b - c)(a - c) \neq 0$.

5 Find A^{10} if

a $A = \begin{bmatrix} 2 & 1 \\ 1 & 2 \end{bmatrix}$ **b** $A = \begin{bmatrix} 2 & -1 & 1 \\ 3 & -2 & 3 \\ 3 & -1 & 0 \end{bmatrix}$

(Hint: First find a diagonal matrix similar to A.)

6 Find a matrix C such that $C^2 = A$, where
$$A = \begin{bmatrix} 2 & 4 & 2 \\ -7 & -12 & -5 \\ 25 & 40 & 15 \end{bmatrix}$$

7 For each of the operators T of Exercise 1, page 204, find a diagonal matrix which is the matrix of T with respect to some basis.

8 Suppose V is the set of all functions of the form $ae^x + be^{-x}$. Find the matrix of the differentiation operator D with respect to the basis e^x, e^{-x}. Why does this not contradict the results of Example 6?

9 Suppose V is the vector space of Example 6 and T is the operation that replaces x by $2x - 1$; that is, $T(a + bx + cx^2) = a + b(2x - 1) + c(2x - 1)^2$.

a Show that T is linear.

b Find the matrix of T with respect to $1, x, x^2$.

c Can you deduce from this matrix that there is a basis for which the matrix of T is diagonal?

d Find three independent polynomials in V which are characteristic vectors for T.

10 Show that if B is diagonal and $B^2 = 0$ then $B = 0$. Deduce from this that if A is similar to a diagonal matrix and $A^2 = 0$ then $A = 0$.

□ **11** Find a *complex* invertible matrix P such that $P^{-1}AP$ is diagonal where

$$A = \begin{bmatrix} 1 & -2 \\ 1 & -1 \end{bmatrix}$$

□ **12** Show that if $A^2 = A$, then A is similar to a diagonal matrix with 1's and 0's on the diagonal. [Hint: Show that if $\bar{u}_1, \bar{u}_2, \ldots, \bar{u}_m$ are a basis for the null space of A, and $\bar{v}_1, \bar{v}_2, \ldots, \bar{v}_k$ are a basis for the null space of $I - A$, these vectors form a basis consisting of characteristic vectors. The relation $I = A + (I - A)$ is useful.]

SECTION 5 Symmetric Matrices

Theorem 19 gives a condition which guarantees that a matrix is similar to a diagonal matrix. This theorem asserts that a matrix is similar to a diagonal matrix if its characteristic polynomial has distinct real roots. If the roots are real and some are repeated, then, as shown in Example 4 of the previous section, further effort is required to see whether there are enough independent characteristic vectors to give a basis. This procedure is of limited use in higher dimensions, because determination of the roots of polynomials of large degree is, in general, quite difficult. Fortunately, there are theorems which, from simple conditions on the entries of the matrix, assert that the matrix is similar to a diagonal matrix. For example, if a matrix is upper (or lower) triangular, with distinct diagonal entries, it is similar to a diagonal matrix. (*See* Exercise 4 of the previous section.)

A much deeper theorem asserts that if a matrix is symmetric, then it is similar to a diagonal matrix. The known proofs of this theorem all require a more sophisticated analysis than we can give at this point, for it must be shown that the characteristic polynomial of a symmetric matrix has *only* real roots and that for each root of multiplicity k, one can find k independent characteristic vectors. The common occurrence of symmetric matrices in applications makes this result particularly important.

We recall that the transpose A^t of A is the matrix obtained from A by interchanging the rows and columns of A. (*See* page 158.) We say that A is **symmetric** if $A^t = A$. For example,

$$A = \begin{bmatrix} 2 & 1 \\ 1 & 3 \end{bmatrix} \quad \text{is symmetric since} \quad A^t = \begin{bmatrix} 2 & 1 \\ 1 & 3 \end{bmatrix} = A$$

while

$$A = \begin{bmatrix} 2 & 1 \\ 2 & 3 \end{bmatrix} \quad \text{is } \textit{not} \text{ symmetric since} \quad A^t = \begin{bmatrix} 2 & 2 \\ 1 & 3 \end{bmatrix} \neq A$$

For symmetric matrices we have the following theorem:

THEOREM 20 If A is symmetric, there is an invertible matrix P such that $B = P^{-1}AP$ is a diagonal matrix.

This theorem is usually called the *spectral theorem*. (A generalization of this result has applications to calculating atomic spectra.) A two-dimensional proof is given in Example 3, below. The reader is referred to the bibliography for general proofs.

The spectral theorem tells us, in particular, that if a matrix is symmetric, its characteristic polynomial must have only real roots. Many methods for approximating these roots have been developed, modern high-speed computers being particularly useful in this task. (*See* bibliography for references to some of these methods.)

If A is symmetric we can actually find an orthogonal matrix P such that $P^{-1}AP$ is diagonal. Recall that an orthogonal matrix is a matrix whose columns are orthonormal. (*See* Example 3, page 160.) This result is a consequence of some elementary tricks with the dot product.

Suppose A has n rows and n columns. For each $\bar{u}$ and $\bar{v}$ in R^n we then have

1 $$(A\bar{u} \cdot \bar{v}) = \bar{u} \cdot (A^t\bar{v})$$

For example, suppose

$$A = \begin{bmatrix} a & b \\ c & d \end{bmatrix}, \quad \bar{u} = \begin{bmatrix} u_1 \\ u_2 \end{bmatrix}, \quad \bar{v} = \begin{bmatrix} v_1 \\ v_2 \end{bmatrix}$$

Then

$$A\bar{u} = \begin{bmatrix} a & b \\ c & d \end{bmatrix}\begin{bmatrix} u_1 \\ u_2 \end{bmatrix} = \begin{bmatrix} au_1 + bu_2 \\ cu_1 + du_2 \end{bmatrix}$$

and therefore

2 $$(A\bar{u}) \cdot \bar{v} = (au_1 + bu_2)v_1 + (cu_1 + du_2)v_2$$

Also, it follows from

$$A^t\bar{v} = \begin{bmatrix} a & c \\ b & d \end{bmatrix}\begin{bmatrix} v_1 \\ v_2 \end{bmatrix} = \begin{bmatrix} av_1 + cv_2 \\ bv_1 + dv_2 \end{bmatrix}$$

that

$$\bar{u} \cdot (A^t \bar{v}) = u_1(av_1 + cv_2) + u_2(bv_1 + dv_2)$$

Comparing this with equation **2**, we see that, indeed,

$$(A\bar{u}) \cdot \bar{v} = \bar{u} \cdot (A^t \bar{v})$$

We can now show that the following statement is true.

3 *If A is symmetric and a_1 and a_2 are distinct characteristic values of A, with corresponding characteristic vectors $\bar{u}_1$ and $\bar{u}_2$, then $\bar{u}_1$ and $\bar{u}_2$ must be orthogonal.*

By assumption $a_1 \neq a_2$ and

4 $$A\bar{u}_1 = a_1\bar{u}_1, \qquad A\bar{u}_2 = a_2\bar{u}_2$$

We therefore have

$$a_1(\bar{u}_1 \cdot \bar{u}_2) - a_2(\bar{u}_1 \cdot \bar{u}_2) = (a_1\bar{u}_1 \cdot \bar{u}_2) - (\bar{u}_1 \cdot a_2\bar{u}_2)$$

We substitute relations **4** into the right-hand side of this and obtain

$$a_1(\bar{u}_1 \cdot \bar{u}_2) - a_2(\bar{u}_1 \cdot \bar{u}_2) = (A\bar{u}_1 \cdot \bar{u}_2) - (\bar{u}_1 \cdot A\bar{u}_2)$$

We now use equation **1** and the assumption that $A = A^t$ to conclude that the right-hand side must be zero. Thus we have

$$(a_1 - a_2)(\bar{u}_1 \cdot \bar{u}_2) = a_1(\bar{u}_1 \cdot \bar{u}_2) - a_2(\bar{u}_1 \cdot \bar{u}_2) = 0$$

Therefore, since $a_1 \neq a_2$, we must have $\bar{u}_1 \cdot \bar{u}_2 = 0$.

In other words, we have shown that $\bar{u}_1$ and $\bar{u}_2$ must be orthogonal, and the proof of statement **3** is completed.

For a given symmetric matrix A, we can modify slightly the procedure of Section 4 to find an orthogonal matrix P such that $P^{-1}AP$ is diagonal. After finding the characteristic polynomial of A and its roots, we then find, for each characteristic value λ, an *orthonormal* basis for the null space of $\lambda I - A$. Theorem 20 guarantees that the collection of such characteristic vectors is then a basis for R^n, while statement **3** guarantees that these basis vectors are orthonormal. Thus the matrix P whose columns are these basis vectors is an orthogonal matrix such that $P^{-1}AP$ is diagonal. The fact that P is orthogonal makes the calculation of P^{-1} quite simple, for we know that

5 *If P is orthogonal, then $P^{-1} = P^t$*

EXAMPLE 1 Suppose

$$A = \begin{bmatrix} 3 & 1 \\ 1 & 3 \end{bmatrix}$$

Then A is symmetric. The characteristic polynomial of A is

$$\begin{aligned}
\det(\lambda I - A) &= \det\left\{\begin{bmatrix} \lambda & 0 \\ 0 & \lambda \end{bmatrix} - \begin{bmatrix} 3 & 1 \\ 1 & 3 \end{bmatrix}\right\} \\
&= \det\begin{bmatrix} \lambda - 3 & -1 \\ -1 & \lambda - 3 \end{bmatrix} \\
&= (\lambda - 3)^2 - 1 \\
&= \lambda^2 - 6\lambda + 8 \\
&= (\lambda - 4)(\lambda - 2)
\end{aligned}$$

so that the characteristic values are $\lambda = 4$, $\lambda = 2$. We now find orthonormal bases for the null spaces of $4I - A$ and $2I - A$. We have

$$4I - A = \begin{bmatrix} 4 & 0 \\ 0 & 4 \end{bmatrix} - \begin{bmatrix} 3 & 1 \\ 1 & 3 \end{bmatrix} = \begin{bmatrix} 1 & -1 \\ -1 & 1 \end{bmatrix}$$

which reduces to $\begin{bmatrix} 1 & -1 \\ 0 & 0 \end{bmatrix}$

so that the vectors in the null space of $4I - A$ are those of the form $\begin{bmatrix} y \\ y \end{bmatrix}$.

Clearly

$$\begin{bmatrix} 1 \\ 1 \end{bmatrix}$$

is a basis for the space. Therefore, if we normalize we have that

$$\bar{u}_1 = \begin{bmatrix} 1/\sqrt{2} \\ 1/\sqrt{2} \end{bmatrix}$$

is an orthonormal basis for the null space of $4I - A$. We also have

$$2I - A = \begin{bmatrix} 2 & 0 \\ 0 & 2 \end{bmatrix} - \begin{bmatrix} 3 & 1 \\ 1 & 3 \end{bmatrix} = \begin{bmatrix} -1 & -1 \\ -1 & -1 \end{bmatrix}$$

which reduces to $\begin{bmatrix} 1 & 1 \\ 0 & 0 \end{bmatrix}$ so that $\bar{u}_2 = \begin{bmatrix} -1/\sqrt{2} \\ 1/\sqrt{2} \end{bmatrix}$

is an orthonormal basis for the null space of $2I - A$.

From our construction we know that $A\bar{u}_1 = 4\bar{u}_1$ and $A\bar{u}_2 = 2\bar{u}_2$ (a fact also easily checked by calculation). We know from statement **3** that

$\bar{u}_1 \cdot \bar{u}_2 = 0$ (which is also easily checked by direct calculation), so that $\bar{u}_1$ and $\bar{u}_2$ are an orthonormal basis for R^2. We see that

$$P = \begin{bmatrix} 1/\sqrt{2} & -1/\sqrt{2} \\ 1/\sqrt{2} & 1/\sqrt{2} \end{bmatrix}$$

is necessarily an orthogonal matrix (since its columns were constructed to be orthonormal). It follows that

$$P^{-1} = P^t = \begin{bmatrix} 1/\sqrt{2} & 1/\sqrt{2} \\ -1/\sqrt{2} & 1/\sqrt{2} \end{bmatrix}$$

Then $B = P^{-1}AP$ is a diagonal matrix. Direct calculation of this product gives

$$B = \begin{bmatrix} 4 & 0 \\ 0 & 2 \end{bmatrix}$$

EXAMPLE 2 Suppose A is the symmetric matrix

$$A = \begin{bmatrix} 1 & 1 & 0 \\ 1 & 1 & 0 \\ 0 & 0 & 2 \end{bmatrix}$$

We have

6 $$\lambda I - A = \begin{bmatrix} \lambda & 0 & 0 \\ 0 & \lambda & 0 \\ 0 & 0 & \lambda \end{bmatrix} - \begin{bmatrix} 1 & 1 & 0 \\ 1 & 1 & 0 \\ 0 & 0 & 2 \end{bmatrix} = \begin{bmatrix} \lambda - 1 & -1 & 0 \\ -1 & \lambda - 1 & 0 \\ 0 & 0 & \lambda - 2 \end{bmatrix}$$

so that

$$\begin{aligned} \det(\lambda I - A) &= (\lambda - 1)\det\begin{bmatrix} \lambda - 1 & 0 \\ 0 & \lambda - 2 \end{bmatrix} - (-1)\det\begin{bmatrix} -1 & 0 \\ 0 & \lambda - 2 \end{bmatrix} \\ &\quad + 0 \det\begin{bmatrix} -1 & \lambda - 1 \\ 0 & 0 \end{bmatrix} \\ &= (\lambda - 1)^2(\lambda - 2) - (\lambda - 2) \\ &= ((\lambda - 1)^2 - 1)(\lambda - 2) \\ &= (\lambda^2 - 2\lambda + 1 - 1)(\lambda - 2) \\ &= (\lambda^2 - 2\lambda)(\lambda - 2) \\ &= \lambda(\lambda - 2)^2 \end{aligned}$$

Thus the characteristic values of A are $\lambda = 0$ and $\lambda = 2$. Using equation **6** we see that $0I - A$ is

$$\begin{bmatrix} -1 & -1 & 0 \\ -1 & -1 & 0 \\ 0 & 0 & -2 \end{bmatrix} \quad \text{which reduces to} \quad \begin{bmatrix} 1 & 1 & 0 \\ 0 & 0 & 1 \\ 0 & 0 & 0 \end{bmatrix}$$

Therefore, the null space of A consists of vectors of the form

$$\begin{bmatrix} -y \\ y \\ 0 \end{bmatrix} \quad \text{so that} \quad \bar{u}_1 = \begin{bmatrix} 1/\sqrt{2} \\ -1/\sqrt{2} \\ 0 \end{bmatrix}$$

is an orthonormal basis for the null space of $0I - A$.

Using equation **6** again we have that $2I - A$ is

$$\begin{bmatrix} 1 & -1 & 0 \\ -1 & 1 & 0 \\ 0 & 0 & 0 \end{bmatrix} \quad \text{which reduces to} \quad \begin{bmatrix} 1 & -1 & 0 \\ 0 & 0 & 0 \\ 0 & 0 & 0 \end{bmatrix}$$

so that the null space of $2I - A$ consists of vectors of the form

$$\begin{bmatrix} y \\ y \\ z \end{bmatrix} = y \begin{bmatrix} 1 \\ 1 \\ 0 \end{bmatrix} + z \begin{bmatrix} 0 \\ 0 \\ 1 \end{bmatrix}$$

Thus

$$\begin{bmatrix} 1 \\ 1 \\ 0 \end{bmatrix} \quad \text{and} \quad \begin{bmatrix} 0 \\ 0 \\ 1 \end{bmatrix}$$

are an orthogonal basis for this null space, and normalizing shows that

$$\bar{u}_2 = \begin{bmatrix} 1/\sqrt{2} \\ 1/\sqrt{2} \\ 0 \end{bmatrix} \quad \text{and} \quad \bar{u}_3 = \begin{bmatrix} 0 \\ 0 \\ 1 \end{bmatrix}$$

are an orthonormal basis for the null space of $2I - A$.

Our construction gives

$$A\bar{u}_1 = 0\bar{u}_1, \qquad A\bar{u}_2 = 2\bar{u}_2, \qquad A\bar{u}_3 = 2\bar{u}_3$$

$$|\bar{u}_1| = |\bar{u}_2| = |\bar{u}_3| = 1 \qquad \text{and} \qquad \bar{u}_2 \cdot \bar{u}_3 = 0$$

while property 3 gives

$$\bar{u}_1 \cdot \bar{u}_2 = 0 \qquad \text{and} \qquad \bar{u}_1 \cdot \bar{u}_3 = 0$$

(These can also be checked by direct calculation.) Therefore $\bar{u}_1$, $\bar{u}_2$, and $\bar{u}_3$ are an orthonormal basis consisting of characteristic vectors for A. Put

$$P = \begin{bmatrix} 1/\sqrt{2} & 1/\sqrt{2} & 0 \\ -1/\sqrt{2} & 1/\sqrt{2} & 0 \\ 0 & 0 & 1 \end{bmatrix}$$

Then, since this is an orthogonal matrix,

$$P^{-1} = P^t = \begin{bmatrix} 1/\sqrt{2} & -1/\sqrt{2} & 0 \\ 1/\sqrt{2} & 1/\sqrt{2} & 0 \\ 0 & 0 & 1 \end{bmatrix}$$

We know that $B = P^{-1}AP$ is diagonal, whose diagonal entries are the characteristic values of A corresponding to the columns of P. Thus

$$B = \begin{bmatrix} 0 & 0 & 0 \\ 0 & 2 & 0 \\ 0 & 0 & 2 \end{bmatrix}$$

which can be checked by calculating $P^{-1}AP$ directly.

EXAMPLE 3 We outline here a proof of the spectral theorem for symmetric matrices with two rows and two columns. This proof uses the quadratic formula and can, with difficulty, be generalized to larger matrices.

Suppose

$$A = \begin{bmatrix} a & b \\ b & c \end{bmatrix}$$

If $b = 0$, A is already diagonal. Thus we can assume $b \neq 0$. The characteristic polynomial is

$$\lambda^2 - (a + c)\lambda + ac - b^2$$

From the quadratic formula we know that this polynomial will have distinct real roots if

7 $$(a + c)^2 - 4(ac - b^2) > 0$$

We shall show that if $b \neq 0$, inequality 7 will always be true, no matter what values a, b, and c have. We multiply out and regroup to obtain

$$\begin{aligned}(a + c)^2 - 4(ac - b^2) &= a^2 + 2ac + c^2 - 4ac + 4b^2 \\ &= a^2 - 2ac + c^2 + 4b^2 \\ &= (a - c)^2 + 4b^2\end{aligned}$$

Thus $(a + c)^2 - 4(ac - b^2)$ can be written as the sum of two squares $(a - c)^2 + 4b^2$, one of which is not zero (since $b \neq 0$ by assumption). We conclude that inequality 7 must always be true if $b \neq 0$. Therefore. the characteristic polynomial has distinct real roots, and we conclude from Theorem 19 that indeed A is similar to a diagonal matrix.

EXERCISES

1 For each of the following matrices A find an orthogonal matrix P such that $P^{-1}AP$ is a diagonal matrix B.

a $\begin{bmatrix} 2 & 1 \\ 1 & 2 \end{bmatrix}$ **b** $\begin{bmatrix} 2 & -1 \\ -1 & 2 \end{bmatrix}$ **c** $\begin{bmatrix} 1 & 1 & 1 \\ 1 & 1 & 1 \\ 1 & 1 & 1 \end{bmatrix}$

d $\begin{bmatrix} -8 & 5 & 4 \\ 5 & 3 & 1 \\ 4 & 1 & 0 \end{bmatrix}$ **e** $\begin{bmatrix} 4 & -2 & 2 \\ -2 & 1 & -1 \\ 2 & -1 & 1 \end{bmatrix}$

2 Find a matrix C such that $C^2 = \begin{bmatrix} 1 & 1 & 1 \\ 1 & 1 & 1 \\ 1 & 1 & 1 \end{bmatrix}$

3 Suppose $A = \begin{bmatrix} 3 & 1 & 2 \\ 0 & 1 & 1 \\ 1 & 0 & 1 \end{bmatrix}$. Find A^t and verify that formula **1** is correct for A.

4 Suppose $\bar{v} = \frac{1}{\sqrt{2}}(1, -1)$ and P is projection onto $\bar{v}$. Show that the matrix of P relative to the standard basis is symmetric and find an orthonormal basis for R^2 consisting of characteristic vectors for P. (Hint: If $\bar{w} \cdot \bar{v} = 0$, then $P\bar{w} = 0$.)

5 Suppose $A = A^t$ and

$$A\begin{bmatrix} 1 \\ 1 \\ 1 \end{bmatrix} = \begin{bmatrix} 2 \\ 2 \\ 2 \end{bmatrix}, \quad A\begin{bmatrix} 1 \\ -2 \\ 1 \end{bmatrix} = \begin{bmatrix} 0 \\ 0 \\ 0 \end{bmatrix}, \quad A\begin{bmatrix} 1 \\ 0 \\ -1 \end{bmatrix} = \begin{bmatrix} -3 \\ 0 \\ 3 \end{bmatrix}$$

Find A.

(Hint: The vectors $\begin{bmatrix} 1 \\ 1 \\ 1 \end{bmatrix}$, $\begin{bmatrix} 1 \\ -2 \\ 1 \end{bmatrix}$, $\begin{bmatrix} 1 \\ 0 \\ -1 \end{bmatrix}$ are orthogonal.

Find an orthogonal matrix P such that $\begin{bmatrix} 2 & 0 & 0 \\ 0 & 0 & 0 \\ 0 & 0 & -3 \end{bmatrix} = P^{-1}AP$.

Then calculate A.)

6 Show that A^tA, AA^t, and $A + A^t$ are symmetric by finding the transpose of each.

7 Find A^{10} if
$$A = \begin{bmatrix} 2 & -1 \\ -1 & 2 \end{bmatrix}$$

8 Show that if A is symmetric and p is a real polynomial, $p(A)$ is symmetric.

9 Show that if $A = A^t$ and $A^2 = 0$ then $A = 0$. (Hint: *See* Exercise 10, page 214. A simple alternative proof can be given by using equation **1** to calculate $A^2\bar{u} \cdot \bar{u}$.)

10 Show that if $A^2 = I$ and $A = A^t$, then A is similar to a matrix with diagonal entries $+1$ or -1.

☐ **11** There are complex versions of Theorem 20. For $z = a + ib$, a and b real, we define the *conjugate* $z^* = a - ib$. For complex A we define the *conjugate* A^* as the matrix obtained by conjugating the entries of A. The *transpose conjugate* (or *adjoint*) is $(A^*)^t$. A matrix A is *unitary* if $(A^*)^t = A^{-1}$; *self-adjoint* if $A = (A^*)^t$; and *normal* if $(A^*)^tA = A(A^*)^t$.

a For $A = \begin{bmatrix} 2-i & i \\ 1+i & 3i \end{bmatrix}$ find A^* and $(A^*)^t$.

b For $A = \begin{bmatrix} i/\sqrt{2} & 1/\sqrt{2} \\ -1/\sqrt{2} & -i/\sqrt{2} \end{bmatrix}$ verify that A is unitary.

c For $A = \begin{bmatrix} 2 & 1-i \\ 1+i & 0 \end{bmatrix}$ verify that A is self-adjoint.

d For $A = \begin{bmatrix} 0 & 2+i \\ -2+i & 0 \end{bmatrix}$ verify that A is normal.

A complex version of Theorem 20 can be stated as follows.

e If A is self-adjoint (or normal), there is a unitary matrix P such that $P^{-1}AP$ is diagonal. If A is self-adjoint, this diagonal matrix has only real entries.

The conditions that P be unitary are the conditions that the columns of P be orthonormal with respect to the dot product of Exercise 17, page 89.

f For $$A = \begin{bmatrix} 1 & i \\ -i & 1 \end{bmatrix}$$

find a unitary matrix P, such that $P^{-1}AP$ is diagonal.

g For $$A = \begin{bmatrix} 0 & -1 \\ 1 & 0 \end{bmatrix}$$

find a unitary matrix P such that $P^{-1}AP$ is diagonal.

SECTION 6 Two Applications of the Spectral Theorem

The spectral theorem of the previous section has many applications. We discuss two such applications in this section: one to a geometric problem and another to systems of differential equations.

EXAMPLE 1 *Reduction of a Quadratic to Standard Form.*

Consider the equation

1 $$ax^2 + bxy + cy^2 = d$$

Put

$$A = \begin{bmatrix} a & b/2 \\ b/2 & c \end{bmatrix} \quad \text{and} \quad \bar{u} = \begin{bmatrix} x \\ y \end{bmatrix}.$$

Then A is symmetric and

$$A\bar{u} \cdot \bar{u} = \begin{bmatrix} ax + \frac{b}{2}y \\ \frac{b}{2}x + cy \end{bmatrix} \cdot \begin{bmatrix} x \\ y \end{bmatrix} = ax^2 + bxy + cy^2$$

so we can rewrite equation **1** as

2 $$A\bar{u} \cdot \bar{u} = d$$

We now apply the spectral theorem to obtain an orthogonal matrix P and a diagonal matrix B such that $B = P^{-1}AP$. We can solve this for A to obtain $A = PBP^{-1}$. Substituting this in equation **2** gives

3 $$PBP^{-1}\bar{u} \cdot \bar{u} = d$$

We have seen how to shift a matrix across the dot product. For any matrix A and any $\bar{u}$ and $\bar{v}$ we have $A\bar{u} \cdot \bar{v} = \bar{u} \cdot A^t\bar{v}$. (*See* formula **1** of the previous section.) Using this to shift P across the dot product, we have

$$PBP^{-1}\bar{u} \cdot \bar{u} = BP^{-1}\bar{u} \cdot P^t\bar{u}$$

Since P is orthogonal we know that $P^t = P^{-1}$. Hence we can rewrite equation **3** as

$$BP^{-1}\bar{u} \cdot P^{-1}\bar{u} = d$$

We can write

$$B = \begin{bmatrix} b_1 & 0 \\ 0 & b_2 \end{bmatrix} \quad \text{and} \quad P^{-1}\bar{u} = \begin{bmatrix} x_1 \\ y_1 \end{bmatrix}$$

Therefore, equation **3** can now be written as

$$\begin{bmatrix} b_1 & 0 \\ 0 & b_2 \end{bmatrix}\begin{bmatrix} x_1 \\ y_1 \end{bmatrix} \cdot \begin{bmatrix} x_1 \\ y_1 \end{bmatrix} = d$$

which, after carrying out these products, gives

4 $$b_1x_1^2 + b_2y_1^2 = d$$

Thus, relative to the x_1, y_1 coordinate system, we can rewrite equation **1** in the form **4**, in which no "xy" term appears. We can easily graph equation **4** in the x_1, y_1 system and thereby obtain the graph of equation **1**.

For example, consider

5 $$3x^2 + 2xy + 3y^2 = 1$$

Put

$$A = \begin{bmatrix} 3 & 1 \\ 1 & 3 \end{bmatrix} \quad \text{and} \quad \bar{u} = \begin{bmatrix} x \\ y \end{bmatrix}$$

and apply the methods of the previous section to find P and B.

The characteristic polynomial of A is

$$\begin{aligned} f(\lambda) &= \det(\lambda I - A) \\ &= \det\begin{bmatrix} \lambda - 3 & -1 \\ -1 & \lambda - 3 \end{bmatrix} \\ &= (\lambda - 3)^2 - 1 \\ &= \lambda^2 - 6\lambda + 8 \\ &= (\lambda - 2)(\lambda - 4) \end{aligned}$$

Therefore, the characteristic roots are $\lambda = 2$, $\lambda = 4$.

The matrices

$$2I - A = \begin{bmatrix} -1 & -1 \\ -1 & -1 \end{bmatrix} \quad \text{and} \quad 4I - A = \begin{bmatrix} 1 & -1 \\ -1 & 1 \end{bmatrix}$$

reduce respectively to

$$\begin{bmatrix} 1 & 1 \\ 0 & 0 \end{bmatrix} \quad \text{and} \quad \begin{bmatrix} 1 & -1 \\ 0 & 0 \end{bmatrix}$$

which give the respective characteristic vectors (normalized to have length 1)

$$\bar{u}_1 = \begin{bmatrix} 1/\sqrt{2} \\ -1/\sqrt{2} \end{bmatrix} \quad \text{and} \quad \bar{u}_2 = \begin{bmatrix} 1/\sqrt{2} \\ 1/\sqrt{2} \end{bmatrix}$$

With

$$P = \begin{bmatrix} 1/\sqrt{2} & 1/\sqrt{2} \\ -1/\sqrt{2} & 1/\sqrt{2} \end{bmatrix}$$

we have

$$P^{-1} = P^t = \begin{bmatrix} 1/\sqrt{2} & -1/\sqrt{2} \\ 1/\sqrt{2} & 1/\sqrt{2} \end{bmatrix}$$

(since P is orthogonal); thus

$$B = P^{-1}AP = \begin{bmatrix} 2 & 0 \\ 0 & 4 \end{bmatrix}$$

Therefore, we can rewrite equation **5** as

6 $$2x_1^2 + 4y_1^2 = 1 \qquad \text{where} \qquad \begin{bmatrix} x_1 \\ y_1 \end{bmatrix} = P^{-1}\begin{bmatrix} x \\ y \end{bmatrix}$$

To graph this equation in the (x_1,y_1) coordinate system we recall that x_1 and y_1 are the coordinates of (x,y) relative to the basis $\bar{u}_1$ and $\bar{u}_2$. (*See* Section 8, Chapter 1.) Since the graph of equation **6** is an ellipse, we obtain the graph shown in Figure 4.

Figure 4 *The graph of* $3x^2 + 2xy + 3y^2 = 1$.

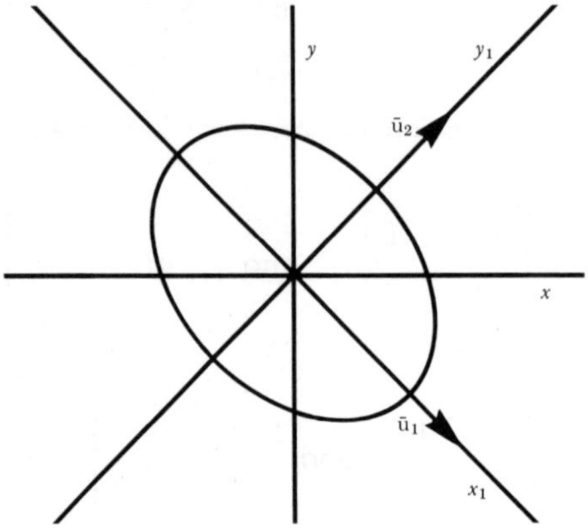

Of course, the matrices P and B are not unique. For example, if we put

$$P = \begin{bmatrix} 1/\sqrt{2} & 1/\sqrt{2} \\ 1/\sqrt{2} & -1/\sqrt{2} \end{bmatrix} \quad \text{so that} \quad P^{-1} = \begin{bmatrix} 1/\sqrt{2} & 1/\sqrt{2} \\ 1/\sqrt{2} & -1/\sqrt{2} \end{bmatrix}$$

we then obtain

$$B = P^{-1}AP = \begin{bmatrix} 4 & 0 \\ 0 & 2 \end{bmatrix}$$

and can thus write equation **5** as

$$7 \quad 4x_2^2 + 2y_2^2 = 1 \quad \text{where} \quad \begin{bmatrix} x_2 \\ y_2 \end{bmatrix} = \begin{bmatrix} 1/\sqrt{2} & 1/\sqrt{2} \\ 1/\sqrt{2} & -1/\sqrt{2} \end{bmatrix} \begin{bmatrix} x \\ y \end{bmatrix}$$

The pair (x_2,y_2) is the set of coordinates of (x,y) relative to the basis $\bar{u}_2$, $\bar{u}_1$. While the graph of equation *7* in the x_2, y_2 system is not the same as the graph of equation **6** in the x_1, y_1 system, these two equations give the same graph in the x, y system (as we should expect). For, merely by labeling the $\bar{u}_2$ axis as the x_2 axis and the $\bar{u}_1$ axis as the y_2 axis, we obtain the same figure shown in Figure 1.

EXAMPLE 2 *Systems of Differential Equations.*

Consider the system of differential equations

8
$$3\frac{dx}{dt} + \frac{dy}{dt} = \sin t$$
$$\frac{dx}{dt} + 3\frac{dy}{dt} = \cos t$$

Put

$$A = \begin{bmatrix} 3 & 1 \\ 1 & 3 \end{bmatrix}, \qquad \bar{u} = \begin{bmatrix} \frac{dx}{dt} \\ \frac{dy}{dt} \end{bmatrix}, \qquad \bar{v} = \begin{bmatrix} \sin t \\ \cos t \end{bmatrix}$$

We can then write system **8** as

9
$$A\bar{u} = \bar{v}$$

With

$$P = \begin{bmatrix} 1/\sqrt{2} & 1/\sqrt{2} \\ -1/\sqrt{2} & 1/\sqrt{2} \end{bmatrix} \quad \text{and} \quad B = \begin{bmatrix} 2 & 0 \\ 0 & 4 \end{bmatrix}$$

we have (as shown in Example 1) $B = P^{-1}AP$. Therefore, solving for A, we have $A = PBP^{-1}$. Substituting this in equation **9** gives $PBP^{-1}\bar{u} = \bar{v}$. Now multiply by P^{-1} to obtain

10
$$BP^{-1}\bar{u} = P^{-1}\bar{v}$$

We put

$$\begin{bmatrix} x_1 \\ y_1 \end{bmatrix} = P^{-1}\begin{bmatrix} x \\ y \end{bmatrix}$$

Since

$$P^{-1} = \begin{bmatrix} 1/\sqrt{2} & -1/\sqrt{2} \\ 1/\sqrt{2} & 1/\sqrt{2} \end{bmatrix}$$

we have $x_1 = \dfrac{1}{\sqrt{2}}(x - y)$ and $y_1 = \dfrac{1}{\sqrt{2}}(x + y)$. We therefore have

$$P^{-1}\bar{u} = \begin{bmatrix} \dfrac{1}{\sqrt{2}}\left(\dfrac{dx}{dt} - \dfrac{dy}{dt}\right) \\ \dfrac{1}{\sqrt{2}}\left(\dfrac{dx}{dt} + \dfrac{dy}{dt}\right) \end{bmatrix} = \begin{bmatrix} \dfrac{dx_1}{dt} \\ \dfrac{dy_1}{dt} \end{bmatrix}$$

Since we also have

$$P^{-1}\bar{v} = \begin{bmatrix} \dfrac{1}{\sqrt{2}}(\sin t - \cos t) \\ \dfrac{1}{\sqrt{2}}(\sin t + \cos t) \end{bmatrix}$$

we can rewrite equation **10** as the system

$$2\frac{dx_1}{dt} = \frac{1}{\sqrt{2}}(\sin t - \cos t)$$

$$4\frac{dy_1}{dt} = \frac{1}{\sqrt{2}}(\sin t + \cos t)$$

This system is easy to solve by integration. Recalling the formulas

$$\int \cos u\, du = \sin u + c, \qquad \int \sin u\, du = -\cos u + c$$

we have

$$x_1 = \frac{1}{2\sqrt{2}}(-\cos t - \sin t) + c_1$$

$$y_1 = \frac{1}{4\sqrt{2}}(-\cos t + \sin t) + c_2$$

where c_1 and c_2 are arbitrary constants. Using the fact that

$$\begin{bmatrix} x \\ y \end{bmatrix} = P\begin{bmatrix} x_1 \\ y_1 \end{bmatrix}$$

we calculate to obtain the general solution to system **8**:

$$x = -\tfrac{1}{8}\sin t - \tfrac{3}{8}\cos t + d_1$$

$$y = \tfrac{3}{8}\sin t + \tfrac{1}{8}\cos t + d_2$$

where

$$\begin{bmatrix} d_1 \\ d_2 \end{bmatrix} = P\begin{bmatrix} c_1 \\ c_2 \end{bmatrix}$$

EXERCISES

1 Use the method of Example 1 to eliminate the xy term and use this information to draw a graph of each of the following.

a $2x^2 + 2xy + 2y^2 = 1$

b $-3x^2 + 8xy + 3y^2 = \sqrt{5}$.

2 Use the method of Example 1 to eliminate the cross product terms in each of the following by first suitably choosing a symmetric matrix A so that the left-hand side is of the form $A\bar{u} \cdot \bar{u}$.

a $2x^2 + 2xy + 2y^2 - 3z^2 = 1$

b $-5x^2 - 5y^2 - 2z^2 + 14xy + 8xz + 8xy = 6$
(Hint: -12 is a root of $\lambda^3 + 12\lambda^2 - 36\lambda - 432 = 0$.)

3 Use the method of Example 2 to find the general solutions to each of the following.

a
$$3\frac{dx}{dt} + \frac{dy}{dt} = \cos t$$
$$\frac{dx}{dt} + 3\frac{dy}{dt} = \sin t$$

b
$$-3\frac{dx}{dt} + 4\frac{dy}{dt} = e^{t}$$
$$4\frac{dx}{dt} + 3\frac{dy}{dt} = e^{-t}$$

4 Use the method of Example 2 to find the general solutions to

$$-5\frac{dx}{dt} + 7\frac{dy}{dt} + 4\frac{dz}{dt} = t$$

$$7\frac{dx}{dt} - 5\frac{dy}{dt} + 4\frac{dz}{dt} = t^2$$

$$4\frac{dx}{dt} + 4\frac{dy}{dt} - 2\frac{dz}{dt} = t^3$$

5 The method of Example 2 does not require that the coefficient matrix be symmetric, but depends only on the fact that it is similar to a diagonal matrix (in which case the calculation of P from P^{-1} cannot be based on the assumption that P is orthogonal). Use this method to describe the solutions to the system

$$-\frac{dx}{dt} + \frac{dy}{dt} = t$$

$$8\frac{dx}{dt} - 3\frac{dy}{dt} = t^2$$

6 We recall that the matrices A and B of Example 1 must have the same determinant. (*See* Example 6, page 194.) Use this information to show that

a If $\det A > 0$, the graph of equation **1** is an ellipse, a single point, or empty.

b If $\det A < 0$, the graph of equation **1** is a hyperbola or two lines.

7 Equations of the form

$$\frac{dx}{dt} = ax + by$$

$$\frac{dy}{dt} = cx + dy$$

can be solved using methods related to those of Example 2. If we put

$$A = \begin{bmatrix} a & b \\ c & d \end{bmatrix}, \quad \bar{u} = \begin{bmatrix} x \\ y \end{bmatrix}, \quad \frac{d\bar{u}}{dt} = \begin{bmatrix} \frac{dx}{dt} \\ \frac{dy}{dt} \end{bmatrix}$$

we can write this as $\frac{d\bar{u}}{dt} = A\bar{u}$. If there is a matrix P such that $B = P^{-1}AP$ is diagonal, we can rewrite this equation as

$$\frac{d\bar{u}}{dt} = PBP^{-1}\bar{u} \quad \text{and obtain} \quad P^{-1}\frac{d\bar{u}}{dt} = BP^{-1}\bar{u}$$

The simple form of the latter makes it easy to solve, using the fact that $(e^{at})' = ae^{at}$, and we can then express our answers in terms of x and y. Use this method to solve the following equations.

a $$\frac{dx}{dt} = 3x + y \qquad \frac{dy}{dt} = x + 3y$$

b $$\frac{dx}{dt} = -x + y \qquad \frac{dy}{dt} = 8x - 3y$$

c $$\frac{dx}{dt} = 4x - 2y + 2z \qquad \frac{dy}{dt} = -2x + y - z \qquad \frac{dz}{dt} = 2x - y + z$$

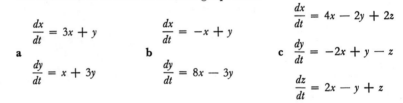

CHAPTER 4

LINEAR DIFFERENTIAL OPERATORS

We have seen that the operation of differentiation is a linear operation. (See *page 102.*) *In this chapter we shall use this fact, along with some elementary differentiation techniques and results about polynomials, to describe the solutions to linear differential equations with constant coefficients, such as*

$$y'' - 3y' + 2y = f$$

Our goal is to describe methods which will enable us to find, for a given function f, the solutions y to such equations.

In outline, our procedure will be as follows. We first observe that if D denotes the differentiation operator and I the identity operator then

$$(D^2 - 3D + 2I)y = y'' - 3y' + 2y$$

The operator $D^2 - 3D + 2I$ is a polynomial in D; that is, if we put $p(\lambda) = \lambda^2 - 3\lambda + 2$, then

$$p(D) = D^2 - 3D + 2I$$

Thus we can rewrite our equation as $p(D)y = f$.

We can then proceed to use the theory of polynomial factorization, and elementary calculus techniques, to find all solutions to the homogeneous problem $p(D)y = 0$. Further effort will enable us to find one solution y_1 to $p(D)y = f$. The operator version of Theorem 6 then tells us that the solutions to $p(D)y = f$ are of the form $y_1 + y_2$, where y_2 is a solution to $p(D)y = 0$. (See *Example 6, page 103.*)

We determine the solutions to $(D - aI)y = 0$ in Section 1. We then show how to solve higher order homogeneous problems in Sections 2, 3, and 4. In Section 5 we discuss methods for solving nonhomogeneous problems. Some applications will be discussed in Section 6.

The differentiation operator can be defined for any collection of functions which have derivatives. To simplify our discussion and to enable us to differentiate as often as we please we shall confine our discussion to the vector space of functions all of whose derivatives exist for all real numbers. We also confine our discussion to operators which can be written as polynomials in D. We do provide occasional examples and exercises which indicate methods for treating more general operators and functions.

SECTION 1 First-order Linear Operators

In this section we discuss the solutions to equations of the form

$$a_1y' + a_2y = f$$

We first discuss the case where $f = 0$, $a_1 = 1$, and a_2 is constant. We can then write our equation as $y' - ay = 0$ by replacing a_2 by $-a$. In operator form this equation is $(D - aI)y = 0$, so the problem of solving the equation $y' - ay = 0$ is the same as the problem of describing the null space of $D - aI$.

We recall from calculus that $De^x = e^x$; therefore, the chain rule gives $De^{ax} = ae^{ax}$ for any real number a. Thus, if L is the operator $L = D - aI$, it follows that $Le^{ax} = 0$.

In other words,

1 *e^{ax} is in the null space of $D - aI$.*

We shall show, in fact, that e^{ax} is a *basis* for the null space of $D - aI$ by using further results from calculus. In other words, it will be seen that

2 *If y is in the null space of $D - aI$, then y is a constant multiple of e^{ax}.*

To do this we use a trick: Suppose $(D - aI)y = 0$. If we put $z = e^{-ax}y$, the product rule then gives

$$\begin{aligned} Dz &= -ae^{-ax}y + e^{-ax}y' \\ &= e^{-ax}(y' - ay) \\ &= e^{-ax}(D - aI)y \\ &= 0 \end{aligned}$$

Thus, since the derivative of z is zero, we know that (from a theorem of calculus) z must be constant; that is, there is a constant c such that $e^{-ax}y = c$. Solving for y gives $y = ce^{ax}$. This proves statement **2**.

We usually summarize statements **1** and **2** by saying that $y = ce^{ax}$ is the **general solution** to $y' - ay = 0$. This means that no matter what value c has, $y = ce^{ax}$ is a solution to this equation, and, conversely, any solution to this equation must be of the form ce^{ax} for some choice of c.

EXAMPLE 1 Consider the equation

3 $$y' = 2y$$

It can be written as

$$Ly = 0 \qquad \text{where} \qquad L = D - 2I$$

so that its general solution is $y = ce^{2x}$.

Suppose we are looking for the solution to equation **3** that satisfies the additional condition

4 $$y(3) = 4$$

We know that if there is a function that satisfies both equation **3** and equation **4**, it must be of the form

5 $$y = ce^{2x}$$

Therefore, we merely need to choose c so that property **4** holds. Putting $x = 3$ in equation **5** and using equation **4**, we have $4 = ce^6$, from which we obtain $c = 4e^{-6}$.

We conclude that $y = 4e^{2x-6}$ is the *only* function that satisfies equation **3** and condition **4**.

EXAMPLE 2 Consider the equation

6 $$y' + 3y = 0$$

We can write this as $Ly = 0$, where $L = D + 3I$, and consequently have the general solution

7 $$y = ce^{-3x}$$

The solution to equation **6** that satisfies

8 $$y(-1) = -2$$

can be found, as in Example 1, by setting $x = -1$ in the general solution **7** and calculating c, using condition **8**. We have $-2 = ce^3$, and, consequently, $c = -2e^{-3}$. Hence $y = -2e^{-3x-3}$ is the solution to equation **6** that satisfies condition **8**.

Problems of this type, for which we are to find a function which satisfies a differential equation and for which the function (and, possibly, one or more of its derivatives) has a specified value at a point, are known as **initial value problems**. This terminology arises from common physical situations in which the functions are functions of t (denoting time) and the conditions are specified for $t = 0$. (*See* Section 6, below.)

EXAMPLE 3 ☐ *Inhomogeneous Equations.*
A useful trick will enable us to solve the inhomogeneous problem

9 $$y' - ay = f$$

where f is assumed to be continuous. The trick is to multiply both sides of this equation by a function so chosen that the left-hand side is the derivative of a known function. Such a function is e^{-ax}. For if we multiply both sides of equation **9** by e^{-ax} we obtain

$$y'e^{-ax} - aye^{-ax} = e^{-ax}f$$

The left-hand side is just $D(ye^{-ax})$, as can be seen by calculating $D(ye^{-ax})$ using the product rule. Thus we have

$$D(ye^{-ax}) = e^{-ax}f$$

Let g be an integral of $e^{-ax}f$; that is, g is any function whose derivative is $e^{-ax}f$. The equation can then be rewritten as $D(ye^{-ax}) = Dg$, and therefore $ye^{-ax}g$ must be constant. Thus $ye^{-ax} = g + c$, which can be rewritten as

10 $$y = e^{ax}g + ce^{ax}$$

This is the general solution to equation **9**. For example, consider the equation

11 $$y' + 2y = x$$

Multiplying this equation by e^{2x} gives $y'e^{2x} + 2ye^{2x} = xe^{2x}$, which can be rewritten as

12 $$D(ye^{2x}) = xe^{2x}$$

To find an integral of xe^{2x} we integrate by parts, with $u = x/2$ and $dv = 2e^{2x}\,dx$. Thus $du = \frac{1}{2}\,dx$ and $v = e^{2x}$, and we have

$$\int xe^{2x}\,dx = (x/2)e^{2x} - \tfrac{1}{2}\int e^{2x}\,dx$$
$$= (x/2)e^{2x} - \tfrac{1}{4}e^{2x}$$

Therefore, since we can rewrite equation **12** as

$$D(ye^{2x}) = D\left(\frac{xe^{2x}}{2} - \frac{e^{2x}}{4}\right)$$

there must be a constant c such that

$$ye^{2x} = \frac{xe^{2x}}{2} - \frac{e^{2x}}{4} + c$$

Multiplying by e^{-2x} then gives the general solution to equation **11**:

13 $$y = x/2 - \tfrac{1}{4} + ce^{-2x}$$

If we are looking for the solution that satisfies the initial condition $y(0) = 2$, we merely substitute $x = 0$ in the general solution **13** to obtain $2 = \frac{0}{2} - \frac{1}{4} + ce^{-0}$. Thus $c = \frac{9}{4}$, and we have

$$y = x/2 - \tfrac{1}{4} + \tfrac{9}{4}e^{-2x}$$

This is the solution to the initial value problem:

$$y' + 2y = x, \; y(0) = 2$$

EXAMPLE 4 ☐ *First-order Continuous Coefficient Operators.*
The trick used in Example 3 can be extended to give the general solution to $y' + p(x)y = f(x)$, if p and f are continuous. The trick is to multiply both sides by

$$e^{q(x)} \qquad \text{where} \qquad q = \int p(x)\,dx$$

so that the equation can be written as

$$D(ye^{q(x)}) = e^{q(x)}f(x)$$

For example, consider

14 $$y' + xy = x$$

Here we have $p(x) = x$ so that $q(x) = \int x\,dx = x^2/2$. Thus multiplying by $e^{x^2/2}$ yields

$$y'e^{x^2/2} + xye^{x^2/2} = xe^{x^2/2}$$

which can be rewritten as

$$D(ye^{x^2/2}) = xe^{x^2/2}$$

Since the function $xe^{x^2/2}$ is the derivative of $e^{x^2/2}$, we can rewrite this as

$$D(ye^{x^2/2}) = D(e^{x^2/2})$$

Therefore, there is a constant c such that

$$ye^{x^2/2} = e^{x^2/2} + c$$

and it follows that the general solution to equation **14** is

$$y = 1 + ce^{-x^2/2}$$

EXERCISES

1 Find the general solution to each of the following problems.

a $y' - y = 0$ **b** $y' + \sqrt{5}y = 0$
c $3y' + 2y = 0$ **d** $2y' = y$
e $y' + ey = 0$

2 For each of the following find the function y that satisfies both the differential equation and the initial condition.

a $y' = 2y, y(0) = 1$ **b** $y' + 2y = 0, y(0) = 1$
c $2y' = y, y(1) = 2$ **d** $4y' + 5y = 0, y(2) = 3$

3 How many solutions does $y' = ay$ have that pass through 0 at 0?

4 Suppose $a < 0$ and y is a solution to the problem

$$y' = ay, \qquad y(0) = b$$

What happens to this solution as $x \to \infty$? as $x \to -\infty$? What happens to the solution as $x \to \infty$ if $a > 0$?

□ 5 Use the method of Example 3 to find the general solution to

a $y' = 2y - x$ **b** $y' + 3y = e^x$
c $y' = \sin x - y$ **d** $y' - y = x^2 + x$

□ 6 For each of the equations of Exercise 4 find the solution that satisfies $y(0) = 1$ and the solution that satisfies $y(1) = 2$.

□ 7 Use the method of Example 4 to find the general solution to

a $y' + x^2 y = 0$ **b** $y' + \dfrac{1}{x} y = x^2$
c $y' + y \log x = x^{-x}$ **d** $y' + y \sin x = 0$

□ 8 For each equation in Exercise 7 find the solution that satisfies $y(1) = 1$.

□ 9 The results **1** and **2** can be derived for complex numbers a by suitably defining e^{ax} and Df for complex functions f. If $a = c + id$, where c and d are real, and $i^2 = -1$, we define e^a by

$$e^a = e^c (\cos d + i \sin d)$$

If $f(x) = f_1(x) + if_2(x)$, where f_1 and f_2 are real, we define

$$Df = Df_1 + i\, Df_2$$

a Show that $De^{ax} = ae^{ax}$ for complex a.
b Show that $D(fg) = f\, Dg + g\, Df$ for complex functions f and g. (Hint: Write $f = f_1 + if_2$ and $g = g_1 + ig_2$, where f_1, f_2, g_1, and g_2 are real functions.)
c Show that if $f = f_1 + if_2$, where f_1 and f_2 are real and have continuous derivatives, and if $Df = 0$, there is a complex number α such that $f = \alpha$.
d Derive property **2** for complex numbers a. (Hint: Proceed as in the derivation of property **2**, using **b** and **c**.)

SECTION 2 Second-order Linear Operators

The differential equation

1 $$y'' + by' + cy = 0$$

can be written as $Ly = 0$, where

2 $$L = D^2 + bD + cI$$

We shall show how to solve equation **1** by suitably factoring expression **2**.

Consider the polynomial

3 $$p(\lambda) = \lambda^2 + b\lambda + c$$

This polynomial is usually called the **characteristic polynomial** of L. Its roots are called the **characteristic roots** of L. Exercise 6, below, shows how this terminology is related to that used for matrices in Chapter 3.

As we know from polynomial theory, polynomial **3** may have two distinct real roots, precisely one real root, or two complex roots. Each of these cases leads to a different form for the general solution to equation **1**.

The roots of p will be denoted by α and β. From the quadratic formula we can write

$$\alpha = \frac{-b + \sqrt{b^2 - 4c}}{2}, \qquad \beta = \frac{-b - \sqrt{b^2 - 4c}}{2}$$

The condition that α and β are real and distinct is simply the condition that $b^2 - 4c > 0$, while the condition that $\alpha = \beta$ is the condition $b^2 - 4c = 0$, and the condition that α and β are complex is the condition $b^2 - 4c < 0$.

We can then factor p as $p(\lambda) = (\lambda - \alpha)(\lambda - \beta)$. This factorization can be used to factor expression **2**. We have (using the product rules of Section 5, Chapter 2)

$$\begin{aligned}(D - \alpha I)(D - \beta I) &= D^2 - \alpha ID - \beta DI + \alpha\beta I^2 \\ &= D^2 - (\alpha + \beta)D + \alpha\beta I\end{aligned}$$

since $ID = DI = D$ and $I^2 = I$. We also have

$$\begin{aligned}(D - \beta I)(D - \alpha I) &= D^2 - \beta ID - \alpha DI + \beta\alpha I^2 \\ &= D^2 - (\alpha + \beta)D + \alpha\beta I\end{aligned}$$

In each case the right-hand side is $p(D)$, since $p(\lambda) = \lambda^2 - (\alpha + \beta)\lambda + \alpha\beta$. We therefore know that $D - \alpha I$ and $D - \beta I$ *commute* and that

4 $$L = (D - \alpha I)(D - \beta I) = (D - \beta I)(D - \alpha I)$$

Case 1: α and β real, $\alpha \neq \beta$.
We can write equation **1** as $Ly = 0$, where $L = D^2 + bD + cI$. We can then express L as a product of $D - \alpha I$ and $D - \beta I$, in either order, by using formula **4**.

The results of Section 1 tell us that

$$(D - \alpha I)e^{\alpha x} = 0 \qquad \text{and} \qquad (D - \beta I)e^{\beta x} = 0$$

Combining these with each expression of formula **4** we have

$$Le^{\alpha x} = (D - \beta I)(D - \alpha I)e^{\alpha x} = (D - \beta I)0 = 0$$
$$Le^{\beta x} = (D - \alpha I)(D - \beta I)e^{\beta x} = (D - \alpha I)0 = 0$$

so we know that

5 $e^{\alpha x}$ *and* $e^{\beta x}$ *are in the null space of* L

These functions are independent, for if $c_1e^{\alpha x} + c_2e^{\beta x} = 0$, we can differentiate to obtain $c_1\alpha e^{\alpha x} + c_2\beta e^{\beta x} = 0$. Setting $x = 0$ in each of these gives the two equations

$$c_1 + c_2 = 0$$
$$c_1\alpha + c_2\beta = 0$$

The determinant of the matrix of coefficients of this system is

$$\det\begin{bmatrix} 1 & 1 \\ \alpha & \beta \end{bmatrix} = \beta - \alpha$$

which, by assumption, is *not* zero, for $\beta \neq \alpha$. We conclude that we must have $c_1 = c_2 = 0$ and, therefore, that $e^{\alpha x}$ and $e^{\beta x}$ are indeed independent.

In Section 4 it will be shown that the null space of L has dimension *at most* two. Since we have found two independent vectors in this null space we conclude from Theorem 10 that

The functions $e^{\alpha x}$ and $e^{\beta x}$ are a basis for the null space of

6 $$L = (D - \alpha I)(D - \beta I),$$

if α and β *are real and* $\alpha \neq \beta$.

We often express this result by saying that

$$y = c_1e^{\alpha x} + c_2e^{\beta x}$$

is the **general solution** to $Ly = 0$. This means that, for any choice of c_1 and c_2, this function is a solution to $Ly = 0$, and that every solution to $Ly = 0$ is of this form, for some c_1 and c_2.

Case 2: α and β real, $\alpha = \beta$.
In this case, we can write (using formula **4**)

$$L = (D - \alpha I)^2$$

Since $(D - \alpha I)e^{\alpha x} = 0$ we see that $e^{\alpha x}$ is in the null space of L. A useful and elementary trick enables us to find a second, independent solution to $Ly = 0$. Since the product rule gives

7 $$D(xe^{\alpha x}) = e^{\alpha x} + \alpha x e^{\alpha x}$$

it follows that

$$(D - \alpha I)(xe^{\alpha x}) = e^{\alpha x}$$

Hence, applying $D - \alpha I$ again, we have

$$\begin{aligned}(D - \alpha I)^2(xe^{\alpha x}) &= (D - \alpha I)[(D - \alpha I)(xe^{\alpha x})]\\ &= (D - \alpha I)e^{\alpha x}\\ &= 0\end{aligned}$$

Therefore, $xe^{\alpha x}$ is *also* in the null space of L.

The functions $e^{\alpha x}$ and $xe^{\alpha x}$ are independent, for if

$$c_1 e^{\alpha x} + c_2 x e^{\alpha x} = 0$$

differentiating gives

$$c_1 \alpha e^{\alpha x} + c_2(e^{\alpha x} + \alpha x e^{\alpha x}) = 0$$

Setting $x = 0$ in each of these gives the two equations

$$\begin{aligned}c_1 &= 0\\ c_1\alpha + c_2 &= 0\end{aligned}$$

Thus, c_1 and c_2 must be zero.

We shall show in Section 4 that the dimension of the null space of L is at most two, so Theorem 10 gives us the following result:

8 *The functions $e^{\alpha x}$ and $xe^{\alpha x}$ are a basis for the null space of $L = (D - \alpha I)^2$. Thus, the general solution to $Ly = 0$ is*

$$c_1 e^{\alpha x} + c_2 x e^{\alpha x}$$

Case 3: α and β complex.
We could use the complex function discussion of Exercise 9 of the previous section to obtain complex solutions of the form given in statement **6**.

Instead, a generalization of result **7** will be used to describe the general solutions in terms of real functions. This will be discussed in the next section.

EXAMPLE 1 Consider the equation $y'' - y = 0$. The associated differential operator is $L = D^2 - I$, whose characteristic polynomial is $p(\lambda) = \lambda^2 - 1 = (\lambda - 1)(\lambda + 1)$. Since the roots are real and unequal, we apply statement **6** to obtain the general solution

$$y = c_1e^x + c_2e^{-x}$$

EXAMPLE 2 Consider the equation $y'' + 4y' - y = 0$, whose associated differential operator is $L = D^2 + 4D - I$. The characteristic polynomial is $p(\lambda) = \lambda^2 + 4\lambda - 1$. The quadratic formula gives the roots

$$\frac{-4 \pm \sqrt{20}}{2} = -2 \pm \sqrt{5}$$

Since these roots are real and unequal, the general solution is

$$y = c_1e^{(-2+\sqrt{5})x} + c_2e^{(-2-\sqrt{5})x}$$

EXAMPLE 3 The associated differential operator for $y'' + 8y' + 16y = 0$ is $L = D^2 + 8D + 16I$. Therefore, the characteristic polynomial is $p(\lambda) = \lambda^2 + 8\lambda + 16 = (\lambda + 4)^2$. Since the roots are real and equal, we apply statement **8** to obtain the general solution

$$y = c_1e^{-4x} + c_2xe^{-4x}$$

EXAMPLE 4 Suppose we wish to solve the initial value problem

9
$$\begin{aligned} y'' - y' - 6y &= 0 \\ y(0) &= 1 \\ y'(0) &= -1 \end{aligned}$$

The associated differential operator is $L = D^2 - D - 6I$, whose characteristic polynomial is $p(\lambda) = \lambda^2 - \lambda - 6 = (\lambda - 3)(\lambda + 2)$. Since the roots are real and distinct, we apply result **6** to obtain the general solution

$$y = c_1e^{3x} + c_2e^{-2x} \qquad \text{to} \qquad y'' - y' - 6y = 0$$

By differentiating we have

$$y' = 3c_1e^{3x} - 2c_2e^{-2x}$$

Setting $x = 0$ in each of these and using the conditions that $y(0) = 1$ and $y'(0) = -1$ gives the two equations

$$c_1 + c_2 = 1$$
$$3c_1 - 2c_2 = -1$$

This system has the unique solution $c_1 = \frac{1}{5}$, $c_2 = \frac{4}{5}$. Thus the solution to the initial value problem **9** is

$$y = \tfrac{1}{5}e^{3x} + \tfrac{4}{5}e^{-2x}$$

EXAMPLE 5 Consider the initial value problem

10
$$\begin{aligned} y'' + 2y' + y &= 0 \\ y(1) &= 0 \\ y'(1) &= 2 \end{aligned}$$

The equation $y'' + 2y' + y = 0$ is the same as $Ly = 0$, where $L = D^2 + 2D + I$.

The characteristic polynomial of L is $p(\lambda) = \lambda^2 + 2\lambda + 1 = (\lambda + 1)^2$. Since the root $\lambda = 1$ is repeated, we obtain the general solution $y = c_1e^{-x} + c_2xe^{-x}$, to $y'' + 2y' + y = 0$. Differentiation gives

$$y' = -c_1e^{-x} + c_2(e^{-x} - xe^{-x})$$

Thus setting $x = 1$ gives the equations

$$0 = c_1e^{-1} + c_2e^{-1}$$
$$2 = -c_1e^{-1} + c_2(e^{-1} - e^{-1})$$

The unique solution to this system is $c_1 = -2e$, $c_2 = 2e$, and, therefore, the solution to initial value problem **10** is

$$y = -2e^{-x+1} + 2xe^{-x+1}$$

EXAMPLE 6 Our method can be extended to equations in which the leading coefficient is a nonzero number other than 1. For example, the system

11
$$10y'' + 13y' - 3y = 0$$

has the same solutions as the system

$$y'' + \tfrac{13}{10}y' - \tfrac{3}{10}y = 0$$

The characteristic polynomial of the latter system is

$$p(\lambda) = \lambda^2 + \tfrac{13}{10}\lambda - \tfrac{3}{10}$$

which has the same roots as

12 $$q(\lambda) = 10\lambda^2 + 13\lambda - 3$$

Thus, to solve equation **11** we form its characteristic polynomial **12**, find its roots, and write down the general solution as before.

The roots are

$$\frac{-13 \pm \sqrt{169 - 4(-3)(10)}}{20} = \frac{-13 \pm 17}{20}$$

which give $\frac{1}{5}$ and $-\frac{3}{2}$. Since these are real and distinct, the general solution to equation **11** is

$$y = c_1 e^{(1/5)x} + c_2 e^{(-3/2)x}$$

EXERCISES

1 By first giving the associated differential operator L and then factoring the characteristic polynomial, find the general solution to each of the following.

a $y'' - 5y' - 6y = 0$ **b** $y'' - 5y' + 6y = 0$
c $y'' + 4y' + 4y = 0$ **d** $y'' + 3y' + y = 0$
e $y'' = 0$ **f** $y'' - 2y = 0$
g $y'' - 6y' + 9y = 0$ **h** $y'' - 2y' - 2y = 0$

2 Solve each of the following initial value problems.

a $y'' - 4y' + 4y = 0$, $y(0) = 0$, $y'(0) = -1$ **b** $y'' + 3y' + 2y = 0$, $y(0) = 2$, $y'(0) = 5$

c $y'' - 4y' + 4y = 0$, $y(3) = -1$, $y'(3) = 2$ **d** $y'' - 3y' + 2y = 0$, $y(10) = 1$, $y'(10) = 0$

3 Suppose y is a solution to $Ly = 0$, where $L = (D - \alpha I)(D - \beta I)$. Use the form of the general solution to answer each of the following

a If α and β are both negative what is $\lim_{x\to\infty} y$? If y is not the zero function does the limit $\lim_{x\to-\infty} y$ exist?

b If $\alpha > 0$ and $\beta < 0$, what must y be in order that $\lim_{x\to\infty} y$ exists? In order that $\lim_{x\to-\infty} y$ exists?

c If α and β are positive and y is not the zero function does $\lim_{x\to\infty} y$ exist? Does $\lim_{x\to-\infty} y$ exist?

4 Find the general solution to (*see* Example 6)

a $3y'' - 17y' + 10y = 0$ **b** $4y'' + 4y' + y = 0$

5 Initial value problems will not, in general, have a unique solution if too many or not enough initial conditions are specified. For each of the following decide whether a solution exists and, if so, whether there is a unique solution.

a $y'' - 3y' + 2y = 0$, $y(0) = 1, y'(0) = 0, y''(0) = 0$

b $y'' = 0$, $y(0) = 1, y'(0) = 2, y''(0) = 0$

c $y'' - 2y' + y = 0$, $y(0) = 1$

□ 6 If $L = D^2 + bD + cI$, the differential equation $y'' + by' + cy = 0$ can be expressed as a system of differential equations, thereby associating a matrix with the operator L. (*See* Exercise 7, page 230.) If $z = y'$, then $z' = y''$; therefore, if the differential equation for y is used, two simultaneous equations for y, z, and their first derivatives can be obtained.

a Let $\bar{u} = \begin{bmatrix} y' \\ z' \end{bmatrix}$ and $\bar{v} = \begin{bmatrix} y \\ z \end{bmatrix}$. Find a matrix A such that $\bar{u} = A\bar{v}$.

b Show that A has the characteristic polynomial $\lambda^2 + b\lambda + c$.

c If the characteristic polynomial of A has distinct real roots, we can find an invertible matrix P such that $B = P^{-1}AP$ is diagonal. Put $\bar{w} = P^{-1}\bar{v}$. Show that the derivatives of the coordinates of $\bar{w}$ are the coordinates of $P^{-1}\bar{u}$ and that $A\bar{v} = \bar{u}$ can be written as $\dfrac{d\bar{w}}{dt} = B\bar{w}$.

d Assuming that the characteristic values of A are real and distinct, we see that the system $d\bar{w}/dt = B\bar{w}$ is easy to solve, for B is diagonal. Show that if $\bar{w}$ is a solution to this system $P\bar{w}$ is a solution to $A\bar{v} = \bar{u}$. Show that the first coordinate of $P\bar{w}$ is then a solution to $y'' + by' + cy = 0$. (This gives an alternative method for solving this equation.)

e Assuming that $\lambda^3 + a\lambda^2 + b\lambda + c = 0$ has three distinct real roots, extend the above methods to solve $y''' + ay'' + by' + cy = 0$. (Hint: First put $z = y'$ and $w = y''$.)

□ 7 Problems other than initial value problems are also common in applications. If the values of y, y', and so on, are specified at two points, the problem is called a *boundary value problem*. In this case we will have either no solution or more than one solution. Discuss the existence and uniqueness of solutions to

a $y'' = 0$, $y(0) = 0$, $y'(1) = 2$

b $y'' + 2y' + y = 0$, $y(0) = 0$, $y'(1) = 3$

c $y'' + 2y' + y = 0$, $y(0) = 0$, $y'(1) = 0$

□ 8 Case 3 can be solved by using the complex function discussion of Exercise 9, page 236. For example, suppose $p(\lambda) = \lambda^2 + b\lambda + c$, with $b^2 - 4c < 0$. With $k = 2\sqrt{4c - b^2}$ and $a = -b/2$, the roots are $a \pm ik$.

a Show that $e^{(a+ik)x}$ and $e^{(a-ik)x}$ are solutions to $y'' + by' + cy = 0$.

b Show that $e^{(a+ik)x}$ and $e^{(a-ik)x}$ are independent.

c Show that $\sin kx = (e^{ikx} - e^{-ikx})/2i$ and $\cos kx = (e^{ikx} + e^{-ikx})/2$.

d Use **a** and **c** to show that $e^{ax} \sin kx$ and $e^{ax} \cos kx$ are solutions to $y'' + by' + cy = 0$.

e Show that $c_1 e^{(a+ik)x} + c_2 e^{(a-ik)x}$ can be written as

$$e^{ax}(d_1 \sin kx + d_2 \cos kx) + ie^{ax}(d_3 \sin kx + d_4 \cos kx)$$

where d_1, d_2, d_3, and d_4 are real.
(Hint: If $c_1 = u_1 + iu_2$, $c_2 = v_1 + iv_2$, where u_1, u_2, v_1, v_2 are real, apply **c** with $d_1 = v_2 - u_2$, $d_2 = u_1 + v_1$, $d_3 = u_1 - v_1$, and $d_4 = u_2 + v_2$.)

f Find the general real solution to $y'' + 2y' + 2y = 0$.
(Hint: Use the real part of the solution of part **e**.)

SECTION 3 The Translation Principle

To complete the discussion of second-order homogeneous equations it is necessary to find the general solution to

1 $$y'' + by' + cy = 0$$

for the case in which $b^2 - 4c < 0$. This is the case in which the roots α and β of $p(\lambda) = \lambda^2 + b\lambda + c$ are complex. We first consider the case in which $b = 0$ and $c = 1$, that is, the equation $y'' + y = 0$. We recall the following two formulas from calculus:

$$(\sin x)' = \cos x, \qquad (\cos x)' = -\sin x$$

Differentiating again we have

$$(\sin x)'' = -\sin x, \qquad (\cos x)'' = -\cos x$$

In other words,

$\sin x$ and $\cos x$ are solutions to $y'' + y = 0$.

In fact we can show that

2 *The functions $\sin x$ and $\cos x$ are a basis for the null space of $L = D^2 + I$, and therefore, the general solution to $y'' + y = 0$ is*

$$y = c_1 \sin x + c_2 \cos x.$$

To prove this it is necessary to show that $\sin x$ and $\cos x$ are independent *and* that they *span* the null space of $D^2 + I$. Suppose

$$c_1 \sin x + c_2 \cos x = 0$$

Differentiating gives

$$c_1 \cos x - c_2 \sin x = 0$$

and putting $x = 0$ in each of these gives

$$c_1 = c_2 = 0$$

which shows that, indeed, $\sin x$ and $\cos x$ are independent. The proof that they span the null space of L is outlined in Exercise 7, below.

The chain rule gives $(\sin kx)' = k \cos kx$ and $(\cos kx)' = -k \sin kx$, so that $\sin kx$ and $\cos kx$ are solutions to $y'' + k^2 y = 0$.

Arguments similar to that above can be used to show that

3 *The general solution to* $y'' + k^2 y = 0$ *is* $c_1 \sin kx + c_2 \cos kx$.

The analysis of

4 $$y'' + by' + cy = 0 \qquad \text{where} \qquad b^2 - 4c < 0$$

is completed by using a translation principle to convert it into an equation of the form $y'' + k^2 y = 0$. We first complete the square on the characteristic polynomial

$$\begin{aligned} p(\lambda) &= \lambda^2 + b\lambda + c \\ &= \lambda^2 + b\lambda + b^2/4 + c - b^2/4 \\ &= (\lambda + b/2)^2 + c - b^2/4 \end{aligned}$$

We know that $c - b^2/4 > 0$, for we have assumed that $b^2 - 4c < 0$. Therefore, we can write

5 $$p(\lambda) = (\lambda - a)^2 + k^2 \qquad \text{where } a = -b/2, \qquad k = \sqrt{c - b^2/2}$$

We have, then, the fact that

6 *If y is a solution to $y'' + k^2 y = 0$, then $e^{ax} y$ is a solution to $y'' + by' + cy = 0$. Conversely, if y is a solution to $y'' + by' + cy = 0$, then $e^{-ax} y$ is a solution to $y'' + k^2 y = 0$.*

Before establishing this result we deduce some of its consequences. The functions $\sin kx$ and $\cos kx$ are a basis for the solutions to $y'' + k^2 y = 0$. Result **6** tells us that

7 $$e^{ax} \sin kx \qquad \text{and} \qquad e^{ax} \cos kx$$

are solutions to equation **4**. If

$$c_1 e^{ax} \sin kx + c_2 e^{ax} \cos kx = 0$$

we can multiply by e^{-ax} to obtain

$$c_1 \sin kx + c_2 \cos kx = 0$$

Thus, the independence of sin kx and cos kx guarantees that $c_1 = c_2 = 0$. In other words, the solutions **7** are independent.

Furthermore, they are a basis for the solutions to $y'' + by' + cy = 0$, for if y is a solution to this equation, then property **6** tells us that $e^{-ax}y$ is a solution to $y'' + k^2y = 0$. Statement **3** tells us, then, that there must be constants c_1 and c_2 such that

$$e^{-ax}y = c_1 \sin kx + c_2 \cos kx$$

so we must have

$$y = c_1e^{ax} \sin kx + c_2e^{ax} \cos kx$$

In summary:

8 *The general solution to* $y'' + by' + cy = 0$, *where* $b^2 - 4c < 0$, *is* $c_1e^{ax} \sin kx + c_2e^{ax} \cos kx$ *where* $a = -b/2$ *and* $k = \sqrt{c - b^2/4}$.

EXAMPLE 1 The equation $y'' + 3y = 0$ is of the form $y'' + k^2y = 0$, where $k = \sqrt{3}$. We apply property **3** to obtain the general solution

$$y = c_1 \sin \sqrt{3}x + c_2 \cos \sqrt{3}x$$

EXAMPLE 2 Consider the equation $y'' + 2y' + 4y = 0$. Here we have $p(\lambda) = \lambda^2 + 2\lambda + 4$ and $2^2 - 4 \cdot 4 < 0$. Therefore, completing the square gives

$$\begin{aligned} p(\lambda) &= (\lambda^2 + 2\lambda + 1) + (4 - 1) \\ &= (\lambda + 1)^2 + 3 \end{aligned}$$

We conclude from result **8** that the general solution is

$$y = c_1e^{-x} \sin \sqrt{3}x + c_2e^{-x} \cos \sqrt{3}x$$

EXAMPLE 3 The characteristic polynomial for $y'' - 6y' + 10y = 0$ is $p(\lambda) = \lambda^2 - 6\lambda + 10$. Completing the square gives

$$\begin{aligned} p(\lambda) &= (\lambda^2 - 6\lambda + 9) + (10 - 9) \\ &= (\lambda - 3)^2 + 1 \end{aligned}$$

Therefore, statement **8** gives the general solution

$$y = c_1e^{3x} \sin x + c_2e^{3x} \cos x$$

EXAMPLE 4 Suppose we wish to solve the initial value problem

$$y'' + 4y = 0$$
$$y(\pi/4) = 1$$
$$y'(\pi/4) = -1$$

The general solution to $y'' + 4y = 0$ is $y = c_1 \sin 2x + c_2 \cos 2x$, whose derivative is $y' = 2c_1 \cos 2x - 2c_2 \sin 2x$. Setting $x = \pi/4$ and using the given conditions gives

$$1 = c_1 \sin \pi/2 + c_2 \cos \pi/2$$
$$-1 = 2c_1 \cos \pi/2 - 2c_2 \sin \pi/2$$

Thus $c_1 = 1$ and $c_2 = \frac{1}{2}$. This gives the solution to our problem:

$$y = \sin 2x + \tfrac{1}{2} \cos 2x$$

EXAMPLE 5 Suppose we wish to solve the initial value problem

$$y'' - 3y' + 3y = 0$$
$$y(0) = -1$$
$$y'(0) = 0$$

The characteristic polynomial of the differential equation is

$$\begin{aligned} p(\lambda) &= \lambda^2 - 3\lambda + 3 \\ &= (\lambda^2 - 3\lambda + \tfrac{9}{4}) + (3 - \tfrac{9}{4}) \\ &= (\lambda - \tfrac{3}{2})^2 + \tfrac{3}{4} \end{aligned}$$

so the general solution is (using statement **8**)

$$y = c_1 e^{3x/2} \sin \frac{\sqrt{3}}{2} x + c_2 e^{3x/2} \cos \frac{\sqrt{3}}{2} x$$

We have

$$\begin{aligned} y' = {} & c_1 \left(\tfrac{3}{2} e^{3x/2} \sin \frac{\sqrt{3}}{2} x + \frac{\sqrt{3}}{2} e^{3x/2} \cos \frac{\sqrt{3}}{2} x \right) \\ & + c_2 \left(\tfrac{3}{2} e^{3x/2} \cos \frac{\sqrt{3}}{2} x - \frac{\sqrt{3}}{2} e^{3x/2} \sin \frac{\sqrt{3}}{2} x \right) \end{aligned}$$

Setting $x = 0$ in each of these, and using the initial conditions, we have

$$-1 = c_2$$
$$0 = \frac{\sqrt{3}}{2} c_1 + \tfrac{3}{2} c_2$$

so that $c_1 = \sqrt{3}$ and $c_2 = -1$. Hence our solution is

$$y = \sqrt{3}e^{3x/2} \sin \frac{\sqrt{3}}{2} x - e^{3x/2} \cos \frac{\sqrt{3}}{2} x$$

DISCUSSION We now turn to the proof of statement **6**. The associated operators for $y'' + by' + cy = 0$ and $y'' + k^2y = 0$ are, respectively,

$$L = D^2 + bD + cI \qquad \text{and} \qquad L_1 = D^2 + k^2I$$

The respective characteristic polynomials are

$$p(\lambda) = \lambda^2 + b\lambda + c \qquad \text{and} \qquad q(\lambda) = \lambda^2 + k^2$$

Formula **5** tells us that $p(\lambda) = q(\lambda - a)$; that is, $p(\lambda)$ is obtained from $q(\lambda)$ by *translation* by $\lambda - a$ (in other words, the replacement of λ by $\lambda - a$). We have

9 $$L(e^{2x}y) = e^{ax}L_1y$$

Result **6** is a consequence of formula **9**, for if y is a solution to $y'' + k^2y = 0$, then $L_1y = 0$, and therefore

$$L(e^{ax}y) = e^{ax}L_1y = 0$$

Thus $e^{ax}y$ is a solution to $y'' + by' + cy = 0$.

Conversely, if y is a solution to $y'' + by' + cy = 0$, then $Ly = 0$. Since $y = e^{ax}(e^{-ax}y)$, formula **9** gives

$$Ly = L[e^{ax}(e^{-ax}y)] = e^{ax}L_1(e^{-ax}y)$$

Therefore, $e^{ax}L_1(e^{-ax}y)$ must be the zero function. Since we know that e^{ax} is never zero, we conclude that $L_1(e^{-ax}y) = 0$, or, in other words, that $e^{-ax}y$ is a solution to $y'' + k^2y = 0$. This completes the proof of the fact that statement **6** is a consequence of formula **9**.

To prove formula **9** we first apply the product and chain rules to obtain

$$D(e^{ax}y) = ae^{ax}y + e^{ax}Dy$$

Observe that $ae^{ax}y = (aI)e^{ax}y$, so we can subtract from each side to obtain

10 $$(D - aI)e^{ax}y = e^{ax}Dy$$

Equation **10** gives us

11 $$(D - aI)^2e^{ax}y = e^{ax}D^2y$$

for we have

$$\begin{aligned}(D - aI)^2 e^{ax} y &= (D - aI)[(D - aI)e^{ax} y] \\ &= (D - aI)(e^{ax} D y)\end{aligned}$$

We then apply formula **10** to this, with $e^{ax}y$ replaced by $e^{ax}Dy$, to obtain

$$(D - aI)^2 e^{ax} y = e^{ax} D^2 y$$

This is the desired formula **11**. Returning to the proof of formula **9**, we observe that since $L = p(D)$ and $p(\lambda) = (\lambda - a)^2 + k^2$ we have

$$L = (D - aI)^2 + k^2 I$$

Thus

$$L(e^{ax} y) = (D - aI)^2 (e^{ax} y) + k^2 I e^{ax} y$$

Applying formula **11** gives

$$L(e^{ax} y) = e^{ax} D^2 y + k^2 I e^{ax} y$$

Since $Ie^{ax}y = e^{ax}y = e^{ax}Iy$, we have

$$\begin{aligned}L(e^{ax} y) &= e^{ax}(D^2 y + k^2 I y) \\ &= e^{ax}(D^2 + k^2 I) y \\ &= e^{ax} L_1 y\end{aligned}$$

This is just formula **9**. These results can be generalized to obtain the following theorem, which is known as the *translation principle*. The proof is left to Exercise 8.

THEOREM 21 If $L_1 = \alpha_n D^n + \alpha_{n-1} D^{n-1} + \cdots + \alpha_1 D + \alpha_0 I$ and
$L = \alpha_n (D - aI)^n + \alpha_{n-1}(D - aI)^{n-1} + \cdots + \alpha_1 (D - aI) + \alpha_0 I$
so that L is obtained from L_1 by replacing D by $D - aI$, then
$L(e^{ax} y) = e^{ax} L_1 y$.

In particular, if $c_1\varphi_1 + c_2\varphi_2 + \cdots + c_n\varphi_n$ is the general solution to $L_1 y = 0$, then

$$e^{ax}(c_1\varphi_1 + c_2\varphi_2 + \cdots + c_n\varphi_n)$$

is the general solution to $Ly = 0$.

This theorem enables us to describe the null space of L once we know the null space of L_1. We shall find it useful in the next section. Example 6 indicates one such use of the translation principle.

EXAMPLE 6 The functions $1, x, x^2, \ldots, x^{n-1}$ are independent and are certainly solutions to $D^n y = 0$. Repeated integration of this equation shows that any solution must be a polynomial of degree $\leq n - 1$. Therefore, the null space of $L_1 = D^n$ has the basis $1, x, x^2, \ldots, x^{n-1}$. The translation principle tells us that the null space of $L = (D - aI)^n$ must have the basis

$$e^{ax}, xe^{ax}, \ldots, x^{n-1}e^{ax}$$

This is the general form of result **8** of the previous section.

We see that the general solution to

$$y'''' + 4y''' + 6y'' + 4y' + y = 0$$

is

$$y = (c_1 + c_2 x + c_3 x^2 + c_4 x^3)e^{-x}$$

since the associated operator is

$$(D + I)^4 = D^4 + 4D^3 + 6D^2 + 4D + I$$

EXERCISES

1 Find the general solution to each of the following.
a $y'' + 4y = 0$ **b** $y'' = -by$
c $3y'' + 7y = 0$ **d** $2y'' = -5y$

2 Using the method of Examples 2 and 3 find the general solution to each of the following.
a $y'' + 2y' + 2y = 0$ **b** $y'' + 4y' + 5y = 0$
c $4y'' - 4y' + 5y = 0$ **d** $y'' - 8y' + 18y = 0$

3 Find the general solution to each of the following.
a $y'' + 6y' + 9y = 0$ **b** $y'' + 6y' + 10y = 0$
c $y'' + 6y' + 8y = 0$ **d** $y'' + 6y' - 10y = 0$

4 Solve each of the following initial value problems.

a $y'' + 4y = 0$, $y(0) = 0$, $y'(0) = 1$

b $4y'' + 9y = 0$, $y(\pi) = 1$, $y'(\pi) = 0$

c $y'' + 2y' + 2y = 0$, $y(\pi/2) = 1$, $y'(\pi/2) = -1$

d $y'' - 4y' + 6y = 0$, $y(0) = 0$, $y'(0) = 1$

5 Find a basis for the null space of each of the following by using the methods of Example 6.
a $(D - 3I)^4$ **b** $(D + 2I)^6$

6 Using Theorem 21 find:
a $(D - 3I)^4(e^{3x}\log x)$ **b** $(D + 2I)^3(x^5 e^{-2x})$
c $(D + I)^5 e^{2x}$ **d** $(D - \sqrt{2}I)^{12}(e^{\sqrt{2}x}\sin x)$

7 This exercise outlines a proof that $\sin x$ and $\cos x$ span the null space of $D^2 + I$. Suppose y is in the null space of $D^2 + I$. Put

$$\begin{aligned} A &= y(0) \\ B &= y'(0) \\ z(x) &= y(x) - A \sin x - B \cos x \\ E(x) &= [z(x)]^2 + [z'(x)]^2 \end{aligned}$$

a Show that $z(0) = z'(0) = 0$.
b Show that $(D^2 + I)z = 0$.
c Show that $DE = 2z'(D^2 + I)z$.
d Deduce that E is constant.
e Use parts **a** and **d** to show that E is the zero function.
f Deduce that z is identically zero.
g Does part **f** show that y is a linear combination of $\sin x$ and $\cos x$?

8 Prove Theorem 21. (Hint: First show that $(D - aI)^k(e^{ax}y) = e^{ax}D^k y$ for $k = 1, 2, \ldots, n$.)

□ 9 Solve each equation of Exercises 1 and 2 by using the method of Exercise 8, page 243.

SECTION 4 Higher-order Linear Operators

The nature of the general solution to

1 $$y^{(n)} + \beta_{n-1}y^{(n-1)} + \cdots + \beta_1 y' + \beta_0 y = 0$$

depends upon the factorization of the characteristic polynomial

$$p(\lambda) = \lambda^n + \beta_{n-1}\lambda^{n-1} + \cdots + \beta_1\lambda + \beta_0$$

Using the theory of such factorization (*see* the bibliography for a reference to a discussion of this), we can write

2 $$p(\lambda) = p_1(\lambda)^{n_1}p_2(\lambda)^{n_2}\ldots p_k(\lambda)^{n_k}$$

where each polynomial p_i is of the form $(\lambda - \alpha_i)$ or $\lambda^2 + b_i\lambda + c_i$ with $b_i^2 - 4c_i < 0$. Furthermore, we can suppose that $p_i \neq p_j$ if $i \neq j$. Since each side of equation 2 must have the same degree, we have

3 $$n = n_1 \text{ degree } p_1 + n_2 \text{ degree } p_2 + \cdots + n_k \text{ degree } p_k$$

Suppose

$$p_i(\lambda) = \lambda - \alpha_i \qquad \text{and} \qquad n_i = 1$$

This factor contributes to the general solution of equation 1 the term $e^{\alpha_i x}$. If $n_i = 2$, we have the two solutions $e^{\alpha_i x}$ and $xe^{\alpha_i x}$.

In general, as shown in Example 6 of the previous section, we have the n_i independent solutions

4 $$e^{\alpha_i x}, xe^{\alpha_i x}, \ldots, x^{n_i-1} e^{\alpha_i x}$$

contributed by the factor $p_i(\lambda)^{n_i} = (\lambda - \alpha_i)^{n_i}$.

If

$$p_i(\lambda) = \lambda^2 + b_i\lambda + c_i \qquad \text{with} \qquad b_i^2 - 4c_i < 0$$

we can complete the square to write

$$p_i(\lambda) = (\lambda - a_i)^2 + k_i^2$$

If $n_i = 1$, this factor contributes the two independent solutions

$$e^{a_i x} \sin k_i x \qquad \text{and} \qquad e^{a_i x} \cos k_i x$$

If $n_i = 2$, this factor contributes the four independent solutions (*see* Exercise 6, below)

$$e^{a_i x} \sin k_i x, \quad e^{a_i x} \cos k_i x, \quad xe^{a_i x} \sin k_i x, \quad \text{and} \quad xe^{a_i x} \cos k_i x$$

In general, we obtain the $2n_i$ independent solutions

5 $$\begin{gathered} e^{a_i x} \sin k_i x, xe^{a_i x} \sin k_i x, \ldots, x^{n_i-1} e^{a_i x} \sin k_i x \\ e^{a_i x} \cos k_i x, xe^{a_i x} \cos k_i x, \ldots, x^{n_i-1} e^{a_i x} \cos k_i x \end{gathered}$$

contributed by the factor $p_i(\lambda)^{n_i} = (\lambda^2 + b_i\lambda + c_i)^{n_i}$.

This process—constructing solutions for each factor $p_i(\lambda)^{n_i}$—gives us n solutions to equation **1** (from formula **3**) which can be shown to be independent. To see that they are a basis for the solutions to equation **1** we refer to the following result, the proof of which is given in Appendix 2.

THEOREM 22 Suppose S and T are linear transformations from V into V, *each* with a finite dimensional null space. Then the null space of ST is finite dimensional, and the dimension of the null space of ST *cannot exceed the sum* of the dimensions of the null space of S and the null space of T.

The associated operator for equation **1** is

$$L = D^n + \beta_{n-1}D^{n-1} + \cdots + \beta_1 D + \beta_0 I$$

We can then write

$$L = p(D) = p_1(D)^{n_1} p_2(D)^{n_2} \ldots p_k(D)^{n_k}$$

so that L is a product of powers of operators of either first or second order.

We have shown that if $p_i(\lambda)$ has degree 1 the null space of $p_i(D)$ has dimension 1. (*See* property 2, page 232.) Exercise 7, page 251, tells us that the null space of $p_i(D)$ has dimension 2 if $p_i(\lambda)$ is of the form $\lambda^2 + k^2$, while property 8, page 246, tells us that this null space has dimension 2 if $p_i(\lambda) = \lambda^2 + b_i\lambda + c_i$ with $b_i^2 - 4c_i < 0$. Thus L is the product of powers of operators whose null spaces have dimension 1 or 2. We can conclude from Theorem 22 and formula 3 that

The dimension of the null space of L cannot exceed n, the order of L.

Since we have constructed n independent solutions to equation 1, we conclude that this null space has dimension at least n. In summary:

THEOREM 23 The dimension of the null space of

$$L = D^n + \beta_{n-1}D^{n-1} + \cdots + \beta_1 D + \beta_0 I$$

is n, the order of L.

EXAMPLE 1 Suppose we are looking for a basis for the null space of

$$L = (D - I)(D + 2I)^3(D^2 + 9I)^2 D^4$$

The factor $D - I$ contributes e^x; the factor $(D + 2I)^3$ contributes e^{-2x}, xe^{-2x}, and x^2e^{-2x}; the factor $(D^2 + 9I)^2$ gives us $\sin 3x$, $\cos 3x$, $x \sin 3x$, and $x \cos 3x$; and D^4 gives 1, x, x^2, and x^3. Thus the general solution to $Ly = 0$ is

$$c_1e^x + c_2e^{-2x} + c_3xe^{-2x} + c_4x^2e^{-2x} + c_5 \sin 3x + c_6 \cos 3x$$
$$+ c_7x \sin 3x + c_8x \cos 3x + c_9 + c_{10}x + c_{11}x^2 + c_{12}x^3$$

EXAMPLE 2 Consider the equation

$$y^{(5)} + y^{(4)} - y^{(3)} - y^{(2)} = 0$$

The associated operator is $L = D^5 + D^4 - D^3 - D^2$, whose characteristic polynomial is

$$\lambda^5 + \lambda^4 - \lambda^3 - \lambda^2 = \lambda^2(\lambda^3 + \lambda^2 - \lambda - 1)$$
$$= \lambda^2(\lambda + 1)^2(\lambda - 1)$$

The factor λ^2 gives the two solutions 1, x; the factor $(\lambda + 1)^2$ gives the two solutions e^{-x}, xe^{-x}; and the factor $\lambda - 1$ gives the solution e^x. Thus the general solution is

$$y = c_1 + c_2x + c_3e^{-x} + c_4xe^{-x} + c_5e^x$$

EXAMPLE 3 To find the general solution to $Ly = 0$, where

$$L = (D^2 + 2D + 2I)^3(D^2 - I),$$

calculate the solutions corresponding to each factor of L. Completing the square for $D^2 + 2D + 2I$ gives

$$D^2 + 2D + 2I = (D + I)^2 + I$$

Therefore $(D^2 + 2D + 2I)^3$ gives the six functions $e^{-x} \sin x$, $e^{-x} \cos x$, $xe^{-x} \sin x$, $xe^{-x} \cos x$, $x^2e^{-x} \sin x$, and $x^2e^{-x} \cos x$. The factor $D^2 - I = (D + I)(D - I)$ gives us e^x and e^{-x}. The general solution is thus

$$\begin{aligned} c_1e^x + e^{-x}(c_2 \sin x + c_3 \cos x + c_4x \sin x \\ + c_5x \cos x + c_6x^2 \sin x + c_7x^2 \cos x + c_8) \end{aligned}$$

EXAMPLE 4 Suppose we wish to solve the initial value problem

$$y^{(5)} + y^{(4)} - y^{(3)} - y^{(2)} = 0$$

$$y(0) = 1,\ y'(0) = -1,\ y''(0) = 0,\ y'''(0) = 1,\ y''''(0) = 0$$

From Example 2 we know that the general solution to the differential equation is

$$y = c_1 + c_2x + c_3e^{-x} + c_4xe^{-x} + c_5e^x$$

so that

$$\begin{aligned} y' &= c_2 - c_3e^{-x} + c_4(e^{-x} - xe^{-x}) + c_5e^x \\ y'' &= c_3e^{-x} + c_4(-2e^{-x} + xe^{-x}) + c_5e^x \\ y''' &= -c_3e^{-x} + c_4(3e^{-x} - xe^{-x}) + c_5e^x \\ y'''' &= c_3e^{-x} + c_4(-4e^{-x} + xe^{-x}) + c_5e^x \end{aligned}$$

Setting $x = 0$ in each of these and using the initial conditions gives the following five equations:

$$\begin{aligned} 1 &= c_1 \quad + c_3 \qquad\quad + c_5 \\ -1 &= \quad c_2 - c_3 + \ \ c_4 + c_5 \\ 0 &= \qquad\quad c_3 - 2c_4 + c_5 \\ 1 &= \qquad - c_3 + 3c_4 + c_5 \\ 0 &= \qquad\quad c_3 - 4c_4 + c_5 \end{aligned}$$

Solving these equations gives the unique solution $c_1 = 1$, $c_2 = -2$, $c_3 = -\frac{1}{2}$, $c_4 = 0$, and $c_5 = \frac{1}{2}$. Therefore, the solution is

$$y = 1 - 2x - \tfrac{1}{2}e^{-x} + \tfrac{1}{2}e^x$$

EXERCISES

1 By factoring the characteristic polynomial find the general solution to each of the following.

a $y'''' + 4y'' + 4y = 0$

b $y''' - 3y'' + 3y' - y = 0$

c $y^{(6)} - 3y^{(5)} - 4y^{(4)} = 0$

d $(y'' + 2y' + 2y)'' = 0$

e $y'''' + y = 0$

f $y''' - y = 0$

2 Find a basis for the null space of each of the following.

a $(D + 3I)^2(D^2 - I)^2(D^2 + I)$

b $D^5(D^2 + 4D + 5I)^3$

c $(D^2 - 3D - 4I)^2(D^2 + D + I)^2$

d $(D^4 - 6D^3 + 13D^2)^2$

3 Solve each of the following initial value problems.

a $y'''' + 4y'' + 4y = 0$
$y(0) = 1, y'(0) = 2, y''(0) = y'''(0) = 0$

b $y'''' - y = 0$
$y(0) = 0, y'(0) = 1, y''(0) = -1, y'''(0) = 1$

c $y''' + 3y'' + 3y' + y = 0$
$y(1) = 1, y'(1) = -1, y''(1) = 0$

d $(D^2 + 2D + 2I)^2(D - I)y = 0$
$y(0) = y'(0) = y''(0) = y'''(0) = 0, y''''(0) = 1$

4 Suppose K and L are constant coefficient linear differential operators.

a Show that KL is a constant coefficient linear differential operator. [Hint: There are polynomials p and q such that $K = p(D)$, $L = q(D)$.]

b Show that $KL = LK$. (Hint: Use the hint of part **a** and the fact that $pq = qp$.)

c Show that the order of KL is the sum of the orders of K and L.

5 Suppose $A = \begin{bmatrix} 1 & 0 \\ 0 & 0 \end{bmatrix}$ and $B = \begin{bmatrix} 2 & 0 \\ 0 & 0 \end{bmatrix}$.

a What is the dimension of the null space of A? of B? of AB?

b Part **a** shows that the dimension of the null space of a product can be smaller than the sum of the dimensions of the null space of each factor. Show that if K and L are constant coefficient linear differential operators, then the dimension of the null space of KL *equals* the sum of the dimensions of the null spaces of K and L. (Hint: Use Theorem 23 and Exercise **4c**.)

6 a Show that $\sin kx$, $\cos kx$, $x \sin kx$, and $x \cos kx$ are solutions to

$$(D^2 + k^2I)^2y = 0$$

b Show that $\sin kx$, $\cos kx$, $x \sin kx$, and $x \cos kx$ are independent.

c Use the translation principle to show that $e^{ax} \sin kx$, $e^{ax} \cos kx$, $xe^{ax} \sin kx$, and $xe^{ax} \cos kx$ are solutions to $((D - aI)^2 + k^2I)^2y = 0$.

d Show that the functions of part **c** are independent.

7 Proceed as in Exercise 6 to show that $e^{ax} \sin kx$, $e^{ax} \cos kx$, $xe^{ax} \sin kx$, $xe^{ax} \cos kx$, $x^2e^{ax} \sin kx$, and $x^2e^{ax} \cos kx$ are independent solutions to

$$((D - aI)^2 + k^2I)^3y = 0$$

SECTION 5 The Method of Undetermined Coefficients

We now turn to the problem of finding the general form of solutions to $Ly = f$, where L is a constant coefficient linear differential operator. We first prove that

1 *If $Ly_1 = f$, then the set of solutions to $Ly = f$ is precisely the set of functions of the form $y_1 + y_2$, where y_2 is in the null space of L.*

For if y_2 is in the null space of L, then

$$L(y_1 + y_2) = Ly_1 + Ly_2 = f + 0 = f$$

Conversely, if $Ly = f$, and we let $y_2 = y - y_1$, then

$$Ly_2 = L(y - y_1) = Ly - Ly_1 = f - f = 0$$

We have shown that if $Ly = f$, then y must be of the form $y = y_1 + y_2$, where y_2 is in the null space of L, and have therefore completed the proof of statement **1**.

The observant student will note that the above result and proof are identical, except for notation changes, with the proof of Theorem 6. We used the linearity properties of L in place of the analogous matrix properties given in Theorem 3.

Suppose $\varphi_1, \varphi_2, \ldots, \varphi_n$ are a basis for the null space of L and that $Ly_1 = f$. The above result tells us that the solutions to $Ly = f$ are precisely the functions of the form

$$y_1 + c_1\varphi_1 + c_2\varphi_2 + \cdots + c_n\varphi_n$$

This is called the **general solution** to $Ly = f$. Observe that it is obtained by finding one solution, namely y_1, to $Ly = f$ and adding it to the general solution to the homogeneous equation $Ly = 0$.

Since the methods for finding the general solution to the homogeneous problem have already been developed, the discussion of constant coefficient linear differential equations can be completed by showing how to find *one* solution to the nonhomogeneous equation. A complicated but general method for finding such a solution for an arbitrary continuous function f is outlined in the exercises. We present here a useful and simple procedure that yields a solution when f is of a special form. To be precise, we assume that

2 *There is a constant coefficient linear differential operator K, such that $Kf = 0$.*

From our discussions in the previous sections about the form of the null space of such a K it is not too difficult to see that this is exactly the condition that f be a linear combination of products and derivatives of x, e^{ax}, and $\sin kx$. Thus, while the method to be presented does not apply to all functions f, it will cover a wide class of functions which arise in practice.

If f satisfies condition 2 and if $Ly = f$, we have

$$(KL)y = K(Ly) = Kf = 0$$

In other words,

3 *If f satisfies condition 2, the solutions to $Ly = f$ are* all *in the null space of KL.*

The operator KL is itself a constant coefficient linear differential operator (*see* Exercise 4, page 255), so we can apply the methods previously learned to find a basis $\varphi_1, \varphi_2, \ldots, \varphi_n$ for the null space of KL. Then condition 3 tells us that we need only choose $c_1, c_2, \ldots, c_n$ so that

$$L(c_1\varphi_1 + c_2\varphi_2 + \cdots + c_n\varphi_n) = f$$

In other words, we merely calculate

$$L(c_1\varphi_1 + c_2\varphi_2 + \cdots + c_n\varphi_n)$$

and determine $c_1, c_2, \ldots, c_n$ so that the result equals f. For this reason, the method is known as the *method of undetermined coefficients*.

We have used the assumption that the equation $Ly = f$ does have a solution in order to know that we can actually find the desired coefficients. In Appendix 2 we shall prove a general result about linear transformations which will give the result that

4 *If f satisfies condition 2, there is a function y in the null space of KL such that $Ly = f$.*

We demonstrate the use of this method with some examples.

EXAMPLE 1 To find a particular solution to

5 $$y'' + 2y = x^2 + 3$$

we set $Ly = y'' + 2y$ and note that $(x^2 + 3)''' = 0$. Therefore, $x^2 + 3$ satisfies condition 2, with $Ky = y'''$. We have

$$L = D^2 + 2I, \qquad K = D^3$$

hence

$$KL = D^3(D^2 + 2I)$$

Thus the null space of KL has the basis $1, x, x^2, \sin\sqrt{2}x, \cos\sqrt{2}x$. We now seek to determine c_1, c_2, c_3, c_4, c_5 so that if $y = c_1 + c_2x + c_3x^2 + c_4 \sin \sqrt{2}x + c_5 \cos \sqrt{2}x$, we will have $Ly = x^2 + 3$. We have

$$Ly = L(c_1 + c_2x + c_3x^2) + L(c_4 \sin \sqrt{2}x + c_5 \cos \sqrt{2}x)$$

The second term is zero for any c_4 and c_5, since $\sin \sqrt{2}x$ and $\cos \sqrt{2}x$ are in the null space of L. Hence we need only choose c_1, c_2, c_3 so that

$$L(c_1 + c_2x + c_3x^2) = x^2 + 3$$

Since

$$L(c_1 + c_2x + c_3x^2) = 2c_1 + 2c_2x + 2c_3x^2 + 2c_3$$

we have the following equations (by equating coefficients of like powers):

$$2c_1 + 2c_3 = 3$$
$$2c_2 = 0$$
$$2c_3 = 1$$

The unique solution to this system is $c_1 = 1,\ c_2 = 0,\ c_3 = \frac{1}{2}$, which gives the function $y_1 = 1 + \frac{1}{2}x^2$ as a solution to equation **5**.

Since the general solution to $Ly = 0$ is

$$c_1 \sin \sqrt{2}x + c_2 \cos \sqrt{2}x$$

we apply property **1** to obtain the general solution to equation **5**,

$$y = 1 + \tfrac{1}{2}x^2 + c_1 \sin \sqrt{2}x + c_2 \cos \sqrt{2}x$$

EXAMPLE 2 Consider the equation

6 $$y'' + y = e^x$$

In this case $L = D^2 + I$, and, since $(D - I)e^x = 0$, we can choose $K = D - I$.

We have

$$KL = (D - I)(D^2 + I)$$

so a basis for the null space of KL is

$$e^x, \sin x, \cos x$$

Thus we want to find c_1, c_2, and c_3 such that

$$y = c_1e^x + c_2 \sin x + c_3 \cos x$$

is a particular solution to equation **6**. We apply L to obtain

$$Ly = c_1Le^x + c_2L \sin x + c_3L \cos x$$

Since

$$L \sin x = L \cos x = 0$$

the choice of c_2 and c_3 is arbitrary. Therefore we need only determine c_1 so that $c_1 L e^x = e^x$.

We have

$$L e^x = (e^x)'' + e^x = 2e^x$$

Therefore $c_1 L e^x = e^x$ gives $2c_1 e^x = e^x$. We can choose $c_1 = \frac{1}{2}$ to obtain the solution $y_1 = \frac{1}{2}e^x$.

The general solution to $Ly = 0$ is (since $L = D^2 + I$)

$$c_1 \sin x + c_2 \cos x$$

so the general solution to equation **6** is the sum of this and a particular solution:

$$y = \tfrac{1}{2}e^x + c_1 \sin x + c_2 \cos x$$

EXAMPLE 3 For the equation

7 $$y'' - y = e^x$$

we have $L = D^2 - I$. We can choose $K = D - I$, since $(D - I)e^x = 0$. We have $KL = (D - I)^2(D + I)$; therefore, e^x, xe^x, and e^{-x} are a basis for the null space of KL. Thus we need to determine c_1, c_2, and c_3 so that

$$L(c_1 e^x + c_2 x e^x + c_3 e^{-x}) = e^x$$

Since $$\begin{aligned} L(c_1 e^x + c_2 x e^x + c_3 e^{-x}) &= c_1 L e^x + c_2 L x e^x + c_3 L e^{-x} \\ &= 0 + c_2 L x e^x + 0 \end{aligned}$$

we need only choose c_2 so that

8 $$c_2 L(xe^x) = e^x$$

Since $$\begin{aligned} L(xe^x) &= (xe^x)'' - xe^x \\ &= 2e^x + xe^x - xe^x = 2e^x \end{aligned}$$

equation **8** gives $2c_2 e^x = e^x$. Hence, if we choose $c_2 = \frac{1}{2}$ we obtain the particular solution $y_1 = \frac{1}{2}xe^x$. The general solution to $Ly = 0$ is $c_1 e^x + c_2 e^{-x}$. Applying property **1** we thus have the general solution to equation **7**:

$$y = \tfrac{1}{2}xe^x + c_1 e^x + c_2 e^{-x}$$

EXAMPLE 4 If L is a linear differential operator and $Lz_1 = f_1$, $Lz_2 = f_2$, then for any scalars a_1, a_2 we have

9 $$L(a_1z_1 + a_2z_2) = a_1Lz_1 + a_2Lz_2 = a_1f_1 + a_2f_2$$

We can use this principle to solve $Ly = f$, when f is a linear combination of functions which satisfy condition **2**. This principle is often called the *superposition principle*. For example, consider

10 $$y'' - y = 4x - 3xe^x$$

We can find particular solutions to each of the equations

$$y'' - y = x \qquad \text{and} \qquad y'' - y = xe^x$$

and then use the superposition principle to solve equation **10**. For $y'' - y = x$ we have $L = D^2 - I$ and $K = D^2$; therefore,

$$KL = D^2(D^2 - I)$$

Thus there is a solution of the form

$$y_1 = c_1 + c_2x + c_3e^x + c_4e^{-x}$$

Applying L we have

$$\begin{aligned} Ly_1 &= c_1L1 + c_2Lx + c_3Le^x + c_4Le^{-x} \\ &= c_1L1 + c_2Lx \\ &= c_1[(1)'' - 1] + c_2[(x)'' - x] \\ &= -c_1 - c_2x \end{aligned}$$

so that the condition $Ly_1 = x$ gives the equation $-c_1 - c_2x = x$. We conclude that $c_1 = 0$ and $c_2 = -1$, so that $y_1 = -x$ is a solution to $y'' - y = x$.

We now find a solution y_2 to the equation $y'' - y = xe^x$. We have $L = D^2 - I$ and $K = (D - I)^2$, for $(D - I)^2(xe^x) = 0$. Thus

$$KL = (D - I)^2(D^2 - I) = (D - I)^3(D + I)$$

Therefore, there is a solution of the form

$$y_2 = c_1e^x + c_2xe^x + c_3x^2e^x + c_4e^{-x}$$

Applying L and using the fact that $Le^x = Le^{-x} = 0$ we see that we need only choose c_2 and c_3 so that

$$c_2L(xe^x) + c_3L(x^2e^x) = xe^x$$

Since we have

$$L(xe^x) = (xe^x)'' - xe^x = 2e^x$$
$$L(x^2e^x) = (x^2e^x)'' - x^2e^x = 2e^x + 4xe^x$$

we must therefore choose c_2 and c_3 so that

$$2c_2e^x + 2c_3e^x + 4c_3xe^x = xe^x$$

holds for all x. As e^x and xe^x are independent, we must have $c_3 = \frac{1}{4}$ and $c_2 = -c_3 = -\frac{1}{4}$, and it follows that $-\frac{1}{4}xe^x + \frac{1}{4}x^2e^x$ is a solution to $y'' - y = xe^x$. Since $-x$ is a solution to $y'' - y = x$, the superposition principle **9** shows that

$$-4x - 3(-\tfrac{1}{4}xe^x + \tfrac{1}{4}x^2e^x) = -4x + \tfrac{3}{4}e^x(x - x^2)$$

is a solution to equation **10**.

EXAMPLE 5 Suppose we wish to solve the initial value problem

11
$$y'' + y = e^x$$
$$y(0) = 1$$
$$y'(0) = 0$$

We saw in Example 2 that the general solution to $y'' + y = e^x$ is

$$y = \tfrac{1}{2}e^x + c_1 \sin x + c_2 \cos x$$

Differentiating this gives

$$y' = \tfrac{1}{2}e^x + c_1 \cos x - c_2 \sin x$$

Setting $x = 0$ in each of these and using the initial conditions gives

$$1 = \tfrac{1}{2} + c_2$$
$$0 = \tfrac{1}{2} + c_1$$

so that $c_1 = -\frac{1}{2}$, $c_2 = \frac{1}{2}$. Therefore the solution to our initial value problem **11** is

$$y = \tfrac{1}{2}e^x - \tfrac{1}{2}\sin x + \tfrac{1}{2}\cos x$$

EXERCISES

1 Find a particular solution to each of the following.

a $y'' - 4y = xe^{-3x}$ **b** $y'' - 4y = e^{2x}$
c $y'' - 6y' + 8y = x^2 + 1$ **d** $y'' + 2y' + y = 2$
e $y'' + 2y' + y = xe^{-x}$ **f** $y'' + 4y' + 5y = x + \cos x$
g $y'' + 9y = 9x^2 + x \sin 3x$ **h** $y'''' - y = e^x + e^{-x} + \sin x$
i $y''' - y'' - 6y' = 1 + x + e^{-x}$ **j** $y'' - 2y' + y = 1 + xe^{2x}$

2 Solve each of the following problems.

a $y'' + 4y = e^x$
$y(\pi) = 1$
$y'(\pi) = 0$

b $y'' - y = e^{-x}$
$y(0) = 1$
$y'(0) = 0$

c $y'' - 3y' + 2y = 4x^2$
$y(0) = y'(0) = 0$

d $y'' + 2y' + y = e^{-x}$
$y(0) = y'(0) = 0$

3 For each of the following show that condition **2** is true by finding such a K.

a $x^2 \cos 2x + e^x$

b $e^{2x} \sin 3x + x^2 e^x$

c $\sin 2x + 3 \cos^2 x$

d $x^3 + 3x^2 + 2$

□ 4 There is a method, known as the method of *variation of parameters*, which gives a solution to $Ly = f$, once the null space of L is known. We illustrate this for $L = D^2 + bD + cI$. Let φ_1 and φ_2 be a basis for the null space of L. Let

12 $y = v_1\varphi_1 + v_2\varphi_2$, where v_1 and v_2 are functions which satisfy the condition

13 $v_1'\varphi_1 + v_2'\varphi_2 = 0$

a Show that $Ly = v_1 L\varphi_1 + v_2 L\varphi_2 + v_1'\varphi_1' + v_2'\varphi_2'$ (Hint: Calculate Dy and D^2y using equations **12** and **13**.)

b Show that if $v_1'\varphi_1' + v_2'\varphi_2' = f$, equation **12** gives a solution to $Ly = f$. (Hint: Use part **a**.)

c Show that if v_1 and v_2 satisfy

$$v_1' = \frac{\det\begin{bmatrix} 0 & \varphi_2 \\ f & \varphi_2' \end{bmatrix}}{\det\begin{bmatrix} \varphi_1 & \varphi_2 \\ \varphi_1' & \varphi_2' \end{bmatrix}}, \qquad v_2' = \frac{\det\begin{bmatrix} \varphi_1 & 0 \\ \varphi_1' & f \end{bmatrix}}{\det\begin{bmatrix} \varphi_1 & \varphi_2 \\ \varphi_1' & \varphi_2' \end{bmatrix}}$$

then $L(v_1\varphi_1 + v_2\varphi_2) = f$. [Hint: Use part **b**, equation **13**, and Cramer's rule (given in Example 9, page 173).]

d Show that if

$$y = \varphi_1 \int \frac{(-f\varphi_2)}{\varphi_1\varphi_2' - \varphi_1'\varphi_2} + \varphi_2 \int \frac{f\varphi_1}{\varphi_1\varphi_2' - \varphi_1'\varphi_2}$$

then $Ly = f$. (Hint: Integrate the equation of part **c**.)

□ 5 Use the method of Exercise 4 to find a particular solution to

a $y'' + y = x$

b $y'' - y = \log x$

c $y'' - 3y' + 2y = \sqrt{x}$

d $y'' - 2y' + y = \sqrt{1 - x^2}$

□ **6** Let $\varphi_1, \varphi_2, \varphi_3$ be a basis for the null space of a third-order operator L. Put

$$\Phi = \det\begin{bmatrix} \varphi_1 & \varphi_2 & \varphi_3 \\ \varphi_1' & \varphi_2' & \varphi_3' \\ \varphi_1'' & \varphi_2'' & \varphi_3'' \end{bmatrix} \qquad \Phi_1 = \det\begin{bmatrix} 0 & \varphi_2 & \varphi_3 \\ 0 & \varphi_2' & \varphi_3' \\ f & \varphi_2'' & \varphi_3'' \end{bmatrix}$$

$$\Phi_2 = \det\begin{bmatrix} \varphi_1 & 0 & \varphi_3 \\ \varphi_1' & 0 & \varphi_3' \\ \varphi_1'' & f & \varphi_3'' \end{bmatrix} \qquad \Phi_3 = \det\begin{bmatrix} \varphi_1 & \varphi_2 & 0 \\ \varphi_1' & \varphi_2' & 0 \\ \varphi_1'' & \varphi_2'' & f \end{bmatrix}$$

a Show that

$$y = \varphi_1 \int \frac{\Phi_1}{\Phi} + \varphi_2 \int \frac{\Phi_2}{\Phi} + \varphi_3 \int \frac{\Phi_3}{\Phi} \text{ is a solution to } Ly = f$$

b Use this method to find a solution to $y''' - y' = \log x$.

□ **7** State a result analogous to the previous three exercises for fourth-order operators.

□ **8** How should the method of Exercises 4 and 6 be modified in order to solve each of the following?

a $2y'' - 5y = x$ **b** $3y''' - y' = \log x$

Use this modification to find one solution to each equation.

SECTION 6 Applications

Linear differential equations with constant coefficients occur often in applied problems. We give some examples of these problems in this section.

EXAMPLE 1 *Growth and Decay.*

In many problems involving growth or decay (such as radioactive decay) experimentation has shown that the rate of growth or decay can often be taken to be proportional to the amount of material on hand. This principle can be given a mathematical formulation. Thus, if $y = y(t)$ represents the amount of material at time t, then y' is the rate of growth (or decay), and the basic assumption consequently is

1 $$y' = ky$$

where k is constant. Growth problems correspond to $k > 0$, decay problems to $k < 0$.

As shown in Section 1, equation **1** has the general solution

2 $$y = ce^{kt}$$

If we set $t = 0$, then $y(0) = c$; thus c is the *initial* amount of material.

If we know the amount of material at some later time then we can find the value of k.

DECAY: For example, suppose equation **1** represents radioactive decay (so that $k < 0$). If at time t_0 the amount of material present is $c/2$, then

$$\frac{c}{2} = y(t_0) = ce^{kt_0}$$

which gives

3
$$t_0 = -\frac{1}{k}\log 2$$

This is called the *half-life* of the material. Therefore, if we know the half-life, we can solve equation **3** for k.

GROWTH: In certain situations bacteria increase at a rate proportional to the number present; thus, if y represents the number present at time t, then $y' = ky$, with $k > 0$. Therefore, $y = ce^{kt}$, and, consequently, if we know the amount present at two different times, we can determine the precise nature of y. For example, if we begin with $y = 10{,}000$ and find from measurement that 1 million are present one hour later, we have

$$10{,}000 = ce^{0k}$$
$$1{,}000{,}000 = ce^{60k}$$

(assuming that t is given in terms of minutes). These give

$$c = 10{,}000$$
$$k = \tfrac{1}{30}\log 10, \qquad \text{which is approximately .078}$$

FRICTION: In some situations friction can be taken to exert a force proportional to the velocity. Thus, if a mass m moves with a velocity $v = v(t)$, subject to such a friction, Newton's second law (force is mass times acceleration) gives

$$m\frac{dv}{dt} = kv$$

If an external force $f(t)$ is applied, we have

4
$$m\frac{dv}{dt} = kv + f(t)$$

Suppose, for example, that f is constant; let us say $f = b$. The general solution to equation **4** is (the student should verify this):

$$v = -\frac{b}{k} + ce^{at} \qquad \text{where } a = \frac{k}{m}$$

Since k is negative (for friction tends to slow the object) we see that as

$t \to \infty$ the term $ce^{at} \to 0$. Thus, after a long time interval, the velocity is nearly constant.

Suppose f is periodic; let us say $f = A \sin \omega t$. The general solution to equation **4** is then seen to be (again, the student should verify this)

$$v = -\frac{A}{a^2 + \omega^2}(\omega \cos \omega t + a \sin \omega t) + ce^{at}, \qquad a = \frac{k}{m}$$

In this case, if t is large, the velocity is nearly equal to

$$-\frac{A}{a^2 + \omega^2}(\omega \cos \omega t + a \sin \omega t)$$

EXAMPLE 2 *Mechanical Vibrations.*

Suppose a mass m is attached to a spring and the spring is pulled back a little and released. We should expect the mass to oscillate back and forth, supposing, of course, that the mass of the spring and the friction present are both so small, relative to m, that their effect can be neglected, and that the oscillations are small (so that the spring is not stretched too far).

Suppose we choose coordinates such that the center of gravity of the mass, with no tension in the spring, is at 0 and that $y = y(t)$ represents the distance from the center of gravity of m from 0 at time t (as shown in Figure 1).

Figure 1 *At* 0 *there is no tension in the spring.*

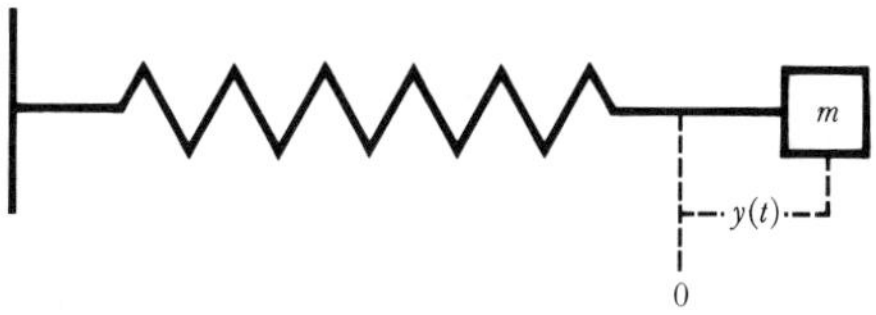

Newton's second law gives

$$my'' = \text{force acting on the mass}$$

Hooke's law (also a result of much experimental observation) asserts that if no external forces are present, this force is proportional to the distance from 0; therefore, we have

5 $$my'' = -ky$$

where k is a positive constant known as the *spring constant* dependent upon the nature of the spring. The minus sign indicates that the force tends to restore the mass to 0.

The general solution to equation **5** is

$$\textbf{6} \qquad y = A \sin \alpha t + B \cos \alpha t, \qquad \alpha = \sqrt{k/m}$$

We have

$$y(0) = B, \qquad y'(0) = \alpha A$$

which give the initial position and velocity of the mass. In particular, if we assume that the mass is moved to y_0 and released from rest so that

$$\textbf{7} \qquad y(0) = y_0, \qquad y'(0) = 0$$

then the unique solution to equation **5** which satisfies initial conditions **7** is $y = y_0 \cos \alpha t$.

We can use trigonometric identities to rewrite equation **6** as

$$y = C \sin (\alpha t + \beta),$$

where

$$C = \sqrt{A^2 + B^2} \qquad \text{and} \qquad \beta = \tan^{-1} \frac{A}{B}$$

(*See* Exercise 8, below.)

The number C is called the *amplitude*, β/α is called the *displacement* or *phase angle*, and $2\pi/\alpha$ is called the *period* of the vibration. Figure 2 indicates the graph of y.

Figure 2 $\quad y = C \sin (\alpha t + \beta)$.

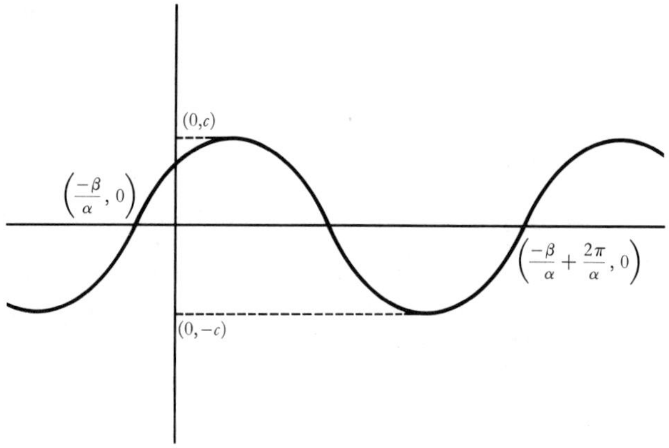

Suppose we attach a damper to the spring of Figure 1 that exerts a damping force proportional to the velocity. We then have the equation

$my'' = -ky - k_1y'$, where k and k_1 are both positive. We can write this as

8 $$y'' + by' + cy = 0 \qquad \text{where } b = \frac{k_1}{m}, \qquad c = \frac{k}{m}$$

The nature of the general solution to equation **8** depends upon whether $b^2 - 4c > 0$, $b^2 - 4c = 0$, or $b^2 - 4c < 0$. We thus have the following possible general solutions to equation **8**:

9

a $y = c_1e^{\alpha t} + c_2e^{\beta t} \qquad \text{if } b^2 - 4c > 0$

b $y = c_1e^{\alpha t} + c_2te^{\alpha t} \qquad \text{if } b^2 - 4c = 0$

c $y = c_1e^{at} \sin kt + c_2e^{at} \cos kt \qquad \text{if } b^2 - 4c < 0$

The behavior of each of these solutions is indicated in Exercise 9, below.

EXAMPLE 3 *A Simple Pendulum.*

Applied problems often give rise to nonlinear differential equations. In some cases, approximate solutions can be obtained by using approximations to obtain a linear equation. An example of this is the differential equation of motion of a pendulum.

Suppose a mass m is hung on a stiff wire, pulled to one side, and released. Let Θ be the angle the wire makes with the vertical. We shall determine the force which is attempting to restore the wire to a vertical position. Neglecting air resistance and the weight of the wire, we find that the only force acting on the mass is the force of gravity, which is vertical. (*See* Figure 3.)

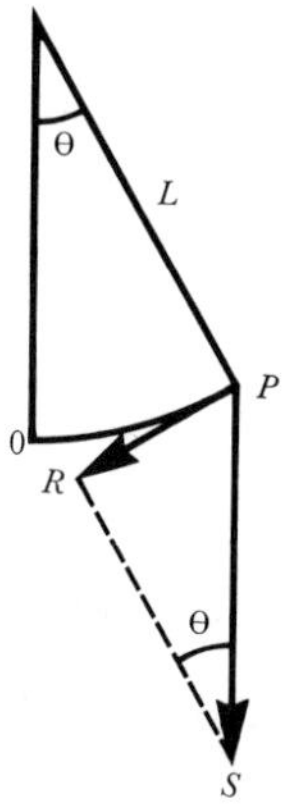

Figure 3 *The pendulum.*

Physical observation has shown that the acceleration due to gravity is (in the English system of measurement) approximately equal to 32 feet per second, so that Newton's second law gives $32m$ as the force due to gravity. We wish to calculate the tangential force PR due to the vertical force $PS = 32m$. We see from Figure 3 that this force is $32m \sin \Theta$. Assuming that the downward direction is negative we therefore find that the tangential, or restoring, force is $-32m \sin \Theta$.

Applying Newton's second law of motion again, we see that if $y = y(t)$ is the distance OP at time t, then $my'' = -32m \sin \Theta$. Since $OP = L\Theta$ we have

$$y'' = L\frac{d^2\Theta}{dt^2}$$

Thus, the equation of motion is

10 $$mL\frac{d^2\Theta}{dt^2} = -32m \sin \Theta$$

If we assume that the mass is released from rest, with the wire at an angle Θ_0 with the vertical, we have

11 $$\Theta(0) = \Theta_0, \qquad \Theta'(0) = 0$$

Thus our function of position, $\Theta = \Theta(t)$, satisfies equation **10** and the initial conditions **11**. We note immediately that the motion does not depend on the amount of mass m, as can be seen from equation **10** (subject, of course, to m being large in relation to the wire weight, so that this equation will hold.)

Equation **10** is nonlinear and very difficult to solve. We recall from calculus that

$$\lim_{\Theta \to 0} \frac{\sin \Theta}{\Theta} = 1$$

so we would expect that a reasonable approximation for small oscillations to the motion $\Theta = \Theta(t)$ can be obtained by replacing equation **10** by

12 $$mL\frac{d^2\Theta}{dt^2} = -32m\Theta$$

Since the general solution to this is

$$\Theta = c_1 \sin (\sqrt{32/L})t + c_2 \cos (\sqrt{32/L})t$$

the solution that satisfies the initial conditions **11** is

$$\Theta(t) = \Theta_0 \cos (\sqrt{32/L})t$$

Experimentation has shown that this solution gives a good approximation to the motion for small oscillations.

EXERCISES

1 Suppose conditions are such that bacterial growth is proportional to the amount present.

a If 1 million bacteria double in one minute, how long will it take for 10 million to be present?

b If 1 million bacteria are present at noon and 10 million are present at 1 P.M., how many are present at 12:30 P.M.?

2 A radioactive material decays at a rate proportional to the amount present. If it takes 1 million years for 10 grams to decay to one gram, what is the half-life of the substance?

3 It is often assumed that human population growth is proportional to the amount present. Use this assumption and the fact that the population of the United States was 106.5 million in 1920 and 132 million in 1940 to determine the population of the United States in 1960. What does this result lead you to conjecture about the truth or falsity of this growth assumption? (The actual population in 1960 was 180 million.)

4 A mass m is dropped in the atmosphere, subject only to air resistance (assumed proportional to velocity) and gravity. Suppose that as $t \to \infty$ the velocity approaches 64 feet per second. How fast is the mass falling after two seconds?

5 Newton's law of cooling states that the rate at which the temperature of a body changes is proportional to the difference between its temperature and that of the surrounding medium. Let y denote the temperature of the body at time t and T the temperature of the surrounding medium.

a Show that $y' = k(y - T)$ where k is constant.

b What happens to the solution as $t \to \infty$?

6 A mass with $m = 10$ is connected to a spring with spring constant $k = 2$. Find the equation of motion if

a The mass is distorted three units to the right and released from rest.

b The mass is distorted four units to the left and released from rest.

c The mass is released from the point of no tension with an initial velocity of five units, directed to the right.

d The mass is distorted three units to the right and released with an initial velocity of two units to the left.

7 Find the period, amplitude, and phase angle for each of the motions of Exercise 6.

8 Show that

$$a \sin \varphi + b \cos \varphi = c \sin (\varphi + \theta)$$

where $c = \sqrt{a^2 + b^2}$ and $\theta = \tan^{-1} a/b$. (Hint: Apply the sum formula to the right-hand side.)

9 A damper is applied to the mass of Figure 1 so that equation **8** holds. The spring is distorted d units to the right and released from rest.

a Does the mass cross the point 0 if $m = 2$, $k_1 = 6$, and $k = 4$? Does your answer depend upon d (if $d \neq 0$)? What happens as $t \to \infty$?

b Answer the questions of part **a** if $m = 2$, $k_1 = 4$, and $k = 2$.
c Answer the questions of part **a** if $m = 2$, $k_1 = 4$, and $k = 4$. Does the mass cross 0 more than once?

10 Suppose the mass of the previous exercise is also subject to an external force $f(t)$. Find the equation of motion if
a $m = 2$, $k_1 = 6$, $k = 4$, and $f(t) = 1$
b $m = 2$, $k_1 = 6$, $k = 4$, and $f(t) = e^{-t}$
c $m = 2$, $k_1 = 4$, $k = 2$, and $f(t) = \sin t$
d $m = 2$, $k_1 = 4$, $k = 2$, and $f(t) = e^{-t}$
e $m = 2$, $k_1 = 4$, $k = 4$, and $f(t) = \sin t$

11 Experimentation has shown that the current I (measured in amperes) in a simple electric series circuit containing a capacitor of capacity C farads, a coil of inductance of L henrys, a resistance of R ohms, and a voltage source of E volts satisfies the equation

$$L\frac{d^2I}{dt^2} + R\frac{dI}{dt} + \frac{1}{C}I = \frac{dE}{dt}$$

What is the general solution to this if
a $R = 0$ and E is constant?
b $R > 0$ and E is constant?
c $R = 0$ and $E = A \sin \omega t$?
d $R > 0$ and $E = A \sin \omega t$?
In which cases does the current become small for large t?

12 Suppose a mass $m = 10$ hangs from a wire 8 units long, is moved to an angle of $\pi/100$ with the vertical, and released. Find the approximate equation of motion. What is the period of the motion? Is the period affected if the mass is doubled? if the initial position is changed?

13 A circular disk of mass m and radius r is suspended on a wire through its center, twisted through an angle Θ_0, and then released from rest. Experience has shown that the torsion in the wire is directly proportional to the amount $\Theta(t)$ of twist and inversely proportional to the square of the radius. Derive the differential equation of motion satisfied by $\Theta(t)$ and find the solution which satisfies the given initial conditions.

APPENDIX 1

ELEMENTARY ANALYTIC GEOMETRY

Vector methods provide a powerful descriptive tool in analytic geometry. In this appendix we give an informal discussion showing how vectors can be used to describe lines, line segments, parallelograms, parallelopipeds, and planes. It is shown how the projection concept of Section 10, Chapter 1, can be used to solve distance problems. The effect of linear transformations upon various figures is then discussed. We also discuss orthogonal transformations. We use freely and interchangeably the various identifications of pairs and triples as points and as arrows.

Equations of Lines

Suppose L is a line which passes through (x_0,y_0) and is parallel to the vector

$$\bar{v} = a\bar{i} + b\bar{j}, \text{ with } \bar{v} \neq \bar{0}$$

Let (x,y) denote an arbitrary point on L. Then the vector

1 $$\bar{u} = (x - x_0)\bar{i} + (y - y_0)\bar{j}$$

is parallel to L and hence parallel to $\bar{v}$. Therefore $\bar{u}$ is a multiple of $\bar{v}$, so there is a number t such that

2 $$\bar{u} = t\bar{v}$$

Conversely if $\bar{u}$ is of the form **1** and satisfies equation **2** then (x,y) must lie on L; thus these relations completely determine L. (*See* Figure 1.)

Figure 1

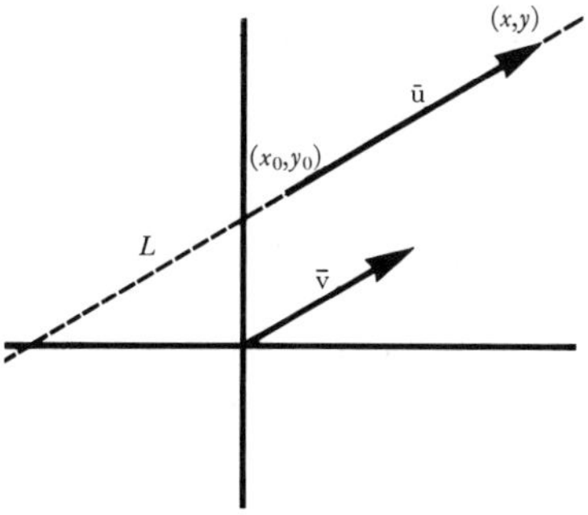

Put $\bar{u}_0 = x_0\bar{i} + y_0\bar{j}$ and $\bar{w} = x\bar{i} + y\bar{j}$ so that $\bar{u} = \bar{w} - \bar{u}_0$. We can then rewrite equation **2** as

3 $$\bar{w} = t\bar{v} + \bar{u}_0$$

Therefore the condition that the terminal point of $\bar{w}$ lies on L is the condition that $\bar{w}$ be the sum of $\bar{u}_0$ and a multiple of $\bar{v}$, as shown in Figure 2. In other words, for a given $\bar{u}_0$ and $\bar{v}$, the *line through the terminal point of* $\bar{u}_0$ *which is parallel to* $\bar{v}$ *consists of the terminal points of the vectors* $t\bar{v} + \bar{u}_0$. We usually summarize this statement by saying that equation **3** is the *vector equation* of this line.

Figure 2

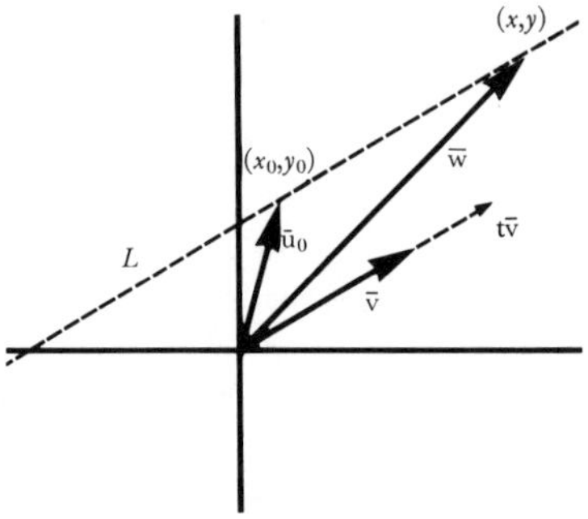

In terms of coordinates we can rewrite equation **3** as the two equations:

4 $$x = at + x_0$$
$$y = bt + y_0$$

Eliminating t we have, if $a \neq 0$ and $b \neq 0$,

5 $$\frac{x - x_0}{a} = \frac{y - y_0}{b}$$

We call the set of equations **4** a *parametric description* of L with *parameter t*, meaning that as t varies, the points (x,y) given by these equations are precisely the points of L. Equation **5** gives the familiar *Cartesian equation* of this line.

The vector description of a line in R^3 is similar to equation **3**. Suppose, for example,

$$\bar{u}_0 = x_0\bar{i} + y_0\bar{j} + z_0\bar{k}$$
$$\bar{v} = a\bar{i} + b\bar{j} + c\bar{k}$$
$$\bar{w} = x\bar{i} + y\bar{j} + z\bar{k}$$

Then the condition

6 $$\bar{w} = t\bar{v} + \bar{u}_0$$

is the same as the condition that *the terminal point of* $\bar{w}$ *lies on the line through the terminal point of* $\bar{u}_0$ *which is parallel to* $\bar{v}$. Thus equation **6** is a *vector equation* of this line. In coordinate form we have the parametric description with parameter t:

7 $$\begin{aligned} x &= at + x_0 \\ y &= bt + y_0 \\ z &= ct + z_0 \end{aligned}$$

Eliminating t and assuming that $a \neq 0$, $b \neq 0$, and $c \neq 0$ we have the Cartesian equations of this line:

8 $$\frac{x - x_0}{a} = \frac{y - y_0}{b} = \frac{z - z_0}{c}$$

We usually write these equations even if one or more of a, b, and c is zero, adopting the convention that this is to mean that the corresponding numerator is zero. For example,

$$\frac{x - 1}{2} = \frac{y + 3}{-4} = \frac{z - 2}{0}$$

means the line given in parametric form by

$$\begin{aligned} x &= 2t + 1 \\ y &= -4t - 3 \\ z &= 2 \end{aligned}$$

or, in other words, the line through $(1,-3,2)$ parallel to $2\bar{\imath} - 4\bar{\jmath}$.

The line through the terminal points of $\bar{u}$ and $\bar{v}$ is just the line through the terminal point of $\bar{u}$ which is parallel to $\bar{v} - \bar{u}$. The vector equation of this line is

9 $$\bar{w} = t(\bar{v} - \bar{u}) + \bar{u} = t\bar{v} + (1 - t)\bar{u}$$

Thus, for example, the line through $(2,1,3)$ and $(-1,0,1)$ has vector form

$$\bar{w} = t(2\bar{\imath} + \bar{\jmath} + 3\bar{k}) + (1 - t)(-\bar{\imath} + \bar{k})$$

Suppose $\bar{v} \neq \bar{0}$. Note that $\bar{w} = t\bar{v}$ is the equation of the line through the origin parallel to $\bar{v}$. This is just the subspace consisting of all multiples of $\bar{v}$. Thus equation **3** (or **6**) shows that a line *not* through the origin is just a translation of a line through the origin, or in other words, a translation of a one-dimensional subspace.

Line Segments

The form **9** enables us to give a useful description of a line segment. The line through the terminal points of $\bar{u}$ and $\bar{v}$ has the vector equation

$$\overline{w} = t\bar{v} + (1 - t)\bar{u}$$

Suppose we let t vary with the restriction $0 \le t \le 1$. Then, as Figure 3 shows, the terminal point of $\overline{w}$ varies over the line segment from $\bar{u}$ to $\bar{v}$.

For example, if $t = 0$, then $\overline{w} = \bar{u}$; if $t = 1$, then $\overline{w} = \bar{v}$; while if $t = \frac{1}{2}$, then

$$\overline{w} = \tfrac{1}{2}\bar{v} + \tfrac{1}{2}\bar{u}$$

the terminal point of which *bisects* the line segment from $\bar{u}$ to $\bar{v}$. Also, the terminal points of $\frac{1}{3}\bar{v} + \frac{2}{3}\bar{u}$ and $\frac{2}{3}\bar{v} + \frac{1}{3}\bar{u}$ *trisect* this line segment.

In summary, the vector description of the *line segment* connecting the terminal points of $\bar{u}$ and $\bar{v}$ is

$$\overline{w} = t\bar{v} + (1 - t)\bar{u}, \qquad 0 \le t \le 1$$

The rays R_1 and R_2 of Figure 4 have the respective descriptions

$$t\bar{v} + (1 - t)\bar{u}, \qquad t \le 0$$
$$t\bar{v} + (1 - t)\bar{u}, \qquad t \ge 1$$

This vector description of line segments and rays enables us to give simple proofs of many theorems of geometry. For example, the terminal

Figure 3

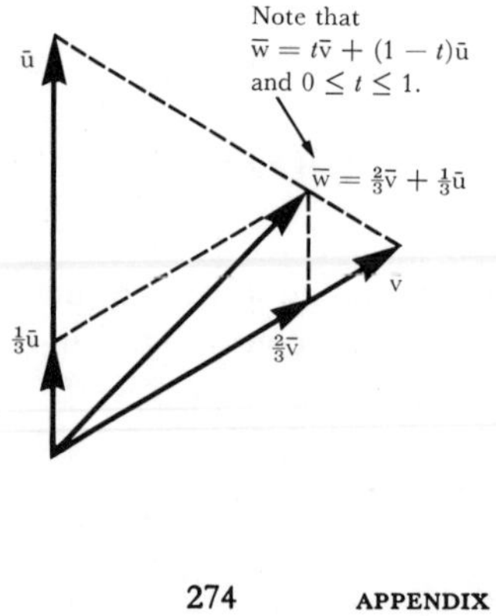

Figure 4

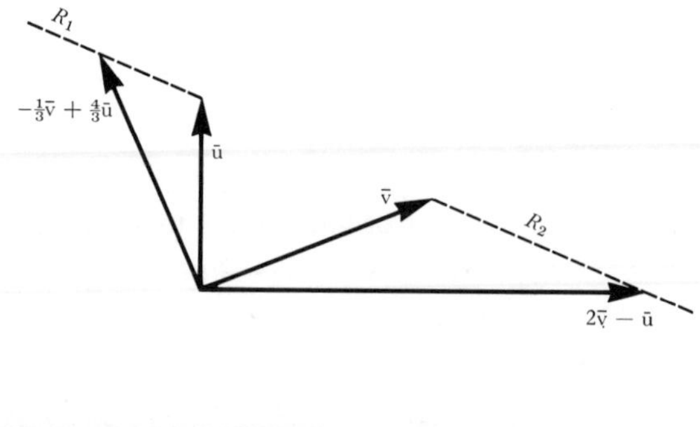

point of $\bar{w} = \frac{1}{2}\bar{v} + \frac{1}{2}\bar{u}$ bisects the line segment connecting the terminal points of $\bar{u}$ and $\bar{v}$. The vector $\bar{v} + \bar{u}$ is the diagonal of the parallelogram determined by $\bar{v}$ and $\bar{u}$. (*See* Figure 5.) Since we also have

$$\bar{w} = \tfrac{1}{2}(\bar{v} + \bar{u})$$

we see that the terminal point of $\bar{w}$ also bisects the vector $\bar{v} + \bar{u}$. This shows that the *diagonals of a parallelogram bisect each other.*

Figure 5

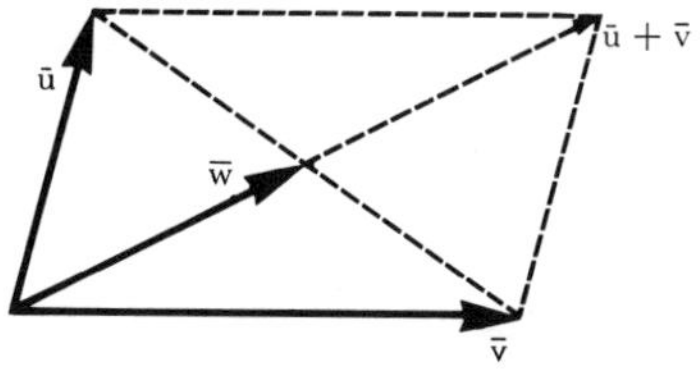

Parallelograms and Parallelopipeds

If $\bar{u}$ and $\bar{v}$ are not parallel, they determine a parallelogram, as shown in Figure 6.

The points inside or on this parallelogram are precisely the vectors of the form

10 $$s\bar{u} + t\bar{v} \quad \text{where} \quad 0 \le s \le 1, \quad 0 \le t \le 1$$

as shown in Figure 7. Thus relation **10** gives a description of the points of this parallelogram.

By the same token, the points of the parallelopiped determined by three independent vectors $\bar{u}$, $\bar{v}$, $\bar{w}$ (*see* Figure 8) are just the terminal points of

11 $$r\bar{u} + s\bar{v} + t\bar{w} \quad \text{with} \quad 0 \le r \le 1, \quad 0 \le s \le 1, \quad 0 \le t \le 1$$

Figure 6

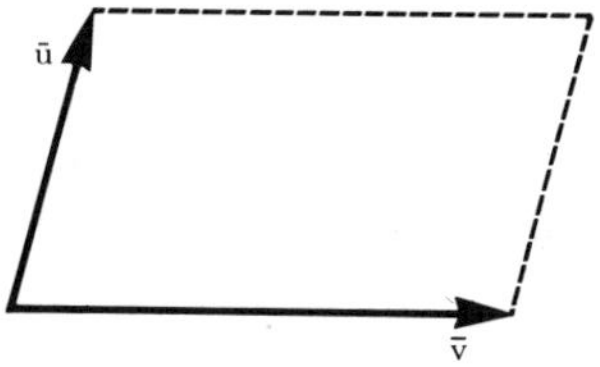

Figure 7 $\bar{w} = s\bar{u} + t\bar{v}$ with $0 < s < 1$. $0 < t < 1$, while $\bar{w}_1 = s\bar{u} + t\bar{v}$ with $t > 1$.

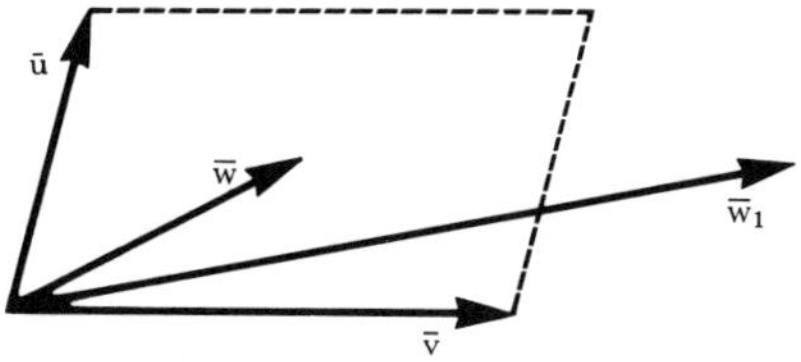

Figure 8

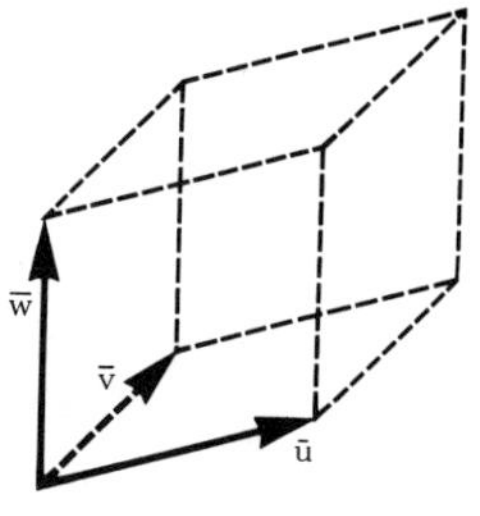

Planes

Suppose $\bar{n} = a\bar{i} + b\bar{j} + c\bar{k}$ is a nonzero vector. The plane through (x_0,y_0,z_0) which is *perpendicular* to $\bar{n}$ can be described as follows: A point (x,y,z) lies in this plane if and only if

$$(x - x_0)\bar{i} + (y - y_0)\bar{j} + (z - z_0)\bar{k}$$

is *orthogonal* to $\bar{n}$. (*See* Figure 9.)

Figure 9

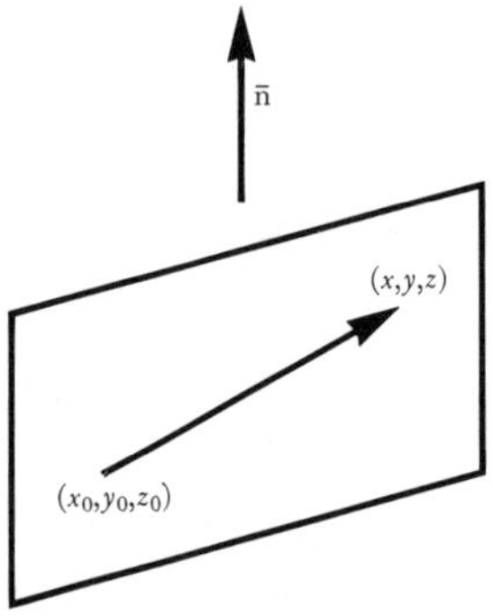

In other words, this plane consists of all points (x,y,z) such that

$$((x - x_0)\bar{i} + (y - y_0)\bar{j} + (z - z_0)\bar{k}) \cdot \bar{n} = 0$$

Calculating this dot product gives the equation

12 $$a(x - x_0) + b(y - y_0) + c(z - z_0) = 0$$

In summary, this must be a *Cartesian equation of the plane through* (x_0,y_0,z_0) *with normal vector* $a\bar{i} + b\bar{j} + c\bar{k}$.

This is often the most useful description of a plane. We can, however, also describe this plane as a translation of a subspace (which is a plane through the origin). For clearly the plane of equation **12** is parallel to the plane

13 $$ax + by + cz = 0$$

since these two planes have the same normal vector. The plane of equation **13** is just the null space of the matrix

$$[a \quad b \quad c]$$

Since, by assumption, $\bar{n} \neq \bar{0}$, at least one of a, b, and c is *not* zero. Thus, since this null space is two-dimensional, it is the subspace spanned by

$\bar{u} = (x_1,y_1,z_1)$ and $\bar{v} = (x_2,y_2,z_2)$, where the vectors $\bar{u}$ and $\bar{v}$ are independent solutions to equation **13**. In other words, the plane **13** consists of all vectors of the form $s\bar{u} + t\bar{v}$.

Put $\bar{w}_0 = (x_0,y_0,z_0)$. Then the plane of equation **12** consists of all vectors $\bar{w}$ of the form

14 $$\bar{w} = s\bar{u} + t\bar{v} + \bar{w}_0$$

With $\bar{w} = (x,y,z)$ we can express this equation in coordinate form:

15 $$\begin{aligned} x &= sx_1 + tx_2 + x_0 \\ y &= sy_1 + ty_2 + y_0 \\ z &= sz_1 + tz_2 + z_0 \end{aligned}$$

Equation **14** is known as a *vector equation* of the plane **12**, while the set of equations **15** is known as a *parametric form* of this plane with *parameters s and t*.

The cross product discussed in Example 4, Section 10, Chapter 1, is a useful tool in discussing planes. For example, if $\bar{u}$ and $\bar{v}$ are independent solutions to equation **13**, then $\bar{u} \times \bar{v}$ is normal to the plane of this equation and hence parallel to $\bar{n}$.

The plane through three noncollinear points $\bar{u}_1$, $\bar{u}_2$, and $\bar{u}_3$ can be described in several ways. We can directly substitute the coordinates of these three vectors for (x,y,z) in equation **12** and solve for a, b, and c in the resulting three equations; or we can use the fact that this plane passes through $\bar{u}_1$ and is parallel to the plane of $\bar{u}_1 - \bar{u}_2$ and $\bar{u}_1 - \bar{u}_3$ to obtain the vector description

$$\bar{w} = s(\bar{u}_1 - \bar{u}_2) + t(\bar{u}_1 - \bar{u}_3) + \bar{u}_1$$

Using the cross product we can obtain a normal vector and then use equation **12**, for the vectors $\bar{u}_1 - \bar{u}_2$ and $\bar{u}_1 - \bar{u}_3$ are parallel to this plane and consequently

$$\bar{n} = (\bar{u}_1 - \bar{u}_2) \times (\bar{u}_1 - \bar{u}_3)$$

is normal to the plane. For example, to describe the plane through (1,2,1), (−1,1,3), and (2,1,0) we find the normal

$$\begin{aligned} \bar{n} &= ((1,2,1) - (-1,1,3)) \times ((1,2,1) - (2,1,0)) \\ &= (2,1,-2) \times (-1,1,1) \\ &= (3,0,3) \end{aligned}$$

so that the equation of this plane is

$$3(x - 1) + 0(y - 2) + 3(z - 1) = 0.$$

Projection Methods

Projection methods are particularly useful in determining distances. For convenience we list here the projection formulas of Section 10, Chapter 1, page 82:

16 *The projection of* $\bar{u}$ *onto* $\bar{v}$ *is* $\dfrac{\bar{u}\cdot\bar{v}}{\bar{v}\cdot\bar{v}}\,\bar{v}$.

17 *The projection of* $\bar{u}$ *orthogonal to* $\bar{v}$ *is* $\bar{u} - \dfrac{\bar{u}\cdot\bar{v}}{\bar{v}\cdot\bar{v}}\,\bar{v}$.

These statements are used below, in a number of examples, to solve distance problems.

a *Distance from a point to a line.*

To find the distance from $(-5,-3)$ to the line L:

$$2x - y = 4$$

we first determine a vector parallel to this line. We can write this equation as

$$\frac{x}{1} = \frac{y+4}{2}$$

so that (from equation **5**) the vector $\bar{v} = \bar{i} + 2\bar{j}$ is parallel to this line. Furthermore $(0,-4)$ lies on this line.

The vector

$$\bar{u} = [0-(-5)]\bar{i} + [-4-(-3)]\bar{j} = 5\bar{i} + \bar{j}$$

connects $(-5,-3)$ to $(0,-4)$. Thus, the projection $\bar{w}$ of $\bar{u}$ orthogonal to $\bar{v}$ is perpendicular to L and can be drawn so as to connect $(-5,-3)$ to L, as shown in Figure 10.

Using formula **17** we have that

$$\begin{aligned}\bar{w} &= \bar{u} - \frac{\bar{u}\cdot\bar{v}}{\bar{v}\cdot\bar{v}}\,\bar{v}\\ &= 5\bar{i} - \bar{j} - \frac{(5-2)}{5}(\bar{i} + 2\bar{j})\\ &= \tfrac{22}{5}\bar{i} - \tfrac{11}{5}\bar{j}\end{aligned}$$

so our desired distance is

$$|\bar{w}| = \sqrt{(\tfrac{22}{5})^2 + (\tfrac{11}{5})^2} = \tfrac{11}{5}\sqrt{5}$$

Figure 10

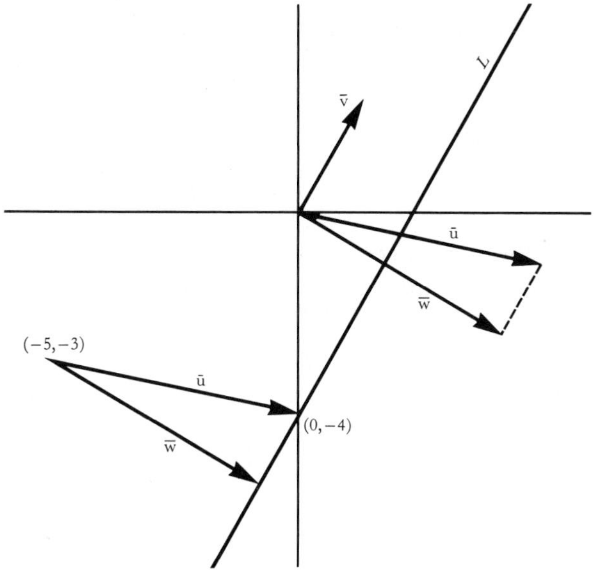

b *Distance from a point to a plane.*

To find the distance from (2,1,3) to the plane

$$x + 2y - 2z = 4$$

we note that $\bar{v} = \bar{i} + 2\bar{j} - 2\bar{k}$ is perpendicular to this plane (from equation **12**) and that (0,0,−2) lies in the plane. Thus

$$\begin{aligned}\bar{u} &= (0 - 2)\bar{i} + (0 - 1)\bar{j} + (-2 - 3)\bar{k} \\ &= -2\bar{i} - \bar{j} - 5\bar{k}\end{aligned}$$

connects (2,1,3) to (0,0,−2). The projection $\bar{w}$ of $\bar{u}$ *onto* $\bar{v}$ is normal to the plane and can be drawn so as to connect (2,1,3) to the plane. (*See* Figure 11.)

Figure 11

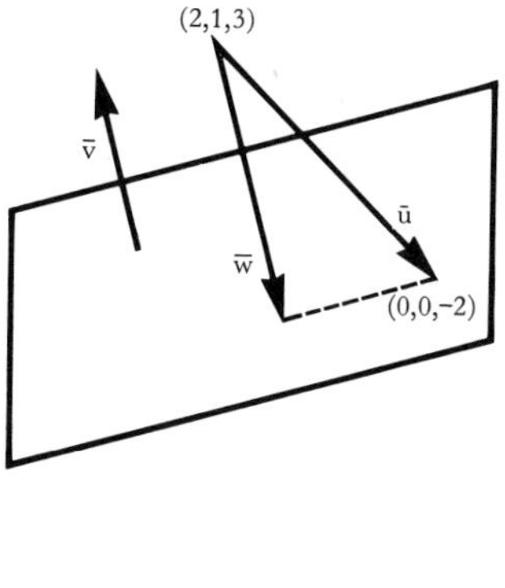

Formula **16** gives

$$\bar{w} = \frac{\bar{u} \cdot \bar{v}}{\bar{v} \cdot \bar{v}} \bar{v} = \tfrac{6}{9}\bar{v} = \tfrac{6}{9}\bar{i} + \tfrac{12}{9}\bar{j} - \tfrac{12}{9}\bar{k}$$

so our desired distance is

$$|\bar{w}| = \sqrt{(\tfrac{6}{9})^2 + (\tfrac{12}{9})^2 + (\tfrac{12}{9})^2} = 2$$

c *Distance between two planes.*

To find the distance between the two parallel planes

$$2x - 3y + 2z = 1 \qquad \text{and} \qquad 2x - 3y + 2z = 3$$

we note that $(0,0,\frac{1}{2})$ and $(0,0,\frac{3}{2})$, respectively, lie on these planes, so that

$$\bar{u} = (\tfrac{1}{2} - \tfrac{3}{2})\bar{k} = -\bar{k}$$

connects these two points. The normal to each plane is $\bar{v} = 2\bar{i} - 3\bar{j} + 2\bar{k}$; therefore, the desired distance is the length of the projection of $\bar{u}$ onto $\bar{v}$. This projection is

$$\bar{w} = \frac{\bar{u} \cdot \bar{v}}{\bar{v} \cdot \bar{v}} \bar{v} = \frac{-2}{17} \bar{v}$$

so our desired distance is

$$|\bar{w}| = \frac{2}{17} |\bar{v}| = \frac{2\sqrt{17}}{17}$$

d *Distance from a point to the intersection of two planes.*

The two planes

$$x + 2y - 3z = 0, \qquad x - 3y + z = -1$$

intersect in a line through (1,1,1). To find the distance from (−1,2,−1) to this line we need to find a vector which is parallel to this line so we can use the method of part **a** above. The respective normals are

$$\bar{n}_1 = \bar{i} + 2\bar{j} - 3\bar{k} \qquad \text{and} \qquad \bar{n}_2 = \bar{i} - 3\bar{j} + \bar{k}$$

so that $\bar{n}_1 \times \bar{n}_2$ is parallel to our line. Since

$$\begin{aligned} \bar{u} &= [1 - (-1)]\bar{i} + (1 - 2)\bar{j} + [1 - (-1)]\bar{k} \\ &= 2\bar{i} - \bar{j} + 2\bar{k} \end{aligned}$$

connects (−1,2,−1) to (1,1,1) our desired distance is just the length of the projection of $\bar{u}$ orthogonal to $\bar{n}_1 \times \bar{n}_2$.

We have

$$\bar{v} = \bar{n}_1 \times \bar{n}_2 = -7\bar{i} - 4\bar{j} - 5\bar{k}$$

$$\bar{u} - \frac{\bar{u} \cdot \bar{v}}{\bar{v} \cdot \bar{v}}\bar{v} = \frac{-4}{9}\bar{i} + \frac{17}{9}\bar{j} - \frac{8}{9}\bar{k}$$

so the distance is $\frac{1}{3}\sqrt{41}$.

Transformations

Suppose T is a linear transformation of R^2 into R^2, or of R^3 into R^3. We can use our descriptions of lines, line segments, and planes and the linearity property

18 $$T(a\bar{u} + b\bar{v}) = aT\bar{u} + bT\bar{v}$$

to show how applying T affects these geometric objects.

a *Linear transformations map lines and planes into lines and planes.*
Suppose T is a linear transformation from R^2 into R^2 and that

19 $$\bar{w} = t\bar{v} + \bar{u}_0$$

is the vector equation of the line through the terminal point of $\bar{u}_0$ which is parallel to $\bar{v}$. Then the linearity property **18** gives

20 $$T\bar{w} = tT\bar{v} + T\bar{u}_0$$

Thus, if $T\bar{v} = \bar{0}$, then T transforms the line **19** into the point $T\bar{u}_0$. If $T\bar{v} \neq \bar{0}$, then equation **20** shows that T transforms the line L of equation **19** into the line L' through the terminal point of $T\bar{u}_0$, which is parallel to $T\bar{v}$. Figures 12 and 13 illustrate two examples of this.

Figure 12 *T is counterclockwise rotation through $\pi/4$.*

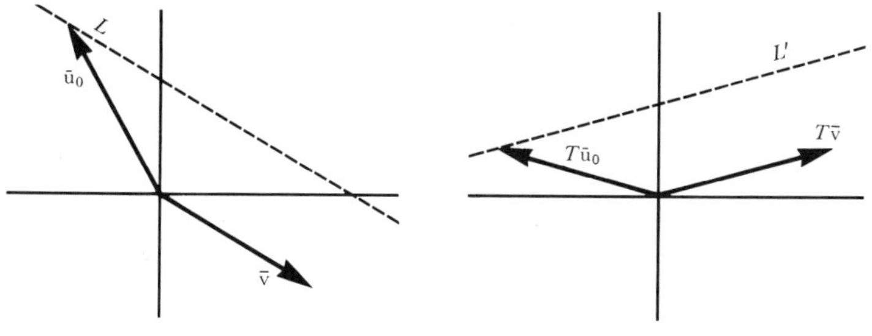

Figure 13 *T is projection onto $\bar{v}_1$, where $\bar{v} \cdot \bar{v}_1 = \bar{0}$, so that each vector from the origin to L is sent into $T\bar{u}_0$.*

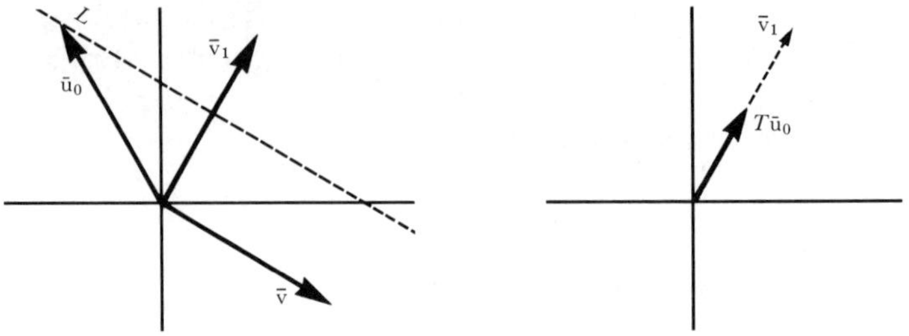

Suppose T is a linear transformation from R^3 into R^3. Just as in the above argument, T transforms the line

$$\bar{w} = t\bar{v} + \bar{u}_0$$

into $T\bar{u}_0$ (if $T\bar{v} = \bar{0}$) or onto the line $tT\bar{v}_0 + T\bar{u}_0$ (if $T\bar{v} \neq \bar{0}$).

The plane

$$\bar{w} = s\bar{u} + t\bar{v} + \bar{w}_0$$

is transformed into

$$T\bar{w} = sT\bar{u} + tT\bar{v} + T\bar{w}_0$$

If $T\bar{u}$ and $T\bar{v}$ are independent, this again is a plane. Otherwise, this is a line (if $T\bar{u}$ and $T\bar{v}$ are dependent but not both zero) or the single point $T\bar{w}_0$ (if $T\bar{u} = T\bar{v} = \bar{0}$).

b *Transformations of line segments, parallelograms, and parallelopipeds.* If T is a linear transformation, then T transforms the line segment

$$t\bar{v} + (1 - t)\bar{u}, \qquad 0 \leq t \leq 1$$

into the set

$$tT\bar{v} + (1 - t)T\bar{u}, \qquad 0 \leq t \leq 1$$

If $T\bar{v} \neq T\bar{u}$, this is just the line segment from $T\bar{v}$ to $T\bar{u}$. If $T\bar{v} = T\bar{u}$, then

$$tT\bar{v} + (1 - t)T\bar{u} = (t + (1 - t))T\bar{v} = T\bar{v}$$

Therefore, this set consists of the single point $T\bar{v}$.

The parallelogram (*see* relation **10**)

21 $$s\bar{u} + t\bar{v}, \qquad 0 \leq s \leq 1, \qquad 0 \leq t \leq 1$$

is transformed into the set

22 $$sT\bar{u} + tT\bar{v}, \qquad 0 \leq s \leq 1, \qquad 0 \leq t \leq 1$$

which is (if $T\bar{u}$ and $T\bar{v}$ are independent) the parallelogram determined by $T\bar{u}$ and $T\bar{v}$. If $T\bar{u}$ and $T\bar{v}$ are dependent, the set described by relation **22** is a line segment or a point. We often call these figures *degenerate parallelograms*. Figures 14, 15, and 16 indicate some of the possibilities. The transformation of Figure 16 is sometimes called a *shear*.

Figure 14 *Rotation through $\pi/4$ sends P onto P'.*

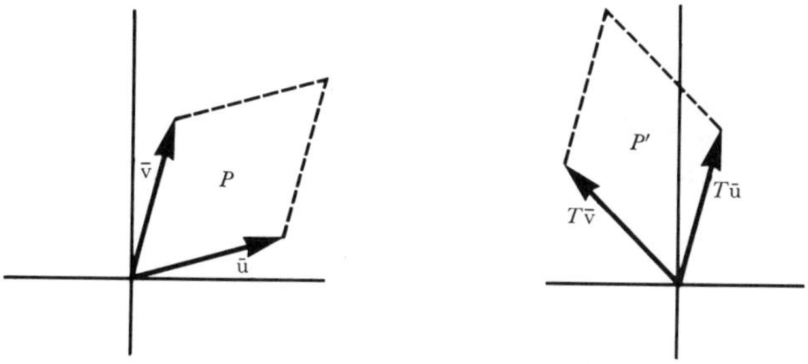

Figure 15 *Projection onto $\bar{w}$ sends P onto the line segment OA.*

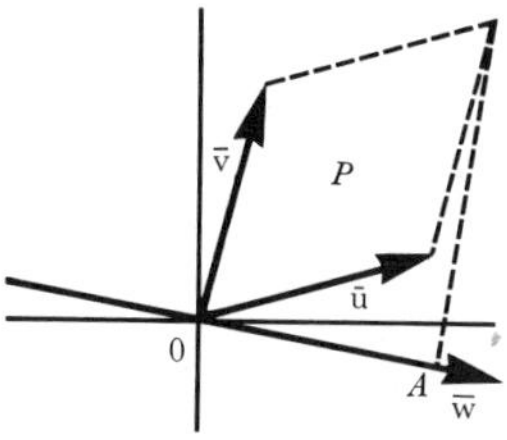

Figure 16 *If* $T\begin{bmatrix} x \\ y \end{bmatrix} = \begin{bmatrix} 1 & 1 \\ 0 & 1 \end{bmatrix}\begin{bmatrix} x \\ y \end{bmatrix}$, *then T transforms P onto P'.*

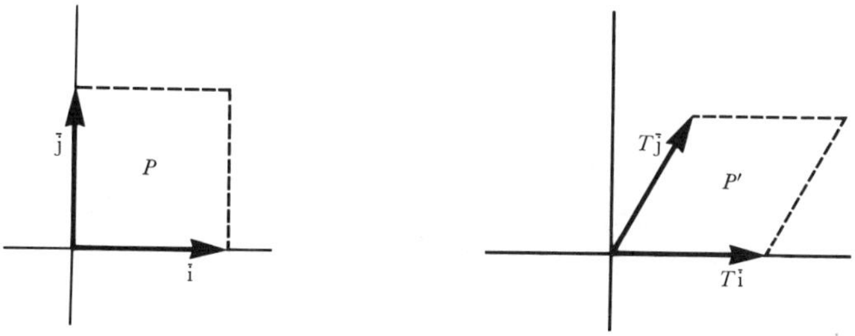

Analogous results show that if $\bar{u}$, $\bar{v}$, and $\bar{w}$ are independent vectors in R^3 and if T is linear, then T transforms the parallelopiped (*see* relation **11**)

$$r\bar{u} + s\bar{v} + t\bar{w}, \qquad 0 \leq r \leq 1, \qquad 0 \leq s \leq 1, \qquad 0 \leq t \leq 1$$

into the set

$$r T\bar{u} + s T\bar{v} + t T\bar{w}, \qquad 0 \le r \le 1, \qquad 0 \le s \le 1, \qquad 0 \le t \le 1$$

which is also a parallelopiped if $T\bar{u}$, $T\bar{v}$, and $T\bar{w}$ are independent.

c *Area and volume.*

Suppose $\bar{u} = (x_1,y_1)$, $\bar{v} = (x_2,y_2)$, and

$$B = \begin{bmatrix} x_1 & x_2 \\ y_1 & y_2 \end{bmatrix}$$

The area of the parallelogram determined by $\bar{u}$ and $\bar{v}$ is $|\det B|$. (*See* Example 6, Section 9, Chapter 2.)

Suppose T has the matrix

$$A = \begin{bmatrix} a & b \\ c & d \end{bmatrix}$$

so that $$T\bar{u} = \begin{bmatrix} ax_1 + by_1 \\ cx_1 + dy_1 \end{bmatrix} \qquad T\bar{v} = \begin{bmatrix} ax_2 + by_2 \\ cx_2 + dy_2 \end{bmatrix}$$

Since $$\begin{bmatrix} ax_1 + by_1 & ax_2 + by_2 \\ cx_1 + dy_1 & cx_2 + dy_2 \end{bmatrix} = AB$$

we see that the area of the parallelogram determined by $T\bar{u}$ and $T\bar{v}$ is $|\det AB|$.

Formula **10**, Section 9, Chapter 2, gives

$$\det AB = \det A \det B$$

so we know that

23 *The ratio of the area of the parallelogram determined by* $T\bar{u}$ *and* $T\bar{v}$ *to the area of the parallelogram determined by* $\bar{u}$ *and* $\bar{v}$ *is* $\det A$, *where* A *is the matrix of* T.

A corresponding result holds for ratios of the volumes of the parallelopipeds determined by $\bar{u}$, $\bar{v}$, and $\bar{w}$ and by $T\bar{u}$, $T\bar{v}$, and $T\bar{w}$.

Orthogonal Transformations

A linear transformation T from R^n into R^n is called an *orthogonal transformation* if its matrix A is an orthogonal matrix, that is, if $A^{-1} = A^t$.

(*See* Example 3, Section 8, Chapter 2.) If we let T^* denote the transformation whose matrix is A^t, then we can write $T\bar{u} = A\bar{u}$ and $T^*\bar{u} = A^t\bar{u}$ for all $\bar{u}$ in R^n. The condition that $A^t = A^{-1}$ is then the same as the condition that $T^* = T^{-1}$.

Suppose T is a counterclockwise rotation in R^2 through the angle θ. The matrices of T and T^* are thus respectively given by (*see* Example 3, Section 2, Chapter 2)

$$A = \begin{bmatrix} \cos\theta & -\sin\theta \\ \sin\theta & \cos\theta \end{bmatrix} \quad \text{and} \quad A^t = \begin{bmatrix} \cos\theta & \sin\theta \\ -\sin\theta & \cos\theta \end{bmatrix}$$

Since $\cos\theta = \cos(-\theta)$ and $\sin\theta = -\sin(-\theta)$, we see that A^t is the matrix of a counterclockwise rotation through the angle $-\theta$. That is, A^t is the matrix of T^{-1}. We therefore know that

24 *A rotation in R^2 is an orthogonal transformation.*

Suppose T is the linear transformation defined for $\bar{u}$ in R^2 by $T\bar{u} = A\bar{u}$ where

$$A = \begin{bmatrix} 0 & 1 \\ 1 & 0 \end{bmatrix}$$

Note that T is a reflection in the line $y = x$.

Since $A^t = A$ and $A^2 = I$ we see that A is an orthogonal matrix, that is,

Reflection in the line $y = x$ is an orthogonal transformation.

We have

$$\det\begin{bmatrix} 0 & 1 \\ 1 & 0 \end{bmatrix} = -1$$

$$\det\begin{bmatrix} \cos\theta & -\sin\theta \\ \sin\theta & \cos\theta \end{bmatrix} = \cos^2\theta + \sin^2\theta = 1$$

so that

25 *A rotation has determinant* 1 *and reflection in the line $y = x$ has determinant* -1.

We shall show that

26 *The determinant of an orthogonal matrix is* ± 1,

from which we shall be able to deduce a partial converse to the result **24**. Suppose $A^t = A^{-1}$ so that $A^tA = I$. We know that $\det I = 1$, $\det A = \det A^t$ (*see* Example 7, Section 9, Chapter 2) and $\det(A^tA) =$

det A^t det A (*see* equation **10**, Section 9, Chapter 2). Thus if $A^tA = I$, we must have $(\det A)^2 = 1$, and statement **26** is therefore true.

We now wish to prove that

27 *An orthogonal transformation of R^2 of determinant 1 is a rotation.*

Suppose T is an orthogonal transformation of determinant 1. We let

$$\bar{u}_1 = T\begin{bmatrix} 1 \\ 0 \end{bmatrix} = T\bar{i}, \qquad \bar{u}_2 = T\begin{bmatrix} 0 \\ 1 \end{bmatrix} = T\bar{j}$$

These are the columns of the matrix of T; and hence

$$\bar{u}_1 \cdot \bar{u}_1 = \bar{u}_2 \cdot \bar{u}_2 = 1 \qquad \bar{u}_1 \cdot \bar{u}_2 = 0$$

Suppose $\bar{u}_1$ is as shown in Figure 17. There are only the two possibilities for $\bar{u}_2$ shown in Figure 17, for $\bar{u}_2$ must be orthogonal to $\bar{u}_1$ and have the same length as $\bar{u}_1$.

Figure 17

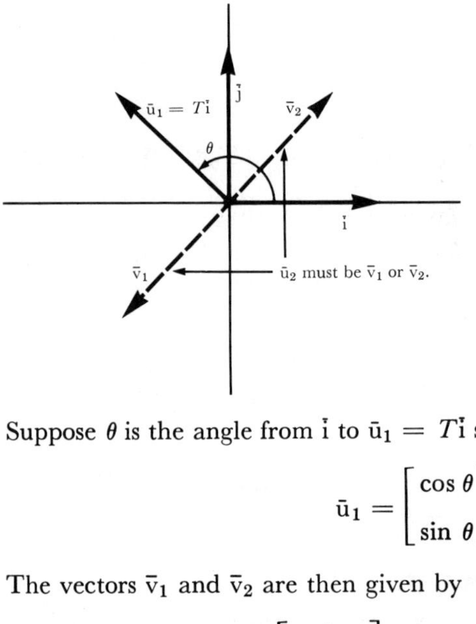

Suppose θ is the angle from $\bar{i}$ to $\bar{u}_1 = T\bar{i}$ so that (in column form)

$$\bar{u}_1 = \begin{bmatrix} \cos\theta \\ \sin\theta \end{bmatrix}$$

The vectors $\bar{v}_1$ and $\bar{v}_2$ are then given by

$$\bar{v}_1 = \begin{bmatrix} -\sin\theta \\ \cos\theta \end{bmatrix}, \qquad \bar{v}_2 = \begin{bmatrix} \sin\theta \\ -\cos\theta \end{bmatrix}$$

(as seen from Figure 17).

Since

$$\det\begin{bmatrix}\cos\theta & \sin\theta\\ \sin\theta & -\cos\theta\end{bmatrix} = -(\cos^2\theta + \sin^2\theta) = -1$$

we cannot have $\bar{u}_2 = \bar{v}_2$. Thus we must have $\bar{u}_2 = \bar{v}_1$, which shows that the matrix of T must be

$$\begin{bmatrix}\cos\theta & -\sin\theta\\ \sin\theta & \cos\theta\end{bmatrix}$$

that is, T is a counterclockwise rotation through the angle θ. Statement **27** is therefore proved. A characterization of orthogonal transformations of R^2 of determinant -1 is given in the exercises. There are references to characterizations of orthogonal transformations in R^3 in the bibliography.

EXERCISES

Equations of Lines

1 Find a vector form for the line through (2,1) parallel to $\bar{i} - 3\bar{j}$.

2 Find a vector form for the line $2x + 5y = 7$. (Hint: Express this equation in the form **4**.)

3 Find a vector form for the line through $(1,-5)$ which is perpendicular to $2\bar{i} - \bar{j}$.

4 Find Cartesian equations for the line through (0,1,0) parallel to $\bar{i} - 2\bar{j} + \bar{k}$.

5 Find a parametric description of the line through (0,1,2) and $(-1,5,1)$.

6 Find Cartesian equations for the line through $(2,-1,3)$ which is perpendicular to $\bar{v}_1 = \bar{i} - \bar{j} + \bar{k}$ and $\bar{v}_2 = 3\bar{i} - 2\bar{j} - \bar{k}$.

Line Segments

7 Describe in vector form the line segment from $(3,-1,2)$ to (5,7,7).

8 What does $\bar{w} = t(1,2) + (1-t)(3,-1)$ with $t \geq 5$ describe?

9 Describe the vectors of the form $s\bar{u} + t\bar{v}$, where $s + t = 1$.

10 Find the points that divide the segment from $(-1,2,1)$ to $(3,1,-1)$ into five equal parts.

Parallelograms and Parallelopipeds

11 Describe in vector form the points of the parallelogram determined by the four vertices (1,0,0), (0,1,0), (0,0,1), $(-2,1,1)$.

12 What point set does

$$s\bar{u} + t\bar{v}, \qquad 0 \leq s \leq 1, \qquad 0 \leq t \leq 1, \qquad s + t \leq 1$$

describe?

13 Give a vector description of the triangle with vertices (1,2,1), (2,−1,1), (1,−1,0).

14 Use vector methods to prove each of the following:

a The diagonals of a parallelogram are perpendicular if and only if the parallelogram is a rhombus.

b The diagonals of a parallelogram have equal length if and only if the parallelogram is a rectangle.

c The altitudes of a triangle meet in a point. (Hint: Express the sides as $\bar{u}$, $\bar{v}$, $\bar{v} - \bar{u}$ and use projection to find the altitudes.)

d The lines from each vertex of a triangle to the midpoint of the opposite side meet in a point.

Planes

15 Find an equation for the plane through (1,2,1) perpendicular to $2\bar{i} - \bar{j} - \bar{k}$.

16 Find a normal vector to the plane

$$2x - 3y + 4z = 1$$

17 Find a vector equation for the plane of Exercise 16.

18 Find in *two* ways a Cartesian equation for the plane through (2,1,0), (−1,1,0), (3,1,1).

19 Find an equation for the plane through (−1,1,1) that is perpendicular to the line of intersection of $x - 2y + 2z = 1$ and $3x - z = 4$.

20 Find a plane through (6,1,2) that is parallel to the plane $x - 3y + 2z = 1$.

21 Show that the line

$$\frac{x+1}{3} = \frac{y}{4} = \frac{z-2}{5}$$

is perpendicular to the plane $3x + 4y + 5z = 10$ and parallel to the plane $5x + 5y - 7z = 1$.

22 Find the point of intersection of the lines

$$\frac{x}{3} = \frac{y}{4} = \frac{z-2}{4} \quad \text{and} \quad x - 1 = \frac{y+4}{-4} = \frac{z}{-2}$$

23 Find the plane determined by the lines of Exercise 22.

Projection Methods

24 Find the distance from (2,1) to $x + 5y = 3$.

25 Find the distance from (3,1,−1) to the line $\dfrac{x-1}{2} = \dfrac{y+1}{3} = \dfrac{z-1}{5}$.

26 Find the distance from (3,1,−1) to the line through (0,1,3) which is parallel to the line of intersection of $x - y + z = 1$, $2x + y = 0$.

27 Find the distance from $(-1,1,2)$ to the line $\bar{w} = t(2,1,1) + (3,1,0)$.

28 Find the distance from $(1,2,-1)$ to the line through $(-1,1,1)$, and $(0,0,1)$.

29 Find the distance from the origin to $2x + y - 3z = 4$.

30 Find the distance between the two parallel lines

$$\frac{x-1}{2} = \frac{y+1}{3} = \frac{z}{4}, \qquad \frac{x}{2} = \frac{y-2}{3} = \frac{z+1}{4}$$

31 Find the distance between the two *skew* lines

$$\frac{x-1}{2} = \frac{y+1}{3} = \frac{z}{4}, \qquad x = y = z - 1$$

(Hint: Find a point on each and a vector orthogonal to each line.)

32 Find the distance between the two planes

$$2x + y + z = 4 \quad \text{and} \quad 2x + y + z = 8.$$

33 Find the distance from the point $(2,-1,1)$ to the intersection of

$$x + y + z = 1 \quad \text{and} \quad x - y + 2z = 0$$

Transformations

34 Suppose $T\bar{u} = \begin{bmatrix} 2 & 1 \\ 1 & 1 \end{bmatrix} \bar{u}$. Into what does T transform the parallelogram determined by $(1,-2)$ and $(3,-1)$?

35 Suppose $T\bar{u} = \begin{bmatrix} 1 & 1 \\ 0 & 1 \end{bmatrix} \bar{u}$. Graph the set of points $tT\bar{v} + T\bar{u}_0$, where

$$\bar{v} = \begin{bmatrix} 3 \\ 1 \end{bmatrix}, \qquad \bar{u}_0 = \begin{bmatrix} -1 \\ 0 \end{bmatrix}$$

36 Show that a rotation preserves the lengths of vectors and the angles between vectors. (Hint: Use the fact that $A\bar{u} \cdot A\bar{v} = \bar{u} \cdot A^tA\bar{v}$ and that $A^t = A^{-1}$ if A is the matrix of a rotation.)

37 Show that if T is linear and $T\bar{u}$ and $T\bar{v}$ are independent, then T maps the triangle Δ, with sides $\bar{u}$, $\bar{v}$, $\bar{v} - \bar{u}$, into a triangle Δ_1. Does T map points inside Δ into points inside Δ_1? (Hint: Describe points inside Δ as sums of certain kinds of multiples of $\bar{u}$ and $\bar{v}$.)

38 Suppose $\det A = 1$. Show that if $T\bar{u} = A\bar{u}$, then T preserves areas of parallelograms.

39 Show that rotations preserve area. What about reflections? projections?

40 Find the area of the parallelogram of Exercise 11. Also, for

$$T\bar{u} = \begin{bmatrix} 1 & 2 & 1 \\ 0 & 1 & 1 \\ 0 & 1 & 3 \end{bmatrix} \bar{u}$$

find the area of the transform of this parallelogram by T.

41 Suppose T is an invertible linear transformation from R^2 into R^2. Show that if $\bar{u}$ and $\bar{v}$ are independent, then $T\bar{u}$ and $T\bar{v}$ are also independent, by using result **23**. Use this same result to show that if T is not invertible and $\bar{u}$ and $\bar{v}$ are independent, then $T\bar{u}$ and $T\bar{v}$ must be dependent. (Hint: The parallelogram determined by $T\bar{u}$ and $T\bar{v}$ is not degenerate if and only if these vectors are independent.)

Orthogonal Transformations

42 Suppose $\bar{u}$ and $\bar{v}$ are orthonormal vectors in R_2. Show that there is an orthogonal linear transformation T from R^2 into R^2 such that $T\bar{i} = \bar{u}$ and $T\bar{j} = \bar{v}$.

43 Suppose $\bar{u}_1, \bar{u}_2$ and $\bar{v}_1, \bar{v}_2$ are each orthonormal sets in R^2. Let A be the matrix with columns $\bar{u}_1$ and $\bar{u}_2$ and B the matrix with columns $\bar{v}_1$ and $\bar{v}_2$. Suppose $\det A = \det B$. Show that there is a rotation T such that $T\bar{u}_1 = \bar{v}_1$ and $T\bar{u}_2 = \bar{v}_2$. (Hint: Use Exercise 42 to find orthogonal transformations T_1 and T_2 such that $T_1\bar{i} = \bar{u}_1$, $T_1\bar{j} = \bar{u}_2$, $T_2\bar{i} = \bar{v}_1$, and $T_2\bar{j} = \bar{v}_2$. Then show that $T = T_2 T_1{}^{-1}$ is a rotation.)

44 Suppose B is an orthogonal matrix of determinant -1 and that

$$A = \begin{bmatrix} 0 & 1 \\ 1 & 0 \end{bmatrix}$$

Put $C = AB$.

a What is $\det C$?

b How is C related to B?

c Show that $B = AC$.

d Use these facts to prove that an orthogonal transformation of R^2 of determinant -1 must be a rotation followed by a reflection in the line $y = x$.

e Replace A by $\quad A = \begin{bmatrix} -1 & 0 \\ 0 & 1 \end{bmatrix}$

and use similar arguments to show that an orthogonal transformation of R^2 of determinant -1 must be a rotation followed by a reflection in the y-axis.

f Suppose the matrix of T is

$$\begin{bmatrix} \sqrt{3}/2 & 1/2 \\ 1/2 & -\sqrt{3}/2 \end{bmatrix}$$

Express T as a rotation followed by a reflection in the line $y = x$. Also express T as a rotation followed by a reflection in the y-axis.

45 Suppose T is a reflection in R^2 in the line through $\overline{w}$. Show that T is an orthogonal transformation of determinant -1.

46 Show that an orthogonal transformation in R^2 preserves the area of parallelograms.

APPENDIX 2

DIMENSION THEORY

We have purposely remained at a fairly elementary level in this book, omitting many proofs and giving other proofs only for low-dimensional cases. To progress further in the study of linear algebra the student must become familiar with certain theoretical techniques as well as with notational devices for treating higher dimensions. To assist in this development we shall present in this appendix proofs of the results about bases stated in Section 9 of Chapter 1. The techniques developed will then also be used to prove some theorems about linear operators, including various results about inverses, characteristic vectors, and null spaces that have been used in this book.

Summation Notation

For convenience in our discussion of dimension we first present a notation for linear combinations which is commonly used. This notation is more compact than the notation

$$c_1\bar{\mathrm{u}}_1 + c_2\bar{\mathrm{u}}_2 + \cdots + c_n\bar{\mathrm{u}}_n$$

which we used previously, and it will greatly simplify our discussions. The usual abbreviation for this sum is

$$\sum_{i=1}^{n} c_i\bar{\mathrm{u}}_i$$

For example,

$$\sum_{i=1}^{3} c_i\bar{\mathrm{u}}_i = c_1\bar{\mathrm{u}}_1 + c_2\bar{\mathrm{u}}_2 + c_3\bar{\mathrm{u}}_3$$

and

$$\sum_{i=1}^{7} d_i\bar{\mathrm{v}}_i = d_1\bar{\mathrm{v}}_1 + d_2\bar{\mathrm{v}}_2 + d_3\bar{\mathrm{v}}_3 + d_4\bar{\mathrm{v}}_4 + d_5\bar{\mathrm{v}}_5 + d_6\bar{\mathrm{v}}_6 + d_7\bar{\mathrm{v}}_7$$

The letter i is a dummy index and can be replaced by any other letter not already in use. For example, we could write

$$\sum_{j=1}^{n} c_j\bar{\mathrm{u}}_j \quad \text{or} \quad \sum_{k=1}^{n} c_k\bar{\mathrm{u}}_k \quad \text{rather than} \quad \sum_{i=1}^{n} c_i\bar{\mathrm{u}}_i$$

We will sometimes encounter a sum such as

$$c_2\bar{\mathrm{u}}_2 + c_3\bar{\mathrm{u}}_3 + \cdots + c_n\bar{\mathrm{u}}_n$$

in which case we will use the symbol

$$\sum_{i=2}^{n} c_i\bar{u}_i \qquad \text{or} \qquad \sum_{j=2}^{n} c_j\bar{u}_j$$

As further examples of this we have

$$\sum_{i=2}^{4} d_i\bar{v}_i = d_2\bar{v}_2 + d_3\bar{v}_3 + d_4\bar{v}_4$$

$$\sum_{j=6}^{9} a_j\bar{u}_j = a_6\bar{u}_6 + a_7\bar{u}_7 + a_8\bar{u}_8 + a_9\bar{u}_9$$

The following rules for manipulating with summation can be shown to be true:

1

a $\sum_{i=1}^{n} c_i\bar{u}_i + \sum_{i=1}^{n} d_i\bar{u}_i = \sum_{i=1}^{n} (c_i + d_i)\bar{u}_i$

b $a\sum_{i=1}^{n} c_i\bar{u}_i = \sum_{i=1}^{n} ac_i\bar{u}_i$

The proof of part **b**, for example, proceeds as follows:

$$\begin{aligned} a\sum_{i=1}^{n} c_i\bar{u}_i &= a(c_1\bar{u}_1 + c_2\bar{u}_2 + \cdots + c_n\bar{u}_n) \\ &= (ac_1)\bar{u}_1 + (ac_2)\bar{u}_2 + \cdots + (ac_n)\bar{u}_n \\ &= \sum_{i=1}^{n} ac_i\bar{u}_i \end{aligned}$$

The definitions of linear combination, independence, dependence, spanning, and basis can be restated in terms of this summation notation and are summarized as follows:

a $\bar{u}$ *is a* linear combination *of* $\bar{u}_1, \bar{u}_2, \ldots, \bar{u}_n$ *if we can find scalars* $c_1, c_2, \ldots, c_n$ *such that* $\bar{u} = \sum_{i=1}^{n} c_i\bar{u}_i$.

b $\bar{u}_1, \bar{u}_2, \ldots, \bar{u}_n$ *are* independent *if the relation* $\sum_{i=1}^{n} c_i\bar{u}_i = \bar{0}$ *necessarily implies that* $c_1 = c_2 = \cdots = c_n = 0$.

2 **c** $\bar{u}_1, \bar{u}_2, \ldots, \bar{u}_n$ *are* dependent *if we can find scalars* $c_1, c_2, \ldots, c_n$, *not all zero, such that* $\sum_{i=1}^{n} c_i\bar{u}_i = \bar{0}$.

d $\bar{u}_1, \bar{u}_2, \ldots, \bar{u}_n$ span *the vector space V if every vector in V is a linear combination of* $\bar{u}_1, \bar{u}_2, \ldots, \bar{u}_n$.

e $\bar{u}_1, \bar{u}_2, \ldots, \bar{u}_n$ *are a* basis *for V if they are independent and span V.*

We gave a somewhat different definition of basis in Section 8 of Chapter 1, but then showed, in the case $n = 2$, that the definition was the same as that given here. The student is asked to give a complete proof of this equivalence in Exercise 6, below.

As an example of the use of this summation notation we give a complete proof of the following statement: (*See* statement **11**, Section 7, Chapter 1.)

3 *The vectors* $\bar{u}_1, \bar{u}_2, \ldots, \bar{u}_n$ *are dependent if and only if one of them is a linear combination of the others.*

For suppose that $\bar{u}_1, \bar{u}_2, \ldots, \bar{u}_n$ are dependent. It is then possible to find $c_1, c_2, \ldots, c_n$, not all zero, such that

$$\sum_{i=1}^{n} c_i\bar{u}_i = \bar{0}.$$

By relabeling, if necessary, we can suppose that $c_1 \neq 0$. We then have

$$(-c_1)\bar{u}_1 = \sum_{i=2}^{n} c_i\bar{u}_i$$

so that dividing by $-c_1$ and using property **1b** gives

$$\bar{u}_1 = \sum_{i=2}^{n} (-c_i/c_1)\bar{u}_i$$

This expresses $\bar{u}_1$ as a linear combination of $\bar{u}_2, \bar{u}_3, \ldots, \bar{u}_n$.

Conversely, suppose one of the $\bar{u}_i$ is a linear combination of the others. Again we can relabel, if necessary, in order to assume that $\bar{u}_1$ is a linear combination of $\bar{u}_2, \bar{u}_3, \ldots, \bar{u}_n$. Thus we can find $d_2, d_3, \ldots, d_n$ such that

$$\bar{u}_1 = \sum_{i=2}^{n} d_i\bar{u}_i$$

With $c_2 = -d_2$, $c_3 = -d_3, \ldots, c_n = -d_n$, and $c_1 = 1$, we can rewrite this as

$$\sum_{i=1}^{n} c_i\bar{u}_i = \bar{0}$$

Since at least one of $c_1, c_2, \ldots, c_n$ is not zero (for $c_1 = 1$), we can conclude that $\bar{u}_1, \bar{u}_2, \ldots, \bar{u}_n$ are dependent and thus complete the proof of statement **3**.

With the aid of this new notation we now proceed to the central dimension theorems.

A Technical Result about Independence

We first prove a fairly technical result about independence which will be one of our primary tools for discussing dimension. This result will be referred to as a *lemma*, a common name for theorems that are useful tools for obtaining further results.

LEMMA 1 Suppose $\bar{u}_1, \bar{u}_2, \ldots, \bar{u}_n$ span the vector space V and that $\bar{v}_1, \bar{v}_2, \ldots, \bar{v}_k$ is an independent set in V. Then *k cannot exceed n.*

Exercise 7, below, shows how this statement can be deduced from Theorem 1. We give an alternative proof that involves a method of substitution. A by-product of this proof is another proof of Theorem 1 that does not involve the method of matrix reduction. (*See* Exercise 8, below.)

We suppose that $\bar{u}_1, \bar{u}_2, \ldots, \bar{u}_n$ and $\bar{v}_1, \bar{v}_2, \ldots, \bar{v}_k$ are as given in Lemma 1. Since $\bar{u}_1, \bar{u}_2, \ldots, \bar{u}_n$ span V, we can find numbers $a_1, a_2, \ldots, a_n$ such that

$$\bar{v}_1 = a_1\bar{u}_1 + a_2\bar{u}_2 + \cdots + a_n\bar{u}_n$$

The vector $\bar{v}_1$ is not zero, for no independent set can contain the zero vector. (*See* Exercise 9.) Thus, at least one of the coefficients a_i is not zero. We can suppose that $a_1 \neq 0$ (otherwise we relabel so that this is so). We can then solve for $\bar{u}_1$ to obtain

4 $$\bar{u}_1 = (1/a_1)\bar{v}_1 + \sum_{i=2}^{n} (-a_i/a_1)\bar{u}_i$$

We also know that we can find $b_1, b_2, \ldots, b_n$ such that

$$\bar{v}_2 = \sum_{i=1}^{n} b_i\bar{u}_i$$

again using the assumption that $\bar{u}_1, \bar{u}_2, \ldots, \bar{u}_n$ span V. We now substitute in the relation **4** to obtain a relation of the form

5 $$\bar{v}_2 = c_1\bar{v}_1 + \sum_{i=2}^{n} c_i\bar{u}_i$$

We have, of course, changed notation by putting

$$c_1 = -b_1/a_1 \qquad \text{and} \qquad c_i = b_i - b_1a_i/a_1 \qquad \text{for } i > 1.$$

We observe that we must have $n \geq 2$, and we cannot have

$$\sum_{i=2}^{n} c_i\bar{u}_i = \bar{0}$$

for then relation **5** would give $\bar{v}_2 = c_1\bar{v}_1$, which from statement **3**, would contradict the assumption that $\bar{v}_1, \bar{v}_2, \ldots, \bar{v}_k$ are independent. Thus, at least one of the numbers $c_2, c_3, \ldots, c_k$ is not zero. We can therefore suppose that $c_2 \neq 0$ (otherwise we relabel so that this is so). We can then rewrite relation **5** as

6 $$\bar{u}_2 = (-c_1/c_2)\bar{v}_1 + (1/c_2)\bar{v}_2 + \sum_{i=3}^{n} (-c_i/c_2)\bar{u}_i$$

The vector $\bar{v}_3$ is a linear combination of $\bar{u}_1, \bar{u}_2, \ldots, \bar{u}_n$, since these span V, so we can write

$$\bar{v}_3 = \sum_{i=1}^{n} d_i\bar{u}_i$$

Replacing $\bar{u}_1$ by its expression **4** and then replacing $\bar{u}_2$ by its expression **6**, we obtain (after changing the notation for the coefficients)

7 $$\bar{v}_3 = e_1\bar{v}_1 + e_2\bar{v}_2 + \sum_{i=3}^{n} e_i\bar{u}_i$$

We again conclude that n is at least 3 and that we cannot have

$$\sum_{i=3}^{n} e_i\bar{u}_i = \bar{0}$$

For, otherwise, equation **7** would be

$$\bar{v}_3 = e_1\bar{v}_1 + e_2\bar{v}_2$$

which would contradict the assumption that $\bar{v}_1, \bar{v}_2, \ldots, \bar{v}_k$ are independent.

Proceeding in this manner we can then (if k is at least 4) obtain for $\bar{v}_4$ the expression

8 $$\bar{v}_4 = f_1\bar{v}_1 + f_2\bar{v}_2 + f_3\bar{v}_3 + \sum_{i=4}^{n} f_i\bar{u}_i$$

where again we must have $n \geq 4$ and

$$\sum_{i=4}^{n} f_i\bar{u}_i \neq \bar{0}$$

We can continue this substitution and relabeling process, each time concluding that n is at least as large as k. We are forced to conclude that indeed k cannot exceed n. This completes the proof of Lemma 1.

A Proof of Theorem 9

Lemma 1 can now be used to give a simple proof of Theorem 9, which is restated as follows:

THEOREM 9 If $\bar{u}_1, \bar{u}_2, \ldots, \bar{u}_n$ are a basis for V, then any other basis for V contains exactly n vectors.

Suppose $\bar{u}_1, \bar{u}_2, \ldots, \bar{u}_n$ and $\bar{v}_1, \bar{v}_2, \ldots, \bar{v}_k$ are both bases for V. Therefore we know in particular that $\bar{u}_1, \bar{u}_2, \ldots, \bar{u}_n$ span V and that $\bar{v}_1, \bar{v}_2, \ldots, \bar{v}_k$ are independent. Lemma 1 then implies that $k \leq n$. We also know that $\bar{v}_1, \bar{v}_2, \ldots, \bar{v}_k$ span V and that $\bar{u}_1, \bar{u}_2, \ldots, \bar{u}_n$ are independent (because both sets are assumed to be bases for V). Applying Lemma 1 again shows that $n \leq k$ and completes the proof of Theorem 9.

If there is a finite set of vectors that is a basis for V we say that V is *finite dimensional*. The number of vectors in such a basis is called the *dimension* of V. Theorem 9 tells us that the dimension of V does not depend upon the basis chosen.

Other Technical Results about Independence

Before proving Theorem 10 we introduce further technical results concerning independence.

LEMMA 2 If $\bar{v}_1, \bar{v}_2, \ldots, \bar{v}_k$ are independent vectors which *do not* span the vector space V, there is a vector $\bar{v}$ in V such that $\bar{v}_1, \bar{v}_2, \ldots, \bar{v}_k, \bar{v}$ is also independent.

For suppose $\bar{v}_1, \bar{v}_2, \ldots, \bar{v}_k$ are independent but do not span V. Then there must be at least one vector $\bar{v}$ in V such that

9 $\bar{v}$ *is not a linear combination of* $\bar{v}_1, \bar{v}_2, \ldots, \bar{v}_k$.

Choose such a $\bar{v}$. We shall show that the vectors $\bar{v}_1, \bar{v}_2, \ldots, \bar{v}_k$ and $\bar{v}$ are independent. For suppose

$$c\bar{v} + \sum_{i=1}^{k} c_i\bar{v}_i = \bar{0}$$

We shall show that we must have $c = c_1 = c_2 = \cdots = c_k = 0$. If $c \neq 0$, this equation can be rewritten to obtain

$$\bar{v} = \sum_{i=1}^{k} (-c_i/c)\bar{v}_i$$

which would contradict property **9**. Therefore we must have $c = 0$. This gives

$$\sum_{i=1}^{k} c_i \bar{v}_i = \bar{0}$$

and thus the assumed independence of $\bar{v}_1, \bar{v}_2, \ldots, \bar{v}_k$ necessarily entails that $c_1 = c_2 = \cdots = c_k = 0$. This completes the proof of Lemma 2.

Our second result is

LEMMA 3 Suppose $n \geq 1$, and $\bar{v}_1, \bar{v}_2, \ldots, \bar{v}_n$ span the vector space V and are *not* independent. The dimension of V, then, is *smaller* than n.

If all the $\bar{v}_i$'s are zero, then V consists only of the zero vector, and this result is certainly true. We will suppose, then, that at least one of the $\bar{v}_i$'s is not zero and, hence, independent. We are also assuming that $\bar{v}_1, \bar{v}_2, \ldots, \bar{v}_n$ are dependent. Therefore, if k is the largest integer with the property that at least k of the vectors $\bar{v}_1, \bar{v}_2, \ldots, \bar{v}_n$ are *independent*, we must have $1 \leq k < n$.

We can relabel, if necessary, so that we can suppose that

10 $\bar{v}_1, \bar{v}_2, \ldots, \bar{v}_k$ are independent.

From the definition of k we then know that the vectors $\bar{v}_1, \bar{v}_2, \ldots, \bar{v}_k, \bar{v}_{k+1}$ are dependent. Therefore, numbers $c_1, c_2, \ldots, c_k, c_{k+1}$, *not* all zero, can be found such that

$$\sum_{i=1}^{k+1} c_i \bar{v}_i = \bar{0}$$

We cannot have $c_{k+1} = 0$, for it would then follow that

$$\sum_{i=1}^{k} c_i \bar{v}_i = \bar{0}$$

and, therefore, assumption **10** would require that $c_1 = c_2 = \cdots = c_k = 0$ also hold. Therefore we must have $c_{k+1} \neq 0$, and hence we can solve for $\bar{v}_{k+1}$ to obtain

$$\bar{v}_{k+1} = \sum_{i=1}^{k} (-c_i/c_{k+1})\bar{v}_i$$

Similar arguments can be used to show that each of the vectors

$$\bar{v}_{k+2}, \bar{v}_{k+3}, \ldots, \bar{v}_n$$

can be expressed as linear combinations of the $\bar{v}_1, \bar{v}_2, \ldots, \bar{v}_k$. Thus in any relation of the form

11 $$\bar{u} = \sum_{i=1}^{n} a_i \bar{v}_i$$

the expressions of $\bar{v}_{k+1}, \bar{v}_{k+2}, \ldots, \bar{v}_n$ as linear combinations of $\bar{v}_1, \bar{v}_2, \ldots, \bar{v}_k$ can be substituted to obtain a relation of the form (after suitable notation change for the coefficients)

12 $$\bar{u} = \sum_{i=1}^{k} b_i \bar{v}_i$$

By assumption, every vector in V can be written in the form **11** and hence also in the form **12**. In other words, the vectors $\bar{v}_1, \bar{v}_2, \ldots, \bar{v}_k$ *must span* V. Therefore, they are an independent set that spans V and consequently are a basis for V. We conclude that V has dimension k, and since k is smaller than n, we have completed the proof of Lemma 3.

Another useful result has also been obtained in this proof:

LEMMA 4 If $\bar{v}_1, \bar{v}_2, \ldots, \bar{v}_n$ are not independent, they can be relabeled so that $\bar{v}_1, \bar{v}_2, \ldots, \bar{v}_k$ are independent and each of the vectors $\bar{v}_{k+1}, \bar{v}_{k+2}, \ldots, \bar{v}_n$ is a linear combination of $\bar{v}_1, \bar{v}_2, \ldots, \bar{v}_k$.

A Proof of Theorem 10

THEOREM 10 A set with n vectors in a space V of dimension n is independent if and only if it spans V.

Suppose V has dimension n, and, therefore, there is a basis $\bar{u}_1, \bar{u}_2, \ldots, \bar{u}_n$ for V. Suppose $\bar{v}_1, \bar{v}_2, \ldots, \bar{v}_n$ is an independent set in V. If this set does not span V, we can apply Lemma 2 to find a vector $\bar{v}$ in V such that $\bar{v}_1, \bar{v}_2, \ldots, \bar{v}_n$ and $\bar{v}$ are independent. We would then have found $n+1$ independent vectors in a space V with a basis containing n vectors. Since such a basis must span V, Lemma 1 would have been contradicted. We are forced to conclude that the set $\bar{v}_1, \bar{v}_2, \ldots, \bar{v}_n$ must span V.

Conversely, suppose V has dimension n and that $\bar{v}_1, \bar{v}_2, \ldots, \bar{v}_n$ span V. If these vectors were not independent, Lemma 3 would tell us that V has dimension smaller than n. We are forced to conclude that $\bar{v}_1, \bar{v}_2, \ldots, \bar{v}_n$ must also be independent, and thus the proof of Theorem 10 has been completed.

Other Results about Bases

We can use our techniques to prove the following statements (*see* statement **8**, Section 9, Chapter 1):

If V is spanned by n vectors, then

13
- **a** V has a basis containing no more than n vectors.
- **b** No independent set in V can contain more than n vectors.
- **c** Any nonzero subspace of V has a basis containing no more than n vectors.

Part **a** is merely a restatement of Lemma 3, and part **b** is a restatement of Lemma 1. Thus the only new result is part **c**, the proof of which follows.

Suppose M is a subspace of V which contains nonzero vectors. We let k be the largest integer such that there are k independent vectors in M. We know from part **b** that such a k exists and that we must have $k \leq n$. Since M contains nonzero vectors we must also have that $k \geq 1$ (for any nonzero vector is independent—see Exercise 10, below). There are (from the definition of k) k independent vectors $\bar{v}_1, \bar{v}_2, \ldots, \bar{v}_k$ in M.

We now show that, in fact, the vectors $\bar{v}_1, \bar{v}_2, \ldots, \bar{v}_k$ must span M and hence are a basis for M. If these vectors did not span M, we could apply Lemma 2 (with V replaced by M) to find $k + 1$ independent vectors in M. This would contradict the defining property of k. We can only conclude that, indeed, $\bar{v}_1, \bar{v}_2, \ldots, \bar{v}_k$ are a basis for M. Since $k \leq n$, the proof of part **c** and, therefore, the proof of statement **13** has been completed.

Proofs of Theorems 13 and 14

We are now ready to prove the following two theorems:

THEOREM 13 A square matrix A is invertible if and only if the equation $A\bar{u} = \bar{0}$ has only one solution (which must, of course, be $\bar{u} = \bar{0}$).

THEOREM 14 If A is a square matrix and $BA = I$, then $AB = I$.

Our method of proof will yield both of these results at the same time. It has already been shown that (*see* statement **2**, Section 6, Chapter 2)

14 *If $BA = I$, then $A\bar{u} = \bar{0}$ has only one solution.*

In order to prove Theorem 13 it is only necessary to prove the converse of this result. Suppose that the only solution to $A\bar{u} = \bar{0}$ is $\bar{u} = \bar{0}$. Theorem 8 tells us that the columns of A must be independent. We can then apply Theorem 10, the fact that R^n has dimension n, and the assumption that A is square to conclude that

If $A\bar{u} = \bar{0}$ *has only one solution, the columns of* A *are a basis for* R^n.

Suppose the columns of A are denoted by $\bar{u}_1, \bar{u}_2, \ldots, \bar{u}_n$. These are a basis for R^n; thus, in particular, we can write

$$\begin{bmatrix} 1 \\ 0 \\ 0 \\ \vdots \\ 0 \end{bmatrix} = b_{11}\bar{u}_1 + b_{21}\bar{u}_2 + \cdots + b_{n1}\bar{u}_n$$

$$\begin{bmatrix} 0 \\ 1 \\ 0 \\ \vdots \\ 0 \end{bmatrix} = b_{12}\bar{u}_1 + b_{22}\bar{u}_2 + \cdots + b_{n2}\bar{u}_n$$

$$\begin{bmatrix} 0 \\ 0 \\ 0 \\ \vdots \\ 1 \end{bmatrix} = b_{1n}\bar{u}_1 + b_{2n}\bar{u}_2 + \cdots + b_{nn}\bar{u}_n$$

These equations can be rewritten as the equation

$$AB = I, \quad \text{where} \quad B = \begin{bmatrix} b_{11} & b_{12} & \cdots & b_{1n} \\ b_{21} & b_{22} & \cdots & b_{2n} \\ \vdots & & & \\ b_{n1} & b_{n2} & \cdots & b_{nn} \end{bmatrix}$$

The student should check that this is so. It may be helpful to first examine the case $n = 2$. (*See* Exercise 11.)

It has been shown, therefore, that the following statement is true:

15 *If* $A\bar{u} = \bar{0}$ *has only one solution, there is a matrix* B *such that* $AB = I$.

Statement **14** can now be applied to $AB = I$ to conclude that $B\bar{u} = \bar{0}$ has only one solution. Property **15** can therefore be applied again, with A replaced by B, to establish the fact that there must be a matrix C such that $BC = I$.

We have therefore shown that

> *If* $A\bar{u} = \bar{0}$ *has only one solution, there are matrices* B *and* C *such that* $AB = BC = I$.

We can easily show that $A = C$, for we have

16 $$A = AI = A(BC) = (AB)C = IC = C$$

We have therefore shown that if $A\bar{u} = \bar{0}$ has only one solution, then there is a matrix B such that $BA = I$, and hence A must be invertible. Thus the proof of Theorem 13 has been completed.

To prove Theorem 14, first suppose that $BA = I$. We can apply property **14** and then property **15** to conclude that there is a matrix B_1 such that $AB_1 = I$. Then, to prove Theorem 14, it is only necessary to show that $B = B_1$. The trick used to establish statement **16** can be applied again. We have

$$B = BI = B(AB_1) = (BA)B_1 = IB_1 = B_1$$

which completes the proof of Theorem 14.

Operator Inverses

The transformation versions of the results of the previous section can be proved as follows: Suppose T is a linear transformation from V into V. We first note that if T is linear it follows that

17 $$T\left(\sum_{i=1}^{n} c_i\bar{u}_i\right) = \sum_{i=1}^{n} c_i T\bar{u}_i$$

This result is obtained by repeated applications of the linearity properties

$$T(\bar{u} + \bar{v}) = T\bar{u} + T\bar{v} \qquad \text{and} \qquad T(a\bar{u}) = a(T\bar{u})$$

We now prove that

18 *If* S *is a linear transformation from* V *into* V *such that* $ST = I$, *the identity operator on* V, *then the null space of* T *contains only the zero vector.*

If $T\bar{u} = \bar{0}$, then

$$\bar{u} = I\bar{u} = (ST)\bar{u} = S(T\bar{u}) = S\bar{0} = \bar{0}$$

Thus, statement **18** is indeed true. We now prove a partial converse ("partial" because in it we assume that V is finite dimensional.)

19 *If V is finite dimensional, T is a linear transformation from V into V, and the null space of T contains only the zero vector, then there is a linear transformation S such that $ST = I$.*

To prove this we select a basis $\bar{u}_1, \bar{u}_2, \ldots, \bar{u}_n$ for V. Suppose

$$\sum_{i=1}^{n} c_i T\bar{u}_i = \bar{0}$$

Applying formula **17** gives

$$T\left(\sum_{i=1}^{n} c_i\bar{u}_i\right) = \bar{0}$$

and then applying the assumption that the null space of T contains only the zero vector gives

$$\sum_{i=1}^{n} c_i\bar{u}_i = \bar{0}$$

We now apply the assumption that $\bar{u}_1, \bar{u}_2, \ldots, \bar{u}_n$ are a basis and hence independent to reach the conclusion that $c_1 = c_2 = \cdots = c_n = 0$.

We have shown that $T\bar{u}_1, T\bar{u}_2, \ldots, T\bar{u}_n$ must be independent. We then apply Theorem 10 to conclude that these vectors are a basis for V. This information can be used to show how to define S. For $\bar{u}$ in V we can write

20 $$\bar{u} = \sum_{i=1}^{n} c_i T\bar{u}_i$$

where $c_1, c_2, \ldots, c_n$ are the (uniquely determined) coordinates of $\bar{u}$ with respect to the basis $T\bar{u}_1, T\bar{u}_2, \ldots, T\bar{u}_n$. We then define S by

21 $$S\bar{u} = \sum_{i=1}^{n} c_i\bar{u}_i$$

The proof that the S so defined is indeed linear is left to the exercises. For any $\bar{v}$ in V we have

$$\bar{v} = \sum_{i=1}^{n} c_i\bar{u}_i$$

where $c_1, c_2, \ldots, c_n$ are the coordinates of $\bar{v}$ with respect to $\bar{u}_1, \bar{u}_2, \ldots, \bar{u}_n$. Formula **17** is then applied to obtain

$$T\bar{v} = \sum_{i=1}^{n} c_i T\bar{u}_i$$

so that $c_1, c_2, \ldots, c_n$ are the coordinates of $T\bar{v}$ with respect to

$$T\bar{u}_1, T\bar{u}_2, \ldots, T\bar{u}_n.$$

Applying S then gives (using formula **21**)

$$(ST)\bar{v} = S(T\bar{v}) = \sum_{i=1}^{n} c_i\bar{u}_i = \bar{v}$$

which shows that $ST = I$ and thereby completes the proof of statement **19**.

It can be shown, using more sophisticated techniques, that the assumption in statement **19** that V is finite dimensional is superfluous. (*See* the Bibliography.)

We can actually establish somewhat more from our formulas **20** and **21**. Applying T to formula **21** and using formula **17** gives

$$(TS)\bar{u} = T(S\bar{u}) = T\left(\sum_{i=1}^{n} c_i\bar{u}_i\right) = \sum_{i=1}^{n} c_iT\bar{u}_i$$

This last sum is just $\bar{u}$ (from formula **20**); therefore, we have, for each $\bar{u}$, $(TS)\bar{u} = \bar{u}$; or in other words, we also have $TS = I$. We have thus obtained an operator form of Theorem 13:

22 *If V is finite dimensional and T is a linear transformation from V into V, then there is a linear transformation S such that $ST = TS = I$ if and only if the null space of T contains only the zero vector.*

Related results, such as an operator version of Theorem 14, are discussed in the exercises.

A Proof of Theorem 19

We now prove

THEOREM 19 Suppose A has n rows and n columns and its characteristic polynomial has n distinct real roots $a_1, a_2, \ldots, a_n$. If $\bar{v}_1, \bar{v}_2, \ldots, \bar{v}_n$ are corresponding characteristic vectors, they are a basis for R^n.

The hypothesis tells us that

23 *$a_i - a_j \neq 0$, if $i \neq j$, and there are vectors $\bar{v}_1, \bar{v}_2, \ldots, \bar{v}_n$ such that $A\bar{v}_i = a_i\bar{v}_i$, and $\bar{v}_i \neq \bar{0}$ for $1 \leq i \leq n$.*

We shall show that these conditions imply that $\bar{v}_1, \bar{v}_2, \ldots, \bar{v}_n$ are independent. Theorem 10 can then be applied to establish that they are a basis for the n-dimensional space R^n.

Suppose that it is possible for $\bar{v}_1, \bar{v}_2, \ldots, \bar{v}_n$ to be dependent. We can then apply Lemma 4 and relabel so that $\bar{v}_1, \bar{v}_2, \ldots, \bar{v}_k$ are independent and $\bar{v}_{k+1}$ is a linear combination of $\bar{v}_1, \bar{v}_2, \ldots, \bar{v}_k$. Therefore, we can find scalars $c_1, c_2, \ldots, c_k$ such that

24
$$\bar{v}_{k+1} = \sum_{i=1}^{k} c_i \bar{v}_i$$

We multiply this by A and use the fact that such multiplication is a linear transformation, so that property **17** gives

$$A\bar{v}_{k+1} = \sum_{i=1}^{k} c_i A\bar{v}_i$$

Using assumption **23** we can rewrite this as

$$a_{k+1}\bar{v}_{k+1} = \sum_{i=1}^{k} c_i a_i \bar{v}_i$$

We then multiply equation **24** by a_{k+1} and subtract from this to obtain (using the rules **1**)

$$\bar{0} = \sum_{i=1}^{k} c_i(a_{k+1} - a_i)\bar{v}_i$$

Since the vectors $\bar{v}_1, \bar{v}_2, \ldots, \bar{v}_k$ are independent it must follow that

$$c_1(a_{k+1} - a_1) = 0, \quad c_2(a_{k+1} - a_2) = 0, \ldots, c_k(a_{k+1} - a_k) = 0$$

Each of the numbers

$$a_{k+1} - a_1, \quad a_{k+1} - a_2, \ldots, a_{k+1} - a_k$$

is not zero (from hypothesis **23**); therefore, we must have

$$c_1 = c_2 = \cdots = c_k = 0$$

Substituting these into equation **24** gives $\bar{v}_{k+1} = \bar{0}$, which contradicts the assumption that each $\bar{v}_i$ is a characteristic vector and hence nonzero.

Thus the assumption that $\bar{v}_1, \bar{v}_2, \ldots, \bar{v}_n$ are dependent has led to a contradiction of the hypothesis. We must therefore conclude that these vectors are independent. This completes the proof of Theorem 19.

A Proof of Theorem 22

We now prove

THEOREM 22 Suppose S and T are linear transformations from V into V, each having a finite dimensional null space. Then the null space of ST is finite dimensional, and the dimension of the null space of ST cannot exceed the sum of the dimensions of the null space of S and the null space of T.

To prove this suppose $\bar{u}_1, \bar{u}_2, \ldots, \bar{u}_n$ are a basis for the null space of S and that $\bar{v}_1, \bar{v}_2, \ldots, \bar{v}_k$ are a basis for the null space of T. We have

$$(ST)\bar{v}_i = S(T\bar{v}_i) = S\bar{0} = \bar{0} \qquad \text{for } i = 1, 2, \ldots, k$$

Therefore, $\bar{v}_1, \bar{v}_2, \ldots, \bar{v}_k$ must also be in the null space of ST.

If $\bar{v}_1, \bar{v}_2, \ldots, \bar{v}_k$ span the null space of ST, then this space has dimension k, which does not exceed $k + n$, and we are finished. If $\bar{v}_1, \bar{v}_2, \ldots, \bar{v}_k$ do not span the null space of ST, we can apply Lemma 2 to find a vector $\overline{w}_1$ in the null space of ST such that $\bar{v}_1, \bar{v}_2, \ldots, \bar{v}_k$, and $\overline{w}_1$ are independent. If these do not span the null space of ST, we apply Lemma 2 again to find $\overline{w}_2$ in the null space of ST such that $\bar{v}_1, \bar{v}_2, \ldots, \bar{v}_k, \overline{w}_1$, and $\overline{w}_2$ are independent. We can proceed in this manner to obtain vectors $\overline{w}_1, \overline{w}_2, \ldots, \overline{w}_m$ in the null space of ST such that

25 $\qquad \bar{v}_1, \bar{v}_2, \ldots, \bar{v}_k, \overline{w}_1, \overline{w}_2, \ldots, \overline{w}_m$ are independent

as long as we do not reach a set which spans this null space. Hence, if the null space of ST were not finite dimensional or if its dimension exceeded $k + n$, we could then find m vectors $\overline{w}_1, \overline{w}_2, \ldots, \overline{w}_m$ in the null space of ST such that property **25** holds, *and* $m > n$. Suppose we have found such vectors; namely, suppose

26 $\qquad$ *There are vectors $\overline{w}_1, \overline{w}_2, \ldots, \overline{w}_m$ in the null space of ST such that $m > n$ and $\bar{v}_1, \bar{v}_2, \ldots, \bar{v}_k, \overline{w}_1, \overline{w}_2, \ldots, \overline{w}_m$ are independent.*

It will be shown that this statement leads to a contradiction. First, note that

If $\overline{w}$ is in the null space of ST, then $T\overline{w}$ is in the null space of S.

Since the hypothesis tells us that $(ST)\overline{w} = \bar{0}$, it follows that $S(T\overline{w}) = (ST)\overline{w} = \bar{0}$, and thus $T\overline{w}$ must be in the null space of S. We conclude from this observation that

$$T\overline{w}_1, T\overline{w}_2, \ldots, T\overline{w}_m \text{ are in the null space of } S$$

We now have m vectors in the null space of S, which is, by assumption, n-dimensional. Furthermore, we have assumed that $m > n$. These vectors must therefore be dependent (from Lemma 1). Therefore we can find $c_1, c_2, \ldots, c_m$ *not* all zero such that

$$\sum_{i=1}^{m} c_i T\bar{w}_i = \bar{0}$$

We then apply formula **17** to obtain

$$T\left(\sum_{i=1}^{m} c_i\bar{w}_i\right) = \bar{0}$$

This tells us that the vector

$$\bar{v} = \sum_{i=1}^{m} c_i\bar{w}_i$$

must be in the null space of T. Since $\bar{v}_1, \bar{v}_2, \ldots, \bar{v}_k$ were assumed to be a basis for this null space it is possible to find $d_1, d_2, \ldots, d_k$ such that

$$\bar{v} = \sum_{i=1}^{k} d_i\bar{v}_i$$

We therefore have

$$\sum_{i=1}^{k} d_i\bar{v}_i = \sum_{i=1}^{m} c_i\bar{w}_i$$

which can be rewritten as

$$\sum_{i=1}^{k} d_i\bar{v}_i + \sum_{i=1}^{m} (-c_i)\bar{w}_i = \bar{0}$$

The assumption **26** then tells us that

$$d_1 = d_2 = \cdots = d_k = -c_1 = -c_2 = \cdots = -c_m = 0$$

This contradicts the fact that at least one of the c_i is *not* zero. Since we have finally reached a contradiction from assumption **26**, we conclude that this assumption must be false. Recall that assumption **26** was a consequence of denying the validity of Theorem 22; we can only conclude that this theorem must be true.

A Related Operator Result

Arguments similar to those above can be used to prove the following statement:

27 *Suppose S and T are linear transformations from V into V such that each has a finite dimensional null space. Suppose also that the dimension of the null space of ST equals the sum of the dimensions of the null space of S and the null space of T. If $\bar{u}$ is in the null space of S, then there is a vector $\bar{v}$ in the null space of ST such that $T\bar{v} = \bar{u}$.*

[Suppose K and L are constant coefficient linear differential operators. We know that the dimension of the null space of such an operator is the order of the operator (Theorem 23). Furthermore, the order of KL is the sum of the orders of K and L. (*See* Exercise 4, Section 4, Chapter 4.) Thus result **27** tells us that if f is in the null space of K, there is a function y in the null space of KL such that $Ly = f$. This is result **4**, Section 5, Chapter 4, which was basic to the method of undetermined coefficients.]

Proceeding to prove statement **27**, we assume that $\bar{u}$ is a vector in the null space of S. We now choose a basis, $\bar{u}_1, \bar{u}_2, \ldots, \bar{u}_n$ for the null space of T. Since, for each i,

$$(ST)\bar{u}_i = S(T\bar{u}_i) = S\bar{0} = \bar{0}$$

it follows that each $\bar{u}_i$ is also in the null space of ST. If the dimension of the null space of S is k, the hypothesis tells us that the dimension of the null space of ST is $n + k$.

We know that $\bar{u}_1, \bar{u}_2, \ldots, \bar{u}_n$ are independent and belong to the null space of ST. If $k = 0$, we can apply Theorem 10 to conclude that these vectors are a basis for the null space of ST. If $k \neq 0$, Theorem 9 shows that they cannot span this null space. Therefore, Lemma 2 can be applied to find a vector $\bar{v}_1$ in the null space of ST such that

$$\bar{u}_1, \bar{u}_2, \ldots, \bar{u}_n \text{ and } \bar{v}_1 \text{ are independent}$$

If these do not span the null space of ST, Lemma 2 can be applied again, and further vectors, $\bar{v}_2, \bar{v}_3, \ldots$, in the null space of ST can be obtained so that

$$\bar{u}_1, \bar{u}_2, \ldots, \bar{u}_n, \bar{v}_1, \bar{v}_2, \bar{v}_3, \ldots, \text{ are independent}$$

We have assumed that the null space of ST has dimension $n + k$, where k is the dimension of the null space of S. Therefore, this process will stop after k such vectors are chosen. For we cannot have more than $n + k$

independent vectors in the null space of ST (from Lemma 1), and no independent set with less than $n + k$ vectors can span this null space (from Theorem 9).

We have shown that with the hypothesis of statement **27** we can find vectors

28 $\bar{v}_1, \bar{v}_2, \ldots, \bar{v}_k$ *in the null space of* ST *such that* $\bar{u}_1, \bar{u}_2, \ldots, \bar{u}_n, \bar{v}_1, \bar{v}_2, \ldots, \bar{v}_k$ *are independent.*

We will show that

29 $T\bar{v}_1, T\bar{v}_2, \ldots, T\bar{v}_k$ *are a basis for the null space of* S,

a fact that will enable us to prove statement **27**. Suppose $\bar{u}$ is in the null space of S. Then we use property **29** to find $c_1, c_2, \ldots, c_k$ such that

$$\bar{u} = \sum_{i=1}^{k} c_i T\bar{v}_i$$

Thus if we put

$$\bar{v} = \sum_{i=1}^{k} c_i \bar{v}_i$$

then $T\bar{v} = \bar{u}$ (from formula **17**), and $\bar{v}$ belongs to the null space of ST (from statement **28**). Therefore we need only prove that property **29** is true. Since we have assumed that the null space of S has dimension k, it is enough (because of Theorem 10) to show that

30 $T\bar{v}_1, T\bar{v}_2, \ldots, T\bar{v}_k$ *are independent and belong to the null space of* S.

Establishing the fact that they belong to the null space of S is easy, for we know that

$$S(T\bar{v}_i) = (ST)\bar{v}_i = \bar{0} \qquad i = 1, 2, \ldots, k$$

because the $\bar{v}_i$'s belong to the null space of ST. The proof of independence is somewhat more difficult, however. Suppose

$$\sum_{i=1}^{k} c_i T\bar{v}_i = \bar{0}$$

We can rewrite this as

$$T\left(\sum_{i=1}^{k} c_i \bar{v}_i\right) = \bar{0}$$

so that the vector

$$\bar{w} = \sum_{i=1}^{k} c_i \bar{v}_i$$

belongs to the null space of T. Since the vectors $\bar{u}_1, \bar{u}_2, \ldots, \bar{u}_n$ were chosen to be a basis for this null space, we can write

$$\bar{w} = \sum_{i=1}^{n} d_i \bar{u}_i$$

Equating these two expressions for $\bar{w}$ gives

$$\sum_{i=1}^{k} c_i \bar{v}_i = \sum_{i=1}^{n} d_i \bar{u}_i$$

and rewriting gives

$$\sum_{i=1}^{k} c_i \bar{v}_i + \sum_{i=1}^{n} (-d_i) \bar{u}_i = \bar{0}$$

Property **28** then tells us that

$$c_1 = c_2 = \cdots = c_k = -d_1 = -d_2 = \cdots = -d_n = 0$$

We have therefore shown that if

$$\sum_{i=1}^{k} c_i T \bar{u}_i = \bar{0}$$

then $c_1 = c_2 = \cdots = c_k = 0$. This concludes the proof of statement **30.**

EXERCISES

The first five exercises are concerned with summation notation.

1 Establish rule **1a**.

2 Show that $\displaystyle\sum_{i=1}^{n} c_i \bar{u}_i - \sum_{i=1}^{n} d_i \bar{u}_i = \sum_{i=1}^{n} (c_i - d_i) \bar{u}_i$

3 Show that $\displaystyle\sum_{j=1}^{k} \sum_{i=1}^{n} a_{ij} = \sum_{i=1}^{n} \sum_{j=1}^{k} a_{ij}$

4 Show that if A_{ij} denotes the entry in the ith row and jth column of A and $C = AB$, then

$$C_{ij} = \sum_{k=1}^{n} A_{ik} B_{kj}$$

5 Use Exercises 3 and 4 to show directly that $(AB)C = A(BC)$.

The next eight exercises are concerned with independence, dependence, and bases. The student may find it helpful to first prove two-dimensional versions of each result.

6 Give the general proof that definition **2e** is the same as the definition of basis used in Section 8 of Chapter 1.

7 Show that Theorem 1 implies Lemma 1. (Hint: We can write

$$\bar{v}_j = \sum_{i=1}^{n} A_{ij}\bar{u}_i \qquad \text{for } j = 1, 2, \ldots, k$$

Let A be the matrix whose entry in the ith row and jth column is A_{ij}. If $k>n$, apply Theorem 1 to choose $\bar{c} \neq \bar{0}$ such that $A\bar{c} = \bar{0}$. Show that

$$\sum_{j=1}^{k} c_j\bar{v}_j = \bar{0}$$

where $c_1, c_2, \ldots, c_k$ are the coordinates of $\bar{c}$.

8 Show that Lemma 1 implies Theorem 1. (Hint: Denote the columns of A by $\bar{v}_1, \bar{v}_2, \ldots, \bar{v}_k$. If A has n rows and $k > n$, apply Lemma 1 to obtain $c_1, c_2, \ldots, c_k$ not all zero such that

$$\sum_{i=1}^{k} c_i\bar{v}_i = \bar{0}$$

Rewrite this as a matrix equation.)

9 Suppose $\bar{v}_1, \bar{v}_2, \ldots, \bar{v}_k$ are independent. Show that each $\bar{v}_i \neq \bar{0}$.

10 Suppose $\bar{v} \neq \bar{0}$. Show that $\bar{v}$ is independent.

11 Suppose $$\bar{v}_j = \sum_{i=1}^{m} b_{ij}\bar{u}_i \qquad \text{for } j = 1, 2, \ldots, n$$

Let A denote the matrix whose columns are $\bar{u}_1, \bar{u}_2, \ldots, \bar{u}_n$, B the matrix whose entry in the ith row and jth column is b_{ij}, and C the matrix whose columns are $\bar{v}_1, \bar{v}_2, \ldots, \bar{v}_n$. Show that $AB = C$.

12 **a** Show that if $\bar{v}_1, \bar{v}_2, \ldots, \bar{v}_n$ span V and $a \neq 0$, then $\bar{v}_1, \bar{v}_2, \ldots, \bar{v}_{i-1}, a\bar{v}_i, \bar{v}_{i+1}, \ldots, \bar{v}_n$ also span V.

b Show that if $\bar{v}_1, \bar{v}_2, \ldots, \bar{v}_n$ span V and $i \neq j$, then $\bar{v}_1, \bar{v}_2, \ldots, \bar{v}_{i-1}, \bar{v}_i + a\bar{v}_j, \bar{v}_{i+1}, \ldots, \bar{v}_n$ span V.

c The *row space* of a matrix A is the subspace spanned by the rows of A. Show that if B is obtained from A by a row operation of the type used in Section 1, Chapter 1, then A and B have the same row space. (Hint: Use parts **a** and **b**.)

d Show that if A is reduced to the reduced matrix R, then the nonzero rows of R are a basis for the row space of A. (Hint: Show that these rows are independent and use part **c**.)

13 Suppose the subspace M of V has the basis $\bar{v}_1, \bar{v}_2, \ldots, \bar{v}_k$ and that $\bar{v}$ is not in M. Show that $\bar{v}_1, \bar{v}_2, \ldots, \bar{v}_k$ and $\bar{v}$ are independent. (Hint: See the proof of Lemma 2.) Use this to show that if V is finite dimensional, then there are vectors $\bar{u}_1, \bar{u}_2, \ldots, \bar{u}_n$ such that $\bar{v}_1, \bar{v}_2, \ldots, \bar{v}_k, \bar{u}_1, \bar{u}_2, \ldots, \bar{u}_n$ is a basis for V.

The remaining exercises are concerned with linear transformations and matrices.

14 If, for any sum, $\sum_{i=1}^{n} c_i\bar{u}_i$, we have $T\left(\sum_{i=1}^{n} c_i\bar{u}_i\right) = \sum_{i=1}^{n} c_i T\bar{u}_i$ show that T is linear.

15 Show that if A and B are square matrices and $AB = aI$ with $a \neq 0$, then $AB = BA$. Is this necessarily true if $a = 0$?

16 Show that the transformation S defined by statement **21** is linear.

17 Suppose $\bar{v}_1, \bar{v}_2, \ldots, \bar{v}_n$ is a basis for V and $\bar{u}_1, \bar{u}_2, \ldots, \bar{u}_n$ are n given vectors in W. Show that there is exactly one linear transformation S from V into W such that $S\bar{v}_i = \bar{u}_i$, $i = 1, 2, \ldots, n$.

(Hint: For $\bar{u} = \sum_{i=1}^{n} c_i\bar{v}_i$ define $S\bar{v}$ to be $\sum_{i=1}^{n} c_i\bar{u}_i$.)

18 Suppose T is linear and $T\bar{u}_1, T\bar{u}_2, \ldots, T\bar{u}_n$ are independent. Show that $\bar{u}_1, \bar{u}_2, \ldots, \bar{u}_n$ are independent.

19 Show that if T is linear and $T\bar{u}_1, T\bar{u}_2, \ldots, T\bar{u}_n$ is an independent set whenver $\bar{u}_1, \bar{u}_2, \ldots, \bar{u}_n$ is independent, then the null space of T is the zero subspace. (Hint: Use Exercises 9 and 10.)

20 Prove the converse of Exercise 19. (Hint: Proceed as in the first part of the proof of statement **19**.)

21 Show that if S and T are linear transformations from V into V such that $ST = I$ and if V is finite-dimensional, then $TS = I$. (Hint: First show that the null space of T is the zero vector, then apply statement **24** and an argument like statement **16**.)

22 Suppose V is finite-dimensional and T is a linear transformation from V into V. The *range* of T is the set of vectors of the form $T\bar{u}$ for $\bar{u}$ in V.

a Show that the range of T is a subspace of V.

b Show that the dimension of V equals the dimension of the range of T plus the dimension of the null space of T. (Hint: Pick a basis $\bar{v}_1, \bar{v}_2, \ldots, \bar{v}_k$ for the null space of T. Apply Exercise 13 to find $\bar{u}_1, \bar{u}_2, \ldots, \bar{u}_n$ such that $\bar{v}_1, \bar{v}_2, \ldots, \bar{v}_k, \bar{u}_1, \bar{u}_2, \ldots, \bar{u}_n$ form a basis for V. Show that

$$T\bar{u}_1, T\bar{u}_2, \ldots, T\bar{u}_n$$

are a basis for the range of T.)

c The dimension of the range of T is sometimes called the *rank* of T. Show that if S is invertible, then rank (ST) = rank T.

d Show that rank $(ST) \leq$ rank S and that rank $(ST) \leq$ rank T.

e Show that T is invertible if and only if the rank of T equals the dimension of V.

ANSWERS TO EXERCISES

CHAPTER 1

SECTION 1

1 (**A**) ↔ (**d**) (**B**) ↔ (**f**) (**C**) ↔ (**e**)
(**D**) ↔ (**g**) (**E**) ↔ (**b**) (**F**) ↔ (**a**) and (**c**)

2
a $x = 0,\ y = 0$
b $x = 0,\ y = 0$
c $x = \frac{1}{4}y,\ y = y$
d $x = 0,\ y = \frac{7}{2}z,\ z = z$
e $x = -\frac{1}{6}y,\ y = y,\ z = 0$
f $x = 0,\ y = 0$
g $x = 0,\ y = 0,\ z = 0$
h $x = -\frac{1}{2}y,\ y = y,\ z = 0$
i $x = -\frac{65}{106}z,\ y = \frac{63}{106}z,\ z = z$
j $x = 0,\ y = 0,\ z = 0$
k $x = \frac{2}{3}y - \frac{1}{3}z,\ y = y,\ z = z$

3 $x = \frac{7}{3}z,\ y = \frac{5}{3}z,\ z = z$ $x = \frac{7}{5}y,\ y = y,\ z = \frac{3}{5}y$ $x = x,\ y = \frac{5}{7}x,\ z = \frac{3}{7}x$

4
a $x = -\frac{3}{7}z,\ y = \frac{8}{7}z,\ z = z$
b $x = 0,\ y = 0$
c $x_1 = -\frac{3}{7}x_3,\ x_2 = \frac{8}{7}x_3,\ x_3 = x_3$
d $x = 0,\ y = 0$
e $x = -2y - 3z - w,\ y = y,\ z = z,\ w = w$
f $x_1 = -2x_5,\ x_2 = 2x_5,\ x_3 = 0,\ x_4 = 0,\ x_5 = x_5$
g $x = 0,\ y = 0$

5 (*See* Exercise 2.)

6
a $x = 0,\ y = 0,\ z = 0,\ w = 0$
b
$$\begin{aligned} x_1 &= \tfrac{7}{3}x_4 - \tfrac{5}{6}x_6 \\ x_2 &= -\tfrac{2}{3}x_4 - \tfrac{1}{3}x_6 \\ x_3 &= -\tfrac{4}{3}x_4 + \tfrac{5}{6}x_6 \\ x_4 &= x_4 \\ x_5 &= -\tfrac{1}{2}x_6 \\ x_6 &= x_6 \end{aligned}$$
c
$$\begin{aligned} x_1 &= \tfrac{7}{5}x_3 - \tfrac{16}{5}x_4 + \tfrac{1}{5}x_5 + \tfrac{6}{5}x_6 \\ x_2 &= \tfrac{7}{5}x_3 + \tfrac{19}{5}x_4 - \tfrac{4}{5}x_5 - \tfrac{9}{5}x_6 \\ x_3 &= x_3 \\ x_4 &= x_4 \\ x_5 &= x_5 \\ x_6 &= x_6 \end{aligned}$$

7 Yes, the solution in which each variable is zero.

8 **a, b**

10 $x = 0,\ y = 0$

13 System B is system S with two variables renamed.

18 **a** $x = \frac{1}{3}iz$
$y = \frac{5}{6}(1 - i)z$
$z = z$

b $x = \left(\dfrac{4 - 6i}{13}\right)z$
$y = \left(\dfrac{16 - 2i}{13}\right)z$
$z = z$

SECTION 2

1 **a** $x = \frac{11}{5}$
$y = \frac{2}{5}$

b No solution.

c No solution.

d $x = z + \frac{2}{3}w + 1$
$y = -2z - \frac{7}{3}w$
$z = z$
$w = w$

e No solution.

f $x_1 = \frac{33}{12}$
$x_2 = -\frac{47}{6}$
$x_3 = \frac{25}{6}$
$x_4 = \frac{5}{6}$
$x_5 = \frac{1}{2}$
$x_6 = -2$

g
$$\begin{aligned} x_1 &= -\tfrac{3}{2}x_4 \qquad\qquad - \tfrac{3}{2}x_6 + 1 \\ x_2 &= -4x_4 - 3x_5 + x_6 - 1 \\ x_3 &= 2x_4 + x_5 - x_6 \\ x_4 &= x_4 \\ x_5 &= x_5 \\ x_6 &= x_6 \end{aligned}$$

6 **a** Unique solution. **b** More than one solution.
c More than one solution. **d** Unique solution.

7 **a** No solution. **b** Unique solution.
c No solution. **d** No solution.

8 **a** Unique solution for any choice of the constants.
b Cannot always be solved; if one solution exists, then more than one solution exists.
c More than one solution for any choice of the constants.
d Cannot always be solved; if one solution exists, then the solution is unique.

9 **a** $x = \dfrac{5 + 7i}{37}$, $y = \dfrac{22 + 16i}{37}$ **b** No solution.

c $x = \dfrac{-2i}{3}z + \dfrac{4 + i}{3}$, $y = \dfrac{-4 - 2i}{3}z + \dfrac{3 - 7i}{3}$, $z = z$

SECTION 3

2 **a** $x = y/2$
$y = y, y \neq 0$

b $x = \frac{1}{2}y$
$y = y, y \neq 0$

c $x = -\frac{10}{41}w$
$y = \frac{23}{41}w$
$z = \frac{35}{41}w$
$w = w, w \neq 0$

d $x = -z$
$y = 0$
$z = z, z \neq 0$

e $x_1 = 0$
$x_2 = -x_5$
$x_3 = -x_5$
$x_4 = 0$
$x_5 = x_5, x_5 \neq 0$

3 The trivial solution in which all the variables are zero.

6 Unique: **a** and **c**

8 **b, d, f, h**

9 No—all solutions are of the form: $x = -2y, \quad y = y, \quad z = 0$

10 **a** Line passes through the origin.
b The lines intersect only in origin (that is, they are not coincidental); the lines are coincident.
c The lines are parallel; they intersect in exactly one point; the lines are coincident.

11 **a** Plane passes through the origin.
b The planes intersect only in origin; the planes intersect in a line through the origin or are coincident.
c The intersection must contain a line.
d The planes do not have a common intersection; the planes meet in exactly one point; the intersection of the planes contains a line.

12 **a** Unique solution: $x = y = 0$. **b** No.

SECTION 4

1 **a** $(0, \frac{5}{4}, \frac{10}{3})$ **b** $(-\frac{3}{2}, \frac{3}{4}, 8)$ **c** $(-1, -\frac{3}{4}, 2)$

2 **a** $(-5, -3, -3, -1, 1)$ **b** $(3, -3, 9, 9, -3)$ **c** $(-2, 2, -2, 2, -2)$

3 $-\bar{x} = (-x_1, -x_2, \ldots, -x_n)$

4 **a** $-2 - 2x + 2x^2 + x^3$ **b** $18x - 6x^2$ **c** $-2 + 7x - x^2 - x^3$

5 Yes.

8 **a** $x(1,2,1,0) + y(-1,1,-1,2)$
b $x_3(-\frac{5}{3},-\frac{1}{5},1,0,0) + x_4(0,0,0,1,0) + x_5(\frac{1}{5},-\frac{3}{5},0,0,1)$

9 **a** $a(1,-\frac{1}{2})$, a any real number. **b** $y = \frac{1}{3}x$ **c** $y\begin{bmatrix}2\\1\\0\end{bmatrix} + z\begin{bmatrix}-1\\0\\1\end{bmatrix}$ **d** No.

10 $(2x_1 - 3y_1 + z_1, 2x_2 - 3y_2, 2x_3 - 3y_3 + 1, 2x_4 - 3y_4 + z_4)$

15 $(-1+4i, 4+i, 5+i) = \bar{u} - 2i\bar{v} + (1+i)\bar{w}$

$$\bar{x} = \left(0, \frac{-3+i}{2}, \frac{1-i}{2}\right)$$

SECTION 5

1 **a** $\begin{bmatrix} -5 \\ -3 \\ 4 \end{bmatrix}$ **b** $\begin{bmatrix} 9 \\ 4 \\ -5 \end{bmatrix}$ **c** $\bar{x} = \begin{bmatrix} -1 \\ 2 \\ 1 \end{bmatrix}$

2 **a** $(-5,-3,4)$ **b** $(9,4,-5)$ **c** $\bar{x} = (-1,2,1)$

3 **a** $\begin{bmatrix} 7 \\ 2 \end{bmatrix}$ **b** $\begin{bmatrix} 4 \\ 6 \end{bmatrix}$ **c** $\begin{bmatrix} 2 \\ 2 \\ 1 \end{bmatrix}$ **d** $\begin{bmatrix} 0 \\ 0 \\ 0 \end{bmatrix}$ **e** $\begin{bmatrix} 1 \\ 3 \\ 1 \end{bmatrix}$ **f** $\begin{bmatrix} 0 \\ 17 \\ 34 \end{bmatrix}$ **g** $\begin{bmatrix} 37 \\ 24 \\ 3 \\ 60 \\ 0 \end{bmatrix}$

4 **a** $\begin{bmatrix} 2 & -1 & 1 \\ 1 & -3 & 1 \\ 1 & 1 & -1 \\ 4 & -1 & 2 \end{bmatrix} \begin{bmatrix} x \\ y \\ z \end{bmatrix} = \begin{bmatrix} 1 \\ 2 \\ 0 \\ 1 \end{bmatrix}$ **b** $[1 \quad -1] \begin{bmatrix} x \\ y \end{bmatrix} = 0$

c $\begin{bmatrix} 0 & 0 & 0 \\ 0 & 0 & 0 \\ 0 & 0 & 0 \end{bmatrix} \begin{bmatrix} x \\ y \\ z \end{bmatrix} = \begin{bmatrix} 0 \\ 0 \\ 0 \end{bmatrix}$

5 **a** No. **b** Yes. **c** Yes. **d** No.

6 No.

8 $A(\bar{u} + \bar{v}) = \begin{bmatrix} 6 \\ 3 \end{bmatrix}$ $A(3\bar{u}) = \begin{bmatrix} 3 \\ -6 \end{bmatrix}$

10 Yes.

11 No.

12 $\begin{bmatrix} 1 & -1 \\ 2 & 3 \end{bmatrix} \begin{bmatrix} c_1 \\ c_2 \end{bmatrix} = \begin{bmatrix} 4 \\ 2 \end{bmatrix}$

13 0

14 $\begin{bmatrix} \frac{3}{4} \\ \frac{5}{4} \\ 0 \end{bmatrix} + a \begin{bmatrix} -\frac{3}{4} \\ -\frac{5}{4} \\ 1 \end{bmatrix}$

(Other forms are possible, depending upon the choice of $\bar{u}$ and $\bar{v}$.)

15 Yes.

16 **a** $\begin{bmatrix} -1 + i \\ 2(1 + i) \end{bmatrix}$ **b** $\begin{bmatrix} 5i \\ -1 + 3i \end{bmatrix}$ **c** $\begin{bmatrix} i & -2i \\ 3 - i & i - 1 \end{bmatrix} \begin{bmatrix} x \\ y \end{bmatrix} = \begin{bmatrix} i \\ \frac{i}{2} \end{bmatrix}$

SECTION 6

1 **a** No. **b** No. **c** Yes. **d** No. **e** Yes.

2 **a** Yes. **b** No. **c** Yes. **d** Yes. **e** No.

3 **a** $a \begin{bmatrix} -3 \\ 5 \\ 1 \end{bmatrix}$ **b** $a \begin{bmatrix} -\frac{1}{3} \\ 1 \\ 0 \\ 0 \end{bmatrix} + b \begin{bmatrix} -\frac{1}{3} \\ 0 \\ 1 \\ 0 \end{bmatrix}$ **c** $\begin{bmatrix} 0 \\ 0 \end{bmatrix}$

d $a_1 \begin{bmatrix} 0 \\ 0 \\ 1 \\ 0 \\ 0 \\ 0 \\ 0 \end{bmatrix} + a_2 \begin{bmatrix} 0 \\ -6 \\ 0 \\ 1 \\ 0 \\ 0 \\ 0 \end{bmatrix} + a_3 \begin{bmatrix} -\frac{1}{2} \\ 0 \\ 0 \\ 0 \\ 1 \\ 0 \\ 0 \end{bmatrix} + a_4 \begin{bmatrix} -\frac{1}{2} \\ 0 \\ 0 \\ 0 \\ 0 \\ 1 \\ 0 \end{bmatrix} + a_5 \begin{bmatrix} \frac{1}{2} \\ -3 \\ 0 \\ 0 \\ 0 \\ 0 \\ 1 \end{bmatrix}$

4 Other choices of a solution to $A\bar{x} = \bar{c}$ will give different first vectors in each case.

a $\begin{bmatrix} 1 \\ -1 \\ 0 \end{bmatrix} + a \begin{bmatrix} -3 \\ 5 \\ 1 \end{bmatrix}$ **b** $\begin{bmatrix} \frac{1}{3} \\ 0 \\ 0 \\ -1 \end{bmatrix} + a \begin{bmatrix} -\frac{1}{3} \\ 1 \\ 0 \\ 0 \end{bmatrix} + b \begin{bmatrix} -\frac{1}{3} \\ 0 \\ 1 \\ 0 \end{bmatrix}$ **c** $\begin{bmatrix} 1 \\ 0 \end{bmatrix}$

d $\begin{bmatrix} 0 \\ 1 \\ 0 \\ 0 \\ 0 \\ 0 \\ 0 \end{bmatrix} + a_1 \begin{bmatrix} 0 \\ 0 \\ 1 \\ 0 \\ 0 \\ 0 \\ 0 \end{bmatrix} + a_2 \begin{bmatrix} 0 \\ -6 \\ 0 \\ 1 \\ 0 \\ 0 \\ 0 \end{bmatrix} + a_3 \begin{bmatrix} -\frac{1}{2} \\ 0 \\ 0 \\ 0 \\ 1 \\ 0 \\ 0 \end{bmatrix} + a_4 \begin{bmatrix} -\frac{1}{2} \\ 0 \\ 0 \\ 0 \\ 0 \\ 1 \\ 0 \end{bmatrix} + a_5 \begin{bmatrix} \frac{1}{2} \\ -3 \\ 0 \\ 0 \\ 0 \\ 0 \\ 1 \end{bmatrix}$

5 **b** Yes. **c** It has a unique solution.

6 **b** No. **c** No.

7 No, $\bar{0}$ is not a solution.

8 Does not have a unique solution.

9 **a** Plane through the origin. **b** Plane parallel to the plane of part **a**.

10 **a** A plane or a line through the origin.
b The planes corresponding to the system of equations are parallel. If the system has a solution, then these planes meet in a line or are coincident.

11 **a** If $A = 0$, all vectors are solutions. If $A \neq 0$, solutions form a plane or a line through the origin or the origin only.
b The planes of the system have no common intersection.
c The origin only. **d** The line through the terminal point of $\bar{u}_1$, parallel to $\bar{u}_2$.

12 **a** One solution. **b** One solution.

14 Other solutions to $A\bar{x} = \begin{bmatrix} 1 \\ i \end{bmatrix}$ will give different first vectors. One form is:

$$\bar{x} = \begin{bmatrix} \frac{1-i}{2} \\ 0 \\ 2 \end{bmatrix} + a \begin{bmatrix} -\frac{1+i}{2} \\ 1 \\ 0 \end{bmatrix}$$

SECTION 7

1 Yes.

2 **a** Dependent. **b** Independent. **c** Independent. **d** Dependent.
e Independent.

3 For example:

a $(-4,3,-5) = 2(1,3,-1) - 3(2,1,1)$ b $(1,-1) = -\frac{5}{11}(1,3) + \frac{4}{11}(4,1)$

c $(1,0,5,3,2) = 3(1,2,1,1,0) - 2(1,3,-1,0,-1)$

4 No.

5 No.

6 $(1,0,3) = \frac{1}{3}(2,1,1) + \frac{1}{3}(1,-1,1) + \frac{7}{3}(0,0,1)$

7 $(x-1)^2 = x^2 - 2x + 1$

13 a No. b Yes. c Yes.

15 c $(3+i, i) = \dfrac{5-2i}{4}(1+i, 2i) + \dfrac{1-5i}{4}(i, 1-i)$

SECTION 8

4 Given in row form. Of course, other bases are possible.

a $(-3,5,1)$

b $(-\frac{1}{3},1,0,0)$, $(-\frac{1}{3},0,1,0)$

c $(0,0,1,0,0,0,0)$, $(0,-6,0,1,0,0,0)$, $(-\frac{1}{2},0,0,0,1,0,0)$, $(-\frac{1}{2},0,0,0,0,1,0)$, $(\frac{1}{2},-3,0,0,0,0,1)$

5 a $\dfrac{-x+3y-z}{14}, \dfrac{3x-2y+3z}{7}, \dfrac{-5x+y+9z}{14}$

b $x, -x+y, -y+z$ c $\dfrac{-x+2y-z}{11}, \dfrac{7x-3y+7z}{22}, \dfrac{14x-6y+3z}{55}$

6 a $\dfrac{x+y+z-w}{4}, \dfrac{x+y-z+w}{4}, \dfrac{x-y+z+w}{4}, \dfrac{-x+y+z+w}{4}$

b $x, -2x+y, x-2y+z, y-2z+w$

7 For example, $(0,1,0)$, $(0,0,1)$

9 $\dfrac{a+b}{2}, \dfrac{a-b}{2}$

SECTION 9

1 a Yes. b No. c No. d Yes.

3 2

4 5

6 Yes.

8 2

10 **a, b, e**

11 **a** 4

b $\dfrac{(x-1)(x-2)(x-3)}{-6}$, $\dfrac{x(x-2)(x-3)}{2}$, $\dfrac{x(x-1)(x-3}{-2}$

$\dfrac{x(x-1)(x-2)}{6}$

c $\dfrac{(x+1)(x-1)(x-2)}{-12}$, $\dfrac{(x+2)(x-1)(x-2)}{6}$,

$\dfrac{(x+2)(x+1)(x-2)}{-6}$, $\dfrac{(x+2)(x+1)(x-1)}{12}$

15 **a** No. **b.** No. **c.** Yes **d** Yes.

SECTION 10

1 **a** 11 **b** 1 **c** $3\bar{w}$

2 **a** 3 **b** 5 **c** $2\bar{w}$

3 **a** 11 **b** 4 **c** $2\bar{w}$

4 **a** $\sqrt{2}$ **b** 3 **c** 6

6 **a** $\dfrac{1}{\sqrt{5}}\bar{u}$ **b** $\dfrac{1}{\sqrt{3}}\bar{u}$ **c** $\dfrac{1}{\sqrt{11}}\bar{u}$ **d** $\frac{1}{3}\bar{u}$

7 **a** $\frac{3}{5}\bar{v}$ **b** $\bar{0}$ **c** $\frac{1}{5}\bar{v}$ **d** $\frac{5}{12}\bar{v}$

8 **a** $(\frac{2}{5},-\frac{1}{5})$ **b** $\bar{u}$ **c** $(\frac{3}{5},2,\frac{6}{5})$ **d** $(\frac{19}{12},-\frac{3}{12},\frac{5}{12},-\frac{5}{12}, 6)$

9 **a** $\bar{w}_1 = (\frac{3}{5},\frac{6}{5})$ $\bar{w}_2 = (\frac{2}{5},-\frac{1}{5})$ **b** $\bar{w}_1 = \bar{0}$ $\bar{w}_2 = \bar{u}$

c $\bar{w}_1 = (\frac{2}{5},0,-\frac{1}{5})$ $\bar{w}_2 = (\frac{3}{5},2,\frac{6}{5})$

d $\bar{w}_1 = (\frac{5}{12},\frac{15}{12},-\frac{5}{12},\frac{5}{12},0)$ $\bar{w}_2 = (\frac{19}{12},-\frac{3}{12},\frac{5}{12},-\frac{5}{12},6)$

10 Projection of $\bar{u}$ onto $\bar{v}$ is $\bar{0}$; projection of $\bar{u}$ orthogonal to $\bar{v}$ is $\bar{u}$.

12 **a** $\sqrt{2}/2$

c The projections onto and orthogonal to 1 are $\frac{1}{2}$ and $x - \frac{1}{2}$, onto and orthogonal to $\cos \pi x$ are $\dfrac{-4}{\pi^2} \cos \pi x$ and $x + \dfrac{4}{\pi^2} \cos \pi x$.

14 $(-1,3,5)$

16 **d** Not in general.

17 **b** $1 - i, -1 - i, 6 - 8i$ **c** $\sqrt{2}, \sqrt{2}$

d $(\frac{1}{2}, i/2), (-\frac{1}{2} + i, 1 + i/2)$ **e** $\bar{u} \cdot \bar{u} > 0$ if $\bar{u} \neq \bar{0}$

SECTION 11

2 **a** $\frac{1}{\sqrt{5}}(1,2);\ \frac{1}{\sqrt{5}}(-2,1)$ **b** $\frac{1}{\sqrt{2}}(1,0,1);\ \frac{1}{\sqrt{3}}(1,1,-1);\ \frac{1}{\sqrt{6}}(-1,2,1)$

c $\frac{1}{\sqrt{2}}(1,0,1,0);\ \frac{1}{\sqrt{3}}(1,1,-1,0);\ \frac{1}{\sqrt{7}}(1,-2,-1,1)$

3 $(3,2,1) = 2(1,0,1) + \frac{4}{3}(1,1,-1) + \frac{1}{3}(-1,2,1)$

5 $\frac{4}{3}(-1,2,1)$

7 Try $\bar{u} = (0,0,1,0)$.

9 **c** $\bar{u}_1 = (1,1,1),\ \bar{u}_2 = (-\frac{1}{3},\frac{2}{3},-\frac{1}{3})$
$\bar{u}_3 = (-\frac{1}{2},0,\frac{1}{2})$

d $\bar{u}_1 = 1$
$\bar{u}_2 = x - \frac{1}{2}$
$\bar{u}_3 = x^2 - x + \frac{1}{6}$

10 **b** $\frac{1}{\sqrt{3}}(1,i,1);\ \frac{1}{\sqrt{2}}(i,0,-i);\ \frac{1}{\sqrt{6}}(i,2,i)$

c $(1,1,i) = \frac{1}{3}(1,i,1) - \frac{i+1}{2}(i,0,-i) + \frac{3-i}{6}(i,2,i)$

CHAPTER 2

SECTION 1

1 **a** $(\frac{5}{9},\frac{10}{9},\frac{10}{9})$ **b** $(\frac{2}{9},\frac{4}{9},\frac{4}{9})$ **c** $(\frac{7}{9},\frac{14}{9},\frac{14}{9})$ **d** $(\frac{20}{9},\frac{40}{9},\frac{40}{9})$ **e** $(\frac{20}{9},\frac{40}{9},\frac{40}{9})$

2 **a** $(-3,2)$ **b** $(1,-4)$ **c** $(-2,-2)$ **d** $(-2,-2)$

4 **a** $\frac{10}{9}(1,-2,2)$ **b** $\frac{2}{9}(1,-2,2)$ **c** $(\frac{2}{9},-\frac{13}{9},\frac{31}{9})$ **d** $(-\frac{14}{9},\frac{1}{9},\frac{17}{9})$

5 $T(1,0) = (1/\sqrt{2},1/\sqrt{2})$ $T(0,1) = (-1/\sqrt{2},1/\sqrt{2})$ $T(1,1) = (0,\sqrt{2})$

6 **a** Reflection in the line $y = x$. **b** Projection onto the y, z plane.
c Reflection in the x-axis. **d** Projection onto the x-axis.

7 $P\bar{u} = \bar{u} - (\bar{u} \cdot \bar{w})\bar{w}$

9 $T(1,2) = (1,2)$
$T(-1,2) = (1,2)$
No; No.

11 **a** $\cos x$ **b** e^x **c** $e^x + \cos x$ **d** $ae^x + b\cos x$

12 **a** $\sin x$ **b** $x^3/3$ **c** $e^x - 1$ **d** $x^3/3 + 3\sin x + 2(e^x - 1)$

13 **a** $1, x, x^2$ is one such basis. **b** $c_1 + c_2x + c_3x^2 + \cos x$

14 The solutions to $Lf = x$ are the functions of the form $c_1e^x + c_2e^{-x} - x$.

15 The solutions to $Lf = 2 + x^2$ are the functions of the form $c_1 \sin x + c_2 \cos x + x^2$.

16 The null space of T consists of all functions f in $C[0,1]$ such that $f(x) = 0$ if $g(x) \neq 0$.

SECTION 2

1 **a** $\begin{bmatrix} 1 & 0 & 0 & 0 \\ 1 & 1 & 0 & 0 \\ 1 & 1 & 1 & 0 \\ 1 & 1 & 1 & 1 \end{bmatrix}$ **b** $\begin{bmatrix} 1 & -1 & 0 \\ 0 & 0 & 1 \end{bmatrix}$ **c** $\begin{bmatrix} 1 & 0 & 0 & 0 \\ 1 & 0 & 0 & 0 \\ 1 & 0 & 0 & 0 \\ 1 & 0 & 0 & 0 \\ 1 & 0 & 0 & 0 \end{bmatrix}$

2 **a** $\begin{bmatrix} 1/\sqrt{2} & -1/\sqrt{2} \\ 1/\sqrt{2} & 1/\sqrt{2} \end{bmatrix}$ **b** $\begin{bmatrix} 0 & -1 \\ 1 & 0 \end{bmatrix}$ **c** $\begin{bmatrix} -1 & 0 \\ 0 & -1 \end{bmatrix}$

d $\begin{bmatrix} -1 & 0 \\ 0 & -1 \end{bmatrix}$ **e** $\begin{bmatrix} 1 & 0 \\ 0 & 1 \end{bmatrix}$

3 **a** $T(1,1) = (0, \sqrt{2})$
$T(2,-3) = (5/\sqrt{2}, -1/\sqrt{2})$

b $T(1,1) = (-1,1)$
$T(2,-3) = (3,2)$

c $T(1,1) = (-1,-1)$
$T(2,-3) = (-2,3)$

d $T(1,1) = (-1,-1)$
$T(2,-3) = (-2,3)$

e $T(1,1) = (1,1)$
$T(2,-3) = (2,-3)$

4 $$P = \begin{bmatrix} \frac{1}{2} & \frac{1}{2} \\ \frac{1}{2} & \frac{1}{2} \end{bmatrix}$$

5 $$T = \begin{bmatrix} 0 & 1 \\ 1 & 0 \end{bmatrix}$$

6 $$P = \begin{bmatrix} \frac{8}{9} & -\frac{2}{9} & -\frac{2}{9} \\ -\frac{2}{9} & \frac{5}{9} & -\frac{4}{9} \\ -\frac{2}{9} & -\frac{4}{9} & \frac{5}{9} \end{bmatrix}$$

7 $\begin{bmatrix} 0 & 0 \\ 0 & 0 \end{bmatrix}$

8 $\begin{bmatrix} 1 & 0 \\ 0 & 1 \end{bmatrix}$

9 $T(x,y,z) = (2x + y + 3z, -y + z)$

10 **a** Reflection in the line $y = x$. **b** Projection onto the x-axis.
c Reflection in the line $y = -x$. **d** Rotation through π.

11 **a** $\begin{bmatrix} 1 \\ 1 \\ 0 \end{bmatrix}$ $\begin{bmatrix} 1 \\ 1 \end{bmatrix}$ **b** The third column of A. **c** $\bar{u} = \begin{bmatrix} 0 \\ 0 \\ 0 \\ 0 \\ 1 \end{bmatrix}$

12 $\begin{bmatrix} -\frac{8}{13} & -\frac{2}{13} \\ \frac{19}{13} & \frac{21}{13} \end{bmatrix}$

14 **a** $\begin{bmatrix} i & -1 \\ 1+i & 0 \end{bmatrix}$ **b** $\begin{bmatrix} 0 & 0 \\ 0 & 0 \\ i & 0 \\ i-1 & 2 \end{bmatrix}$ **c** $\begin{bmatrix} \frac{1}{2} & i/2 \\ -i/2 & \frac{1}{2} \end{bmatrix}$

SECTION 3

1 **a** $\begin{bmatrix} -1 & 3 \\ 1 & 4 \end{bmatrix}$ **b** $\begin{bmatrix} -5 & -2 & -1 & 4 \\ 3 & 7 & -1 & 0 \end{bmatrix}$ **c** $\begin{bmatrix} 0 & 0 \\ 0 & 0 \\ 0 & 0 \end{bmatrix}$

3 **a** [15, 6] **b** [−8,4] **c** $\begin{bmatrix} 2 & 1 \\ 0 & 0 \end{bmatrix}$ $\begin{bmatrix} 3 & -1 \\ 2 & 0 \end{bmatrix}$ $\begin{bmatrix} 5 & 0 \\ 2 & 0 \end{bmatrix}$

4 $\begin{bmatrix} 5 & 0 & 0 \\ 1 & 0 & 0 \\ 2 & 1 & 1 \\ 1 & 0 & 1 \end{bmatrix}$ $\begin{bmatrix} -3 & 0 & 0 \\ 1 & 0 & 0 \\ 0 & -1 & -1 \\ 1 & 0 & -1 \end{bmatrix}$ $\begin{bmatrix} 8 & 0 & 0 \\ 0 & 0 & 0 \\ 2 & 2 & 2 \\ 0 & 0 & 2 \end{bmatrix}$ $\begin{bmatrix} -5 & 0 & 0 \\ 3 & 0 & 0 \\ 1 & -2 & -2 \\ 3 & 0 & -2 \end{bmatrix}$

5 $m = p$ $n = q$

6 If P is projection onto $\bar{w}$, then $I-P$ is projection onto M, and $2(I-P)-I = I - 2P$ is reflection through M.

7 **a** 0 **b** $6x$ **c** $1 + 7e^{2x}$ $\cos x$ belongs to the null space of $T + D$

8 $T = \frac{3}{2}R - S - \frac{1}{2}I$

9 $\begin{bmatrix} \lambda - a_{11} & -a_{12} \\ -a_{21} & \lambda - a_{22} \end{bmatrix}$ $A\bar{u} = \lambda\bar{u}$, if $\bar{u}$ is in the null space of $\lambda I - A$.

11 $m \cdot n$

12 No.

13 **a** $((3i + 1)x + (2i + 2)y, -x - iy)$ **c** $\begin{bmatrix} -3 + i & -1 \\ 0 & 0 \end{bmatrix}$

SECTION 4

1 **a** Counterclockwise rotation through $\pi/2$.
b Counterclockwise rotation through 2π.
c Counterclockwise rotation through π.
d Counterclockwise rotation through $5\pi/4$.
e Counterclockwise rotation through $5\pi/2$.
f Counterclockwise rotation through 2π.

2 Do not commute.

3 **a** Do not commute. **b** S_1S is reflection through the origin $S_1S = SS_1$.

c $T_1T = TT_1$

6 **a** 1 **b** $x^3/3$ **c** $-\cos x$ **d** $\frac{1}{2}x - (\sin 2x)/4$ **e** $\cos x - 1$ **f** $\cos x$

g $6 + \frac{2}{3}x^3$ D and T do not commute.

7 **a** $\begin{bmatrix} -2 & 2 \\ -1 & 2 \end{bmatrix}$ **b** $\begin{bmatrix} 0 & 5 \\ 0 & -1 \end{bmatrix}$ **c** $\begin{bmatrix} 19 & 22 \\ 43 & 50 \end{bmatrix}$ **d** $\begin{bmatrix} 1 & 0 \\ 0 & 1 \end{bmatrix}$

8 **a** $\begin{bmatrix} 5 & -7 & -3 \\ 7 & -3 & -1 \\ 7 & 1 & 1 \end{bmatrix}$ **b** $\begin{bmatrix} -3 & 1 & 1 \\ 1 & -3 & 1 \\ 1 & 1 & -3 \end{bmatrix}$ **c** $\begin{bmatrix} 14 & -16 & 18 \\ 26 & -31 & 36 \\ 38 & -46 & 54 \end{bmatrix}$ **d** $\begin{bmatrix} 1 & 1 & 2 \\ 2 & 1 & 1 \\ 1 & 2 & 1 \end{bmatrix}$

9 **a** $\begin{bmatrix} 3 & 0 & 7 \\ 1 & 3 & 4 \end{bmatrix}$ **b** 1 **c** $\begin{bmatrix} 0 & 4 & -6 & -1 & -5 \\ 6 & 7 & 7 & 4 & -9 \\ -5 & -12 & -1 & -5 & -6 \\ 0 & 7 & 3 & 7 & -4 \\ 3 & 2 & 1 & 0 & 2 \end{bmatrix}$ **d** $\begin{bmatrix} -7 & 7 \\ -4 & 4 \\ -6 & 6 \end{bmatrix}$

10 **a** $\begin{bmatrix} 1 & 2 \\ 0 & 1 \end{bmatrix}$ $\begin{bmatrix} 1 & 3 \\ 0 & 1 \end{bmatrix}$ $\begin{bmatrix} 1 & 4 \\ 0 & 1 \end{bmatrix}$ $\begin{bmatrix} 1 & 4 \\ 0 & 1 \end{bmatrix}$ **b** $\begin{bmatrix} 1 & 0 \\ 0 & 1 \end{bmatrix}$ $\begin{bmatrix} 0 & 1 \\ 1 & 0 \end{bmatrix}$ $\begin{bmatrix} 1 & 0 \\ 0 & 1 \end{bmatrix}$ $\begin{bmatrix} 1 & 0 \\ 0 & 1 \end{bmatrix}$

c $\begin{bmatrix} 7 & 10 \\ 15 & 22 \end{bmatrix}$ $\begin{bmatrix} 37 & 54 \\ 81 & 118 \end{bmatrix}$ $\begin{bmatrix} 199 & 290 \\ 435 & 634 \end{bmatrix}$ $\begin{bmatrix} 199 & 290 \\ 435 & 634 \end{bmatrix}$

d $\begin{bmatrix} 5 & 1 & 1 \\ 2 & 4 & 0 \\ 5 & 1 & 3 \end{bmatrix}$ $\begin{bmatrix} 12 & 6 & 2 \\ 8 & -2 & 4 \\ 14 & 10 & 4 \end{bmatrix}$ $\begin{bmatrix} 32 & 10 & 8 \\ 18 & 18 & 2 \\ 42 & 12 & 14 \end{bmatrix}$ $\begin{bmatrix} 32 & 10 & 8 \\ 18 & 18 & 2 \\ 42 & 12 & 14 \end{bmatrix}$

11 **a** $\begin{bmatrix} 8 & 1 \\ -1 & 0 \end{bmatrix}$ **b** $\begin{bmatrix} 15 & 1 \\ -2 & 0 \end{bmatrix}$ **c** $\begin{bmatrix} 15 & 1 \\ -2 & 0 \end{bmatrix}$ **d** $\begin{bmatrix} 16 & 2 \\ -9 & -1 \end{bmatrix}$

e $\begin{bmatrix} 5 & 4 & 2 \\ 5 & 1 & -2 \\ -1 & 1 & 2 \end{bmatrix}$ **f** Not defined. **g** Not defined. **h** Not defined. **i** $\begin{bmatrix} 4 & 1 \\ 2 & -1 \end{bmatrix}$ **j** Not defined.

12 Number of columns of A = number of rows of B. AB has the same number of rows as A and the same number of columns as B.

13 Third row of A and fourth column of B.

14 $TS(x,y) = (6x + 3y, 4x + 2y)$, $ST(x, y) = (8x - 2y, 0)$

$\begin{bmatrix} 2 & 1 \\ 0 & 0 \end{bmatrix}$ $\begin{bmatrix} 3 & -1 \\ 2 & 0 \end{bmatrix}$ $\begin{bmatrix} 8 & -2 \\ 0 & 0 \end{bmatrix}$ $\begin{bmatrix} 6 & 3 \\ 4 & 2 \end{bmatrix}$

15 **a**

$$P_0 = \begin{bmatrix} \frac{1}{9} & \frac{2}{9} & \frac{2}{9} \\ \frac{2}{9} & \frac{4}{9} & \frac{4}{9} \\ \frac{2}{9} & \frac{4}{9} & \frac{4}{9} \end{bmatrix} \qquad T_0 = \begin{bmatrix} -\frac{7}{9} & \frac{4}{9} & \frac{4}{9} \\ \frac{4}{9} & -\frac{1}{9} & \frac{4}{9} \\ \frac{4}{9} & \frac{4}{9} & -\frac{1}{9} \end{bmatrix}$$

16 **a**

$$P_0 = \begin{bmatrix} \frac{1}{5} & \frac{2}{5} \\ \frac{2}{5} & \frac{4}{5} \end{bmatrix} \qquad Q_0 = \begin{bmatrix} \frac{4}{5} & -\frac{2}{5} \\ -\frac{2}{5} & \frac{1}{5} \end{bmatrix}$$

17 **a** $\begin{bmatrix} 2 & 2i - 1 \\ 2 - 3i & 2i + 1 \end{bmatrix}$ **b** $\begin{bmatrix} 3 + 2i & 2 \\ 2 - 2i & 1 + 2i \end{bmatrix}$

c $\begin{bmatrix} i & 1 + i \\ i & 0 \end{bmatrix}$ $\begin{bmatrix} 0 & -1 + i \\ -1 & 0 \end{bmatrix}$ $\begin{bmatrix} 0 & -1 + i \\ 0 & 0 \end{bmatrix}$

SECTION 5

2 $B = \frac{2}{3}A - \frac{1}{3}AC$

4 No.

5 $R(ST)$ and $(RS)T$ are counterclockwise rotations through $\theta + \varphi + \psi$. $R(S^2T^3)$ and $(RS^2)T^3$ are counterclockwise rotations through $3\varphi + 2\psi + \theta$.

6 **a** $\begin{bmatrix} 0 & 0 \\ 0 & 0 \end{bmatrix}$ **b** $\begin{bmatrix} 0 & 0 & 0 \\ 0 & 0 & 0 \end{bmatrix}$ **c** $\begin{bmatrix} 1 & 2 \\ 1 & 1 \end{bmatrix}$ **d** $\begin{bmatrix} 1 & 2 & 1 \\ 1 & 1 & 1 \end{bmatrix}$ **e** $\begin{bmatrix} 0 & 0 \\ 0 & 0 \end{bmatrix}$

f $\begin{bmatrix} 3 & 1 \\ 2 & -1 \\ 0 & 1 \\ 1 & 1 \end{bmatrix}$ **g** Not defined.

7 **a** $\begin{bmatrix} 7 & 5 \\ 0 & 0 \end{bmatrix}$ **b** $\begin{bmatrix} -1 & 0 \\ 0 & 0 \end{bmatrix}$ **c** $\begin{bmatrix} 0 & 13 & 6 & 25 \\ 0 & 0 & 0 & 0 \\ 0 & 0 & 0 & 0 \end{bmatrix}$ **d** $\begin{bmatrix} 9 & 3 & 0 \\ 0 & 0 & 0 \\ 3 & 1 & 0 \end{bmatrix}$

8 **a** $\begin{bmatrix} 12 & 6 & 18 & \frac{3}{2} \\ 2 & -1 & 0 & \frac{1}{2} \end{bmatrix}$ **b** $\begin{bmatrix} -24 & -24 & -4 & -24 \\ -\frac{1}{2} & 0 & \frac{1}{2} & \frac{1}{2} \\ 0 & 3 & 9 & 0 \\ 0 & -1 & \frac{1}{2} & -\frac{1}{2} \end{bmatrix}$

c $\begin{bmatrix} -24 & 3 & 3 & -3 \\ 4 & 0 & 3 & -\frac{1}{2} \\ 0 & \frac{1}{2} & 9 & 0 \\ 0 & 1 & -3 & -\frac{1}{2} \end{bmatrix}$ **d** $\begin{bmatrix} 1 & \frac{3}{2} \\ \frac{1}{2} & 0 \\ \frac{1}{2} & \frac{3}{2} \\ \frac{1}{2} & -\frac{3}{2} \end{bmatrix}$

9 **a** $\begin{bmatrix} 1 & 0 & 0 \\ 0 & 8 & 0 \\ 0 & 0 & 27 \end{bmatrix}$ **b** $\begin{bmatrix} 9 & 0 & 0 \\ 0 & 0 & 0 \\ 0 & 0 & -8 \end{bmatrix}$ **c** $\begin{bmatrix} 1 & 0 & 0 \\ 0 & -1 & 0 \\ 0 & 0 & 1 \end{bmatrix}$

d $\begin{bmatrix} 0 & 0 & 0 & 0 \\ 0 & 1 & 0 & 0 \\ 0 & 0 & 27 & 0 \\ 0 & 0 & 0 & -1 \end{bmatrix}$

10 **a** $p(A) = \begin{bmatrix} 1 & 4 \\ 0 & -3 \end{bmatrix}$ $q(A) = \begin{bmatrix} -2 & 2 \\ 0 & -4 \end{bmatrix}$ $r(A) = \begin{bmatrix} -2 & 0 \\ 0 & -2 \end{bmatrix}$

b $p(A) = \begin{bmatrix} 30 & 9 & 3 \\ 21 & -3 & 6 \\ 24 & 9 & 9 \end{bmatrix}$ $q(A) = \begin{bmatrix} 0 & 1 & 0 \\ 2 & -4 & 1 \\ 1 & 1 & -1 \end{bmatrix}$ $r(A) = \begin{bmatrix} 18 & 4 & 2 \\ 10 & 4 & 2 \\ 14 & 4 & 6 \end{bmatrix}$

c $p(A) = \begin{bmatrix} 52 & 0 & 0 \\ 0 & -3 & 0 \\ 0 & 0 & 6 \end{bmatrix}$ $q(A) = \begin{bmatrix} 1 & 0 & 0 \\ 0 & -4 & 0 \\ 0 & 0 & -1 \end{bmatrix}$ $r(A) = \begin{bmatrix} 28 & 0 & 0 \\ 0 & -2 & 0 \\ 0 & 0 & 4 \end{bmatrix}$

11 $p(A) = \begin{bmatrix} p(a) & 0 & 0 \\ 0 & p(b) & 0 \\ 0 & 0 & p(c) \end{bmatrix}$ In particular, $p(A) = \begin{bmatrix} 0 & 0 & 0 \\ 0 & 0 & 0 \\ 0 & 0 & 0 \end{bmatrix}$

when $p(\lambda) = (\lambda - a)(\lambda - b)(\lambda - c)$.

12 $B = \begin{bmatrix} 2 & 0 & 0 \\ 0 & 3 & 0 \\ 0 & 0 & -2 \end{bmatrix}$ is one such matrix.

13 $\begin{bmatrix} -3 & 0 & 0 \\ 0 & -4 & 0 \\ 0 & 0 & 1 \end{bmatrix}$ and $\begin{bmatrix} 0 & 6 \\ 6 & 6 \end{bmatrix}$

20 **a** $\begin{bmatrix} 1 & -1 & 1 \\ 3 & 2 & 1 \\ 2 & 1 & 1 \end{bmatrix}$ **b** $\begin{bmatrix} 3 & 2 & 1 \\ \frac{1}{2} & -\frac{1}{2} & \frac{1}{2} \\ 2 & 1 & 1 \end{bmatrix}$ **c** $\begin{bmatrix} 3 & 2 & 1 \\ 10 & 5 & 4 \\ 2 & 1 & 1 \end{bmatrix}$ **d** $\begin{bmatrix} 3 & 2 & 1 \\ -8 & -7 & -2 \\ 2 & 1 & 1 \end{bmatrix}$

21 **a** $\begin{bmatrix} 0 & 1 & 0 \\ 1 & 0 & 0 \\ 0 & 0 & 1 \end{bmatrix}$ **b** $\begin{bmatrix} 1 & 0 & 0 \\ 0 & 2 & 0 \\ 0 & 0 & 1 \end{bmatrix}$ **c** $\begin{bmatrix} 1 & 0 & 0 \\ -3 & 1 & 0 \\ 0 & 0 & 1 \end{bmatrix}$ **d** $\begin{bmatrix} 1 & 0 & 0 \\ 3 & 1 & 0 \\ 0 & 0 & 1 \end{bmatrix}$

22 $EDCBA = \begin{bmatrix} 1 & 0 \\ 0 & 1 \end{bmatrix}$. Put $A' = EDCB$.

24 **a** $\begin{bmatrix} 0 & 0 \\ 0 & 0 \end{bmatrix}$ **b** $\begin{bmatrix} i & 2i \\ 1+i & 3-i \end{bmatrix}$ **c** $\begin{bmatrix} 1+3i & 3+3i \\ 0 & 0 \end{bmatrix}$ **d** $\begin{bmatrix} 0 & -1+2i \\ 0 & 2 \end{bmatrix}$

e $\begin{bmatrix} -1 & -2 \\ -2+2i & 2+6i \end{bmatrix}$ **f** $\begin{bmatrix} -1 & -4 \\ -1+i & 2+6i \end{bmatrix}$ **g** $\begin{bmatrix} 1 & 0 \\ 0 & 1 \end{bmatrix}$

SECTION 6

2 **a** $\begin{bmatrix} \frac{2}{11} & -\frac{1}{22} \\ -\frac{1}{11} & \frac{3}{11} \end{bmatrix}$ **b** $\begin{bmatrix} -\frac{1}{2} & \frac{1}{2} \\ -\frac{1}{2} & -\frac{1}{2} \end{bmatrix}$ **c** $\begin{bmatrix} -2 & 1 \\ \frac{3}{2} & -\frac{1}{2} \end{bmatrix}$ **d** $\begin{bmatrix} 1 & 0 \\ -2 & 1 \end{bmatrix}$

e $\begin{bmatrix} 2 & -2 & 1 \\ \frac{1}{2} & -\frac{1}{2} & \frac{1}{2} \\ -\frac{7}{2} & \frac{9}{2} & -\frac{5}{2} \end{bmatrix}$ **f** $\begin{bmatrix} 1 & -1 & 0 \\ 0 & 1 & -1 \\ 0 & 0 & 1 \end{bmatrix}$ **g** $\begin{bmatrix} -\frac{1}{9} & \frac{1}{9} & \frac{8}{9} \\ \frac{10}{9} & -\frac{1}{9} & -\frac{26}{9} \\ \frac{1}{9} & -\frac{1}{9} & \frac{1}{9} \end{bmatrix}$

h $\begin{bmatrix} 1 & -1 & 2 & 2 \\ 0 & \frac{1}{2} & 0 & \frac{1}{2} \\ 0 & 0 & -2 & -2 \\ 0 & 0 & 0 & -1 \end{bmatrix}$ **i** $\begin{bmatrix} -\frac{1}{2} & \frac{1}{2} & \frac{1}{2} & \frac{1}{2} \\ \frac{1}{2} & 0 & 0 & -\frac{1}{2} \\ \frac{1}{2} & 0 & -\frac{1}{2} & 0 \\ \frac{1}{2} & -\frac{1}{2} & 0 & 0 \end{bmatrix}$

3 **a** $\begin{bmatrix} 1 & -1 \\ 0 & 1 \end{bmatrix}$ **b** $\begin{bmatrix} 1 & -1 & 0 \\ 0 & 1 & -1 \\ 0 & 0 & 1 \end{bmatrix}$ **c** $\begin{bmatrix} 1 & -1 & 0 & 0 & 0 \\ 0 & 1 & -1 & 0 & 0 \\ 0 & 0 & 1 & -1 & 0 \\ 0 & 0 & 0 & 1 & -1 \\ 0 & 0 & 0 & 0 & 1 \end{bmatrix}$

4 **a** $\begin{bmatrix} \frac{1}{2} & 0 \\ 0 & -\frac{1}{2} \end{bmatrix}$ **b** $\begin{bmatrix} 4 & 0 & 0 \\ 0 & 2 & 0 \\ 0 & 0 & 3 \end{bmatrix}$ **c** $\begin{bmatrix} 1 & 0 & 0 & 0 & 0 \\ 0 & \frac{1}{4} & 0 & 0 & 0 \\ 0 & 0 & \frac{1}{2} & 0 & 0 \\ 0 & 0 & 0 & -1 & 0 \\ 0 & 0 & 0 & 0 & \frac{1}{3} \end{bmatrix}$

5 **a** Not invertible. **b** $\begin{bmatrix} \frac{1}{3} & -\frac{1}{3} & -\frac{1}{3} \\ 0 & \frac{1}{2} & 1 \\ 0 & 0 & -1 \end{bmatrix}$ **c** $\begin{bmatrix} \frac{1}{3} & -\frac{1}{3} & 0 & -\frac{1}{3} \\ 0 & 1 & -\frac{1}{2} & \frac{5}{2} \\ 0 & 0 & \frac{1}{2} & \frac{1}{2} \\ 0 & 0 & 0 & -1 \end{bmatrix}$

d Not invertible. **e** $\begin{bmatrix} \frac{1}{2} & 0 & 0 & 0 \\ -\frac{1}{6} & \frac{1}{3} & 0 & 0 \\ \frac{1}{3} & -\frac{1}{6} & \frac{1}{2} & 0 \\ -\frac{1}{2} & -\frac{1}{2} & -\frac{1}{2} & 1 \end{bmatrix}$

9 a $\begin{bmatrix} i & 1 \\ 2 & -i \end{bmatrix}$ b $\begin{bmatrix} (1-i)/2 & 0 \\ 0 & (1+i)/2 \end{bmatrix}$

SECTION 7

1 a $\begin{bmatrix} \frac{3}{2} & 2 & \frac{5}{2} \\ \frac{1}{2} & -1 & \frac{3}{2} \end{bmatrix}$ b $\begin{bmatrix} -\frac{3}{2} & \frac{3}{2} \\ \frac{7}{2} & -\frac{5}{2} \end{bmatrix}$ c $\begin{bmatrix} \frac{7}{6} & \frac{19}{6} & 0 & \frac{9}{6} & -\frac{5}{6} \\ \frac{1}{6} & \frac{19}{6} & 0 & -\frac{3}{6} & \frac{1}{6} \\ \frac{3}{6} & -\frac{21}{6} & 0 & -\frac{3}{6} & \frac{9}{6} \end{bmatrix}$

2 a $\begin{bmatrix} \frac{1}{5} \\ \frac{1}{5} \end{bmatrix}$ b $\begin{bmatrix} \frac{3}{5} \\ -\frac{7}{5} \end{bmatrix}$ c $\begin{bmatrix} \frac{4}{5} \\ -\frac{1}{5} \end{bmatrix}$ d $\begin{bmatrix} 0 \\ 0 \end{bmatrix}$

3 A is not invertible.

4 No.

6 $(x,y,z) = (2x + \frac{1}{2}y - \frac{7}{2}z)(2,1,1)$
$+ (-2x - \frac{1}{2}y + \frac{9}{2}z)(1,3,1)$
$+ (x + \frac{1}{2}y - \frac{5}{2}z)(-1,4,0)$

7 $\begin{bmatrix} 2 & 1 & -5 \\ -1 & -1 & 4 \\ 1 & 1 & -3 \end{bmatrix}$

8 a Counterclockwise rotation through $\theta = -\pi/4, 3\pi/2, -\pi$.
b Counterclockwise rotation through -2θ.
c Multiples of π. d Multiples of $\pi/2$.

9 $T^{-1}(x,y) = (\frac{2}{7}x + \frac{1}{7}y, -\frac{1}{7}x + \frac{3}{7}y)$

10 T^{-1} is reflection followed by the opposite rotation.

12 a $(A^{-1})^3$ b $\frac{1}{3}A^{-1}$ c $-A^{-4}$ d A^2

13 $\frac{1}{3}(A + 2I), -\frac{1}{2}(A^5 - 5A^3 + 3A)$

14 a $B = (A + aI)^{-1}D$, if $A + aI$ is invertible.
b $B = 2(D - A)^{-1}C$, if $D - A$ is invertible.
c $B = (A - 3I)^{-1}C$, if $A - 3I$ is invertible.
d $B = C(A + C)^{-1}$, if $A + C$ is invertible.
e $B = C$, if A is invertible.

15 $T^{-1}f = \frac{1}{g}f$

17 **a** $\begin{bmatrix} \frac{-1-7i}{2} & 2+i \\ -\frac{i}{2} & 1 \end{bmatrix}$ **b** $\frac{1-2i}{5}y, \frac{1+i}{2}x - \frac{1+3i}{10}y$

SECTION 8

1 **a** Not invertible. **b** Invertible. **c** Invertible. **d** Not invertible.

6 **a** $\begin{bmatrix} 1/\sqrt{2} & -1/\sqrt{2} \\ 1/\sqrt{2} & 1/\sqrt{2} \end{bmatrix}$ **b** $\begin{bmatrix} 0 & 1 \\ 1 & 0 \end{bmatrix}$ **c** $\begin{bmatrix} 1/\sqrt{3} & 1/\sqrt{2} & 1/\sqrt{6} \\ 1/\sqrt{3} & -1/\sqrt{2} & 1/\sqrt{6} \\ 1/\sqrt{3} & 0 & -2/\sqrt{6} \end{bmatrix}$

SECTION 9

1 28

3 **a** 3 **b** 0 **c** 0 **d** −23 **e** 0 **f** 0 **g** 6 **h** 0 **i** 0

4 **a**, **d** and **g** are invertible.

9 **a** $\lambda^2 - 5\lambda + 7$ **b** $\lambda^3 - 2\lambda^2 - 4\lambda + 6$

12 $-1 - i$; Yes.

13 2

14 **a** 0; Dependent. **b** 0; Independent.

17 $\begin{bmatrix} 0 & 0 & 0 \\ 14 & -4 & 2 \\ -7 & 2 & -1 \end{bmatrix}$

18 **a** $x = \frac{5}{3}$, $y = -\frac{7}{3}$ **b** $x = -2$, $y = \frac{1}{2}$ **c** $x = 5$, $y = 0$, $z = -3$ **d** $x = -\frac{1}{15}$, $y = -\frac{13}{15}$, $z = \frac{1}{3}$

CHAPTER 3

SECTION 1

1
$$D = \begin{bmatrix} 0 & 1 & 0 & 0 \\ 0 & 0 & 2 & 0 \\ 0 & 0 & 0 & 3 \\ 0 & 0 & 0 & 0 \end{bmatrix}$$

2
$$D^2 = \begin{bmatrix} 0 & 0 & 2 & 0 \\ 0 & 0 & 0 & 6 \\ 0 & 0 & 0 & 0 \\ 0 & 0 & 0 & 0 \end{bmatrix} \quad D^3 = \begin{bmatrix} 0 & 0 & 0 & 6 \\ 0 & 0 & 0 & 0 \\ 0 & 0 & 0 & 0 \\ 0 & 0 & 0 & 0 \end{bmatrix} \quad D^4 = \begin{bmatrix} 0 & 0 & 0 & 0 \\ 0 & 0 & 0 & 0 \\ 0 & 0 & 0 & 0 \\ 0 & 0 & 0 & 0 \end{bmatrix}$$

3
$$\begin{bmatrix} -\frac{11}{6} & 3 & -\frac{3}{2} & \frac{1}{3} \\ -\frac{1}{3} & -\frac{1}{2} & 1 & -\frac{1}{6} \\ \frac{1}{6} & -1 & \frac{1}{2} & \frac{1}{3} \\ -\frac{1}{3} & \frac{3}{2} & -3 & \frac{11}{6} \end{bmatrix}$$

4 The matrix I; the matrix 0; the matrix aI.

5 **a** $B = \begin{bmatrix} 3 & 0 \\ 0 & -2 \end{bmatrix}$ **b** $\begin{bmatrix} 1 & 1 \\ 0 & 1 \end{bmatrix}$

6 For 5**a** **a** $\begin{bmatrix} 27 & 0 \\ 0 & -8 \end{bmatrix}$ **b** $\begin{bmatrix} 4 & 0 \\ 0 & -1 \end{bmatrix}$ **c** $\begin{bmatrix} 657 & 0 \\ 0 & 52 \end{bmatrix}$ **d** $\begin{bmatrix} \frac{1}{3} & 0 \\ 0 & -\frac{1}{2} \end{bmatrix}$

For 5**b** **a** $\begin{bmatrix} 1 & 3 \\ 0 & 1 \end{bmatrix}$ **b** $\begin{bmatrix} 2 & 1 \\ 0 & 2 \end{bmatrix}$ **c** $\begin{bmatrix} 1 & 4 \\ 0 & 1 \end{bmatrix}$ **d** $\begin{bmatrix} 1 & -1 \\ 0 & 1 \end{bmatrix}$

7 **a** $\begin{bmatrix} -1 & 0 & 0 \\ 0 & -1 & 0 \\ 0 & 0 & 2 \end{bmatrix}$ **b** $\begin{bmatrix} 1 & 0 & 0 \\ 0 & 1 & 0 \\ 0 & 0 & 64 \end{bmatrix}$

8 Columns are interchanged.

9 **a** $\begin{bmatrix} 3 & 5 \\ 1 & 2 \end{bmatrix}$ **b** $\begin{bmatrix} -1 & -1 & -3 \\ 1 & 0 & -1 \\ 0 & 1 & 3 \end{bmatrix}$

10 **a** $x^2/3 + 1$ **b** $1 - x/2$ **c** $A = \begin{bmatrix} 1 & 0 & 0 \\ 0 & \frac{1}{2} & 0 \\ 0 & 0 & \frac{1}{3} \end{bmatrix}$ **d** $A^{-1} = \begin{bmatrix} 1 & 0 & 0 \\ 0 & 2 & 0 \\ 0 & 0 & 3 \end{bmatrix}$

$T^{-1}(1) = 1 \qquad T^{-1}(x) = 2x \qquad T^{-1}(x^2) = 3x^2$

11 $\begin{bmatrix} 1 & 0 & 0 \\ \frac{5}{12} & \frac{2}{3} & -\frac{1}{12} \\ \frac{1}{6} & \frac{2}{3} & \frac{1}{6} \end{bmatrix}$

13 $P = \begin{bmatrix} 1 & 0 & 0 \\ -\frac{3}{2} & 2 & -\frac{1}{2} \\ \frac{1}{2} & -1 & \frac{1}{2} \end{bmatrix} \qquad Q = \begin{bmatrix} 1 & 0 & 0 \\ 1 & 1 & 1 \\ 1 & 2 & 4 \end{bmatrix}$

14 **a** $\begin{bmatrix} 1+i & 0 \\ 0 & -1 \end{bmatrix}$ **b** $\begin{bmatrix} 4i & -3 \\ -1 & -i \end{bmatrix}$

SECTION 2

1 Because P and A may not commute.

2 **a** $\begin{bmatrix} 3 & -1 & 0 \\ 1 & 0 & -1 \\ -3 & 1 & 1 \end{bmatrix}$ **b** $\begin{bmatrix} 6 & 9 & 8 \\ 2 & 4 & 3 \\ -5 & -9 & -7 \end{bmatrix}$

3 **a** $\begin{bmatrix} -1 & 0 & -1 \\ 3 & 3 & 4 \\ -1 & -1 & -1 \end{bmatrix}$ **b** $\begin{bmatrix} -1 & 0 & 0 \\ 0 & -1 & 0 \\ 0 & 0 & 2 \end{bmatrix}$ **e** $\begin{bmatrix} 190 & 189 & 189 \\ 63 & 64 & 63 \\ -189 & -189 & -188 \end{bmatrix}$

f $q(A) = \begin{bmatrix} 0 & 0 & 0 \\ 0 & 0 & 0 \\ 0 & 0 & 48 \end{bmatrix} \qquad q(B) = \begin{bmatrix} 144 & 144 & 144 \\ 48 & 48 & 48 \\ -144 & -144 & -144 \end{bmatrix}$

4 **b** $\begin{bmatrix} 9\sqrt{3} - 8 & -6\sqrt{3} + 6 \\ 12\sqrt{3} - 12 & -8\sqrt{3} + 9 \end{bmatrix}$ **c** $\begin{bmatrix} 9\sqrt[3]{3} - 8 & -6\sqrt[3]{3} + 6 \\ 12\sqrt[3]{3} - 12 & -8\sqrt[3]{3} + 9 \end{bmatrix}$

5 abc

6 I

7 0

8 **a** 0

9 **b** $\begin{bmatrix} 0 & 0 & 0 \\ 0 & 0 & 0 \\ 0 & 0 & 0 \end{bmatrix}$ **c** $\begin{bmatrix} 0 & 0 & 0 \\ 0 & 0 & 0 \\ 0 & 0 & 0 \end{bmatrix}$

16 **a** $P^{-1} = \begin{bmatrix} 4i & -3 \\ -1 & -i \end{bmatrix}$ $B = \begin{bmatrix} 7 + 4i & -12 + 24i \\ -1 + 2i & -7 - 3i \end{bmatrix}$

b $B^8 = \begin{bmatrix} 61 & 180i \\ 15i & -44 \end{bmatrix}$

SECTION 3

1 **a** The nonzero vectors parallel to $\overline{w}$ are characteristic vectors belonging to $\lambda = 1$; those perpendicular to $\overline{w}$ belong to $\lambda = -1$.

b The nonzero vectors parallel to $\overline{w}$ are characteristic vectors belonging to $\lambda = 0$; those perpendicular to $\overline{w}$ belong to $\lambda = 1$.

c *See* answer to part **a**.

d The nonzero vectors parallel to $\overline{w}$ are characteristic vectors belonging to $\lambda = 1$; those perpendicular to $\overline{w}$ belong to $\lambda = 0$.

e *See* answer to part **b**.

f Nonzero multiples of $(\cos \pi/8, -\sin \pi/8)$ belong to $\lambda = 1$; while nonzero multiples of $(\cos 3\pi/8, \sin 3\pi/8)$ belong to $\lambda = -1$.

3 3 and 1, respectively.

4 **a** $\lambda^2 - \lambda$, $\lambda = 0, 1$ **b** $\lambda^2 - 6\lambda + 8$, $\lambda = 2, 4$ **c** $\lambda^3 - 8\lambda^2 + 20\lambda - 16$, $\lambda = 2, 4$

d $\lambda^3 - 8\lambda^2 + 16\lambda$, $\lambda = 0, 4$ **e** $(\lambda - 1)(\lambda - 2)(\lambda - 3)$, $\lambda = 1, 2, 3$ **f** λ^4, $\lambda = 0$

5 These answers are not unique.

a For $\lambda = 0$, $\begin{bmatrix} -1 \\ 1 \end{bmatrix}$ For $\lambda = 1$, $\begin{bmatrix} 1 \\ 1 \end{bmatrix}$

b For $\lambda = 2$, $\begin{bmatrix} -1 \\ 1 \end{bmatrix}$ For $\lambda = 4$, $\begin{bmatrix} 1 \\ 1 \end{bmatrix}$

c For $\lambda = 2$, $\begin{bmatrix} -1 \\ 1 \\ 0 \end{bmatrix}$ or $\begin{bmatrix} 0 \\ 0 \\ 1 \end{bmatrix}$ For $\lambda = 4$, $\begin{bmatrix} 1 \\ 1 \\ 0 \end{bmatrix}$

d For $\lambda = 0$, $\begin{bmatrix} -1 \\ 3 \\ 2 \end{bmatrix}$ For $\lambda = 4$, $\begin{bmatrix} -1 \\ 1 \\ 0 \end{bmatrix}$ or $\begin{bmatrix} -1 \\ 0 \\ 1 \end{bmatrix}$

e For $\lambda = 1$, $\begin{bmatrix} 1 \\ 0 \\ 0 \end{bmatrix}$ For $\lambda = 2$, $\begin{bmatrix} 2 \\ 1 \\ 0 \end{bmatrix}$ For $\lambda = 3$, $\begin{bmatrix} 3 \\ 2 \\ 2 \end{bmatrix}$

f For $\lambda = 0$, $\begin{bmatrix} 1 \\ 0 \\ 0 \\ 0 \end{bmatrix}$

7 **b** $\lambda_1^2, \lambda_2^2, \ldots, \lambda_k^2$ **c** of A^2, $\lambda = 1, 9$ of A^3, $\lambda = 1, -1, 27$

8 **b** $q(\lambda_1), q(\lambda_2), \ldots, q(\lambda_k)$

10 $\lambda = 2, -1, 3$

11 i and $-i$, respectively.

12 **a** $\lambda^2 - (1 + 2i)\lambda - 1 + i$; $\lambda = 1 + i, i$; $\begin{bmatrix} 2 \\ -1 + 2i \end{bmatrix}$ $\begin{bmatrix} 1 \\ -1 + i \end{bmatrix}$ respectively.

b $\lambda^2 + 1$; $\lambda = i, -i$; $\begin{bmatrix} 1 \\ -i \end{bmatrix}$ $\begin{bmatrix} -i \\ 1 \end{bmatrix}$ respectively.

SECTION 4

1 Other answers are possible.

a $\begin{bmatrix} -1 & 1 \\ 1 & 1 \end{bmatrix}$ **b** $\begin{bmatrix} -1 & 1 \\ 1 & 1 \end{bmatrix}$ **c** $\begin{bmatrix} -1 & 1 & 0 \\ 1 & 1 & 0 \\ 0 & 0 & 1 \end{bmatrix}$ **d** $\begin{bmatrix} 1 & 2 & 3 \\ 0 & 1 & 2 \\ 0 & 0 & 2 \end{bmatrix}$

e $\begin{bmatrix} -1 & -1 & -1 \\ 3 & 1 & 0 \\ 2 & 0 & 1 \end{bmatrix}$ **f** $\begin{bmatrix} 7 & 9 & 2 \\ -3 & -3 & -1 \\ 4 & 5 & 1 \end{bmatrix}$

2 For $A = \begin{bmatrix} 2 & -6 \\ -2 & 1 \end{bmatrix}$ $P = \begin{bmatrix} -2 & 3 \\ 1 & 2 \end{bmatrix}$

For $A = \begin{bmatrix} 3 & -1 \\ 2 & 0 \end{bmatrix}$ $P = \begin{bmatrix} 1 & 1 \\ 1 & 2 \end{bmatrix}$

5 **a** $\frac{1}{2}\begin{bmatrix} 3^{10}+1 & 3^{10}-1 \\ 3^{10}-1 & 3^{10}+1 \end{bmatrix}$ **b** $\begin{bmatrix} 4 & -1 & -1 \\ 9 & -2 & -3 \\ 3 & -1 & 0 \end{bmatrix}$

6 $\begin{bmatrix} -2 & -2 & 0 \\ 1 & 0 & -1 \\ 5 & 10 & 5 \end{bmatrix}$ is one possibility.

7 Other answers are possible (by permutation of the diagonal entries).

a $\begin{bmatrix} 1 & 0 \\ 0 & -1 \end{bmatrix}$ **b** $\begin{bmatrix} 0 & 0 \\ 0 & 1 \end{bmatrix}$ **c** $\begin{bmatrix} 1 & 0 & 0 \\ 0 & -1 & 0 \\ 0 & 0 & -1 \end{bmatrix}$ **d** $\begin{bmatrix} 1 & 0 & 0 \\ 0 & 0 & 0 \\ 0 & 0 & 0 \end{bmatrix}$

e $\begin{bmatrix} 0 & 0 & 0 \\ 0 & 1 & 0 \\ 0 & 0 & 1 \end{bmatrix}$ **f** $\begin{bmatrix} 1 & 0 \\ 0 & -1 \end{bmatrix}$

8 $\begin{bmatrix} 1 & 0 \\ 0 & -1 \end{bmatrix}$

9 **b** $\begin{bmatrix} 1 & -1 & 1 \\ 0 & 2 & -4 \\ 0 & 0 & 4 \end{bmatrix}$ **d** For example, $1, x-1, (x-1)^2$

11 For example, $P = \begin{bmatrix} 2 & 2 \\ 1-i & 1+i \end{bmatrix}$

SECTION 5

1 Possible answers are

a $\begin{bmatrix} -1/\sqrt{2} & 1/\sqrt{2} \\ 1/\sqrt{2} & 1/\sqrt{2} \end{bmatrix}$ **b** $\begin{bmatrix} 1/\sqrt{2} & -1/\sqrt{2} \\ 1/\sqrt{2} & 1/\sqrt{2} \end{bmatrix}$

c $\begin{bmatrix} -1/\sqrt{2} & -1/\sqrt{6} & 1/\sqrt{3} \\ 1/\sqrt{2} & -1/\sqrt{6} & 1/\sqrt{3} \\ 0 & 2/\sqrt{6} & 1/\sqrt{3} \end{bmatrix}$ **d** $\begin{bmatrix} 1/\sqrt{66} & 1/\sqrt{6} & -3/\sqrt{11} \\ -4/\sqrt{66} & 2/\sqrt{6} & 1/\sqrt{11} \\ 7/\sqrt{66} & 1/\sqrt{6} & 1/\sqrt{11} \end{bmatrix}$

e $\begin{bmatrix} 0 & -1/\sqrt{3} & 2/\sqrt{6} \\ 1/\sqrt{2} & -1/\sqrt{3} & -1/\sqrt{6} \\ 1/\sqrt{2} & 1/\sqrt{3} & 1/\sqrt{6} \end{bmatrix}$

2 $\begin{bmatrix} 1/\sqrt{3} & 1/\sqrt{3} & 1/\sqrt{3} \\ 1/\sqrt{3} & 1/\sqrt{3} & 1/\sqrt{3} \\ 1/\sqrt{3} & 1/\sqrt{3} & 1/\sqrt{3} \end{bmatrix}$

4 $\dfrac{1}{\sqrt{2}}(1,-1), \dfrac{1}{\sqrt{2}}(1,1)$

5 $A = \begin{bmatrix} -\frac{5}{6} & \frac{2}{3} & \frac{13}{6} \\ \frac{2}{3} & \frac{2}{3} & \frac{2}{3} \\ \frac{13}{6} & \frac{2}{3} & -\frac{5}{6} \end{bmatrix}$

7 $\dfrac{1}{2}\begin{bmatrix} 1+3^{10} & 1-3^{10} \\ 1-3^{10} & 1+3^{10} \end{bmatrix}$

11 **f** $\begin{bmatrix} i/\sqrt{2} & i/\sqrt{2} \\ 1/\sqrt{2} & -1/\sqrt{2} \end{bmatrix}$ **g** Same as **f**.

SECTION 6

1 Possible answers are **a** $3x_1^2 + y_1^2 = 1$ **b** $\dfrac{5}{\sqrt{5}}x_1^2 - \dfrac{5}{\sqrt{5}}y_1^2 = 1$

2 Possible answers are **a** $x_1^2 + 3y_1^2 - 3z_1^2 = 1$ **b** $x_1^2 - y_1^2 - 2z_1^2 = 1$

3 **a** $x = \frac{3}{8}\sin t + \frac{1}{8}\cos t + C_1$
$y = -\frac{1}{8}\sin t - \frac{3}{8}\cos t + C_2$

b $x = -\frac{3}{25}e^t - \frac{4}{25}e^{-t} + C_1$
$y = \frac{4}{25}e^t - \frac{3}{25}e^{-t} + C_2$

4 $x = \frac{1}{432}(-3t^2 + 10t^3 + 12t^4) + d_1$
$y = \frac{1}{432}(15t^2 - 2t^3 + 12t^4) + d_2$
$z = \frac{1}{432}(24t^2 + 16t^3 + 6t^4) + d_3$

5 $x = \frac{3}{10}t^2 + \frac{1}{15}t^3 + C_1$
$y = \frac{8}{10}t^2 + \frac{1}{15}t^3 + C_2$

7 **a** $x = c_1e^{2t} + c_2e^{4t}$
$y = -c_1e^{2t} + c_2e^{4t}$

b $x = c_1e^t + c_2e^{-5t}$
$y = 2c_1e^t - 4c_2e^{-5t}$

c $x = -c_2 + 2c_3e^{6t}$
$y = c_1 - c_2 - c_3e^{6t}$
$z = c_1 + c_2 + c_3e^{6t}$

CHAPTER 4

SECTION 1

1 **a** $y = ce^{x}$ **b** $y = ce^{-\sqrt{5}x}$ **c** $y = ce^{-(2/3)x}$
d $y = ce^{(1/2)x}$ **e** $y = ce^{-ex}$

2 **a** $y = e^{2x}$ **b** $y = e^{-2x}$ **c** $y = 2e^{(1/2)x-1/2}$ **d** $y = 3e^{-(5/4)x+5/2}$

3 One, namely, $y = 0$.

4 $y \to 0$; $|y| \to +\infty$; $|y| \to +\infty$

5 **a** $y = ce^{2x} + x/2 + \frac{1}{4}$ **b** $y = ce^{-3x} + \frac{1}{4}e^{x}$
c $y = ce^{-x} + \dfrac{\sin x}{2} - \dfrac{\cos x}{2}$ **d** $y = ce^{x} - x^2 - 2x - 2$

6 **a** $y(0) = 1: y = \frac{3}{4}e^{2x} + x/2 + \frac{1}{4}$
$y(1) = 2: y = \frac{5}{4}e^{2x-2} + x/2 + \frac{1}{4}$
b $y(0) = 1: y = \frac{3}{4}e^{-3x} + \frac{1}{4}e^{x}$
$y(1) = 2: y = 2e^{-3x+3} - \frac{1}{4}e^{-3x+4} + \frac{1}{4}e^{x}$
c $y(0) = 1: y = \frac{3}{2}e^{-x} + \dfrac{\sin x}{2} - \dfrac{\cos x}{2}$

$$y(1) = 2: y = \left(2 + \frac{\cos 1}{2} - \frac{\sin 1}{2}\right)e^{-x+1} + \frac{\sin x}{2} - \frac{\cos x}{2}$$

d $y(0) = 1: y = 3e^{x} - x^2 - 2x - 2$
$y(1) = 2: y = 7e^{x-1} - x^2 - 2x - 2$

7 **a** $y = ce^{-x^3/3}$ **b** $y = c/x + x^3/4$ **c** $y = x^{-x}(-1 + ce^{x})$ **d** $y = ce^{\cos x}$

8 **a** $y = e^{-(1/3)(x^3-1)}$ **b** $y = 3/4x + x^3/4$
c $y = x^{-x}(-1 + 2e^{x-1})$ **d** $y = e^{\cos x - \cos 1}$

SECTION 2

1 **a** $y = c_1e^{6x} + c_2e^{-x}$ **b** $y = c_1e^{3x} + c_2e^{2x}$
c $y = c_1e^{-2x} + c_2xe^{-2x}$ **d** $y = c_1e^{-(3/2+\sqrt{5}/2)x} + c_2e^{-(3/2-\sqrt{5}/2)x}$
e $y = c_1 + c_2x$ **f** $y = c_1e^{\sqrt{2}x} + c_2e^{-\sqrt{2}x}$
g $y = c_1e^{3x} + c_2xe^{3x}$ **h** $y = c_1e^{(1+\sqrt{3})x} + c_2{}^{(1-\sqrt{3})x}$

2 **a** $y = -xe^{2x}$ **b** $y = -7e^{-2x} + 9e^{-x}$
c $y = -13e^{2x-6} + 4xe^{2x-6}$ **d** $y = -e^{2x-20} + 2e^{x-10}$

3 **a** 0; No. **b** $y = ce^{\beta x}$ $y = ce^{\alpha x}$ **c** No; Yes.

4 **a** $y = c_1e^{5x} + c_2e^{(2/3)x}$ **b** $y = c_1e^{-(1/2)x} + c_2xe^{-(1/2)x}$

5 **a** No solution. **b** unique: $y = 1 + 2x$
c Not unique: $y = e^x + c_2xe^x$ for any c_2

6 **a** $\begin{bmatrix} 0 & 1 \\ -c & -b \end{bmatrix}$

7 **a** Unique: $y = 2x$ **b** No solution. **c** Not unique: $y = c_2\,xe^{-x}$ for any c_2

8 **f** $y = c_1e^{-x}\sin x + c_2e^{-x}\cos x$

SECTION 3

1 **a** $y = c_1 \sin 2x + c_2 \cos 2x$
b $y = c_1 \sin \sqrt{b}x + c_2 \cos \sqrt{b}x \qquad b > 0$
$y = c_1e^{\sqrt{b}x} + c_2e^{-\sqrt{b}x} \qquad b < 0$
$y = c_1 + c_2x \qquad b = 0$
c $y = c_1 \sin \sqrt{7/3}x + c_2 \cos \sqrt{7/3}x$ **d** $y = c_1 \sin \sqrt{5/2}x + c_2 \cos \sqrt{5/2}x$

2 **a** $y = c_1e^{-x}\sin x + c_2e^{-x}\cos x$ **b** $y = c_1e^{-2x}\sin x + c_2e^{-2x}\cos x$
c $y = c_1e^{(1/2)x}\sin x + c_2e^{(1/2)x}\cos x$ **d** $y = c_1e^{4x}\sin \sqrt{2}x + c_2e^{4x}\cos \sqrt{2}x$

3 **a** $y = c_1e^{-3x} + c_2xe^{-3x}$ **b** $y = c_1e^{-3x}\sin x + c_2e^{-3x}\cos x$
c $y = c_1e^{-4x} + c_2e^{-2x}$ **d** $y = c_1e^{(-3+\sqrt{76}/2)x} + c_2e^{(-3-\sqrt{76}/2)x}$

4 **a** $y = \frac{1}{2}\sin 2x$ **b** $y = -\frac{3}{2}\sin x$
c $y = e^{-x+\pi/2}\sin x$ **d** $y = \dfrac{1}{\sqrt{2}}e^{2x}\sin \sqrt{2}x$

a $e^{3x}, xe^{3x}, x^2e^{3x}, x^3e^{3x}$ **b** $e^{-2x}, xe^{-2x}, x^2e^{-2x}, x^3e^{-2x}, x^4e^{-2x}, x^5e^{-2x}$

6 **a** $e^{3x}D^4(\log x)$ **b** $e^{-2x}D^3(x^5)$
c $e^xD^5(e^{3x})$ **d** $e^{\sqrt{2}x}D^{12}(\sin x)$

SECTION 4

1 **a** $y = c_1 \sin \sqrt{2}x + c_2 \cos \sqrt{2}x + c_3x \sin \sqrt{2}x + c_4x \cos \sqrt{2}x$
b $y = c_1e^x + c_2xe^x + c_3x^2e^x$
c $y = c_1 + c_2x + c_3x^2 + c_4x^3 + c_5e^{4x} + c_6e^{-x}$
d $y = c_1 + c_2x + c_3e^{-x}\sin x + c_4e^{-x}\cos x$
e $y = c_1e^{-x/\sqrt{2}}\sin(x/\sqrt{2}) + c_2e^{-x/\sqrt{2}}\cos(x/\sqrt{2}) + c_3e^{x/\sqrt{2}}\sin(x/\sqrt{2})$
$+ c_4e^{x/\sqrt{2}}\cos(x/\sqrt{2})$
f $y = c_1e^x + c_2e^{-(1/2)x}\sin(\sqrt{3}/2)x + c_3e^{-(1/2)x}\cos(\sqrt{3}/2)x$

2 **a** $e^{-3x}, xe^{-3x}, e^x, xe^x \quad e^{-x}, xe^{-x}, \sin x, \cos x$

b $1, x, x^2, x^3, x^4, e^{-2x}\sin x, e^{-2x}\cos x, xe^{-2x}\sin x, xe^{-2x}\cos x,$
$x^2e^{-2x}\sin x, x^2e^{-2x}\cos x$

c $e^{4x}, xe^{4x}, e^{-x}, xe^{-x}, e^{-(1/2)x}\sin(\sqrt{3}/2)x, e^{-(1/2)x}\cos(\sqrt{3}/2)x,$
$xe^{-(1/2)x}\sin(\sqrt{3}/2)x, xe^{-(1/2)x}\cos(\sqrt{3}/2)x$

d $1, x, x^2, x^3, e^{3x}\sin 2x, e^{3x}\cos 2x, xe^{3x}\sin 2x, xe^{3x}\cos 2x$

3 **a** $y = (3/\sqrt{2})\sin\sqrt{2}x + \cos\sqrt{2}x + (1/\sqrt{2})x\sin\sqrt{2}x - x\cos\sqrt{2}x$

b $y = \frac{1}{2}\cos x + \frac{1}{4}e^x - \frac{3}{4}e^{-x}$ **c** $y = (\frac{1}{2} + x - \frac{1}{2}x^2)e^{-x+1}$

d $y = -\frac{3}{10}\sin x + \frac{1}{10}\cos x - \frac{1}{5}e^{-x}\cos x + \frac{1}{10}e^x$

5 **a** 1, 1, 0

SECTION 5

1 **a** $y = \frac{1}{5}xe^{-3x} + \frac{6}{25}e^{-3x}$ **b** $y = \frac{1}{4}xe^{2x}$ **c** $y = \frac{1}{8}x^2 + \frac{3}{16}x + \frac{15}{64}$
d $y = 2$ **e** $y = \frac{1}{6}x^3e^{-x}$ **f** $y = \frac{1}{5}(x-1) + \frac{1}{8}(\sin x + \cos x)$
g $y = x^2 - \frac{2}{9} - \frac{1}{12}x^2\cos 3x + \frac{1}{36}x\sin 3x$
h $y = \frac{1}{4}xe^x - \frac{1}{4}xe^{-x} - \frac{1}{4}x\cos x$
i $y = -\frac{1}{12}x^2 - \frac{5}{36}x + \frac{1}{4}e^{-x}$ **j** $y = 1 - 2e^{2x} + xe^{2x}$

2 **a** $y = \frac{1}{5}e^x + (\frac{1}{2}e^{-2\pi} - \frac{3}{20}e^{-\pi})e^{2x} + (-\frac{1}{2}e^{2\pi} + \frac{1}{20}e^{3\pi})e^{-2x}$
b $y = -\frac{1}{2}xe^{-x} + \frac{3}{4}e^x + \frac{1}{4}e^{-x}$ **c** $y = 2x^2 + 6x + 7 + e^{2x} - 8e^x$
d $y = \frac{1}{2}x^2e^{-x}$

3 **a** $K = (D^2 + I)^3(D - I)$ **b** $K = (D^2 - 4D + 13I)(D - I)^3$
c $K = (D^2 + 4I)D$ **d** $K = D^4$

5 **a** $y = x$
b With $z_1 = \int e^{-x}\log x\,dx$, $z_2 = \int e^x\log x\,dx$, then
$$y = \tfrac{1}{2}e^x z_1 - \tfrac{1}{2}e^{-x}z_2$$
c With $z_1 = \int \sqrt{x}e^{-x}\,dx$, $z_2 = \int \sqrt{x}e^{-2x}\,dx$, then
$$y = -e^x z_1 + e^{2x}z_2$$
d With $z_1 = \int xe^{-x}\sqrt{1-x^2}\,dx$, $z_2 = \int e^{-x}\sqrt{1-x^2}\,dx$,
$$y = -e^x z_1 + xe^x z_2$$

6 **b** With $z_1 = \int \frac{\log x}{x}\,dx$, $z_2 = \int \frac{e^{-x}(x+1)\log x}{2x}\,dx$, and
$$z_3 = \int \frac{e^x(x-1)\log x}{2x}\,dx,\ y = -xz_1 + e^x z_2 + e^{-x}z_3$$

8 **a** $y = -\frac{1}{5}x$

b With $z_1 = \int \frac{\log x}{x}\,dx$, $z_2 = \frac{1}{2}\int \frac{e^{-\sqrt{1/3}x}(x+\sqrt{3})\log x}{x}\,dx$

$$z_3 = \frac{1}{2}\int \frac{e^{\sqrt{1/3}x}(x-\sqrt{3})\log x}{x}\,dx$$

$$y = -xz_1 + e^{\sqrt{1/3}x}z_2 + e^{-\sqrt{1/3}x}z_3$$

SECTION 6

1 **a** $t = \dfrac{\log 10}{\log 2}$ minutes **b** $10^6 \cdot \sqrt{10}$

2 $10^6 \dfrac{\ln 2}{\ln 10}$ years

3 163.7 million

4 $64(1 - e^{-1})$

5 **b** $t \to T$

6 **a** $y = 3\cos\sqrt{\frac{1}{5}}t$ **b** $y = -4\cos\sqrt{\frac{1}{5}}t$ **c** $y = 5\sqrt{5}\sin\sqrt{\frac{1}{5}}t$
d $y = -2\sqrt{5}\sin\sqrt{\frac{1}{5}}t + 3\cos\sqrt{\frac{1}{5}}t$

APPENDIX 1

1 $\overline{w} = (2,1) + t(1,-3) = (2+t,1-3t)$

2 $\overline{w} = (\frac{7}{2},0) + t(\frac{7}{2},-\frac{7}{5}) = (\frac{7}{2}+\frac{7}{2}t,-\frac{7}{5}t)$

3 $\overline{w} = (1,-5) + t(1,2) = (1+t,-5+2t)$

4 $\dfrac{x}{1} = \dfrac{y-1}{-2} = \dfrac{z}{1}$

5 $x = t, y = 1 - 4t, z = 2 + t$

6 $\dfrac{x-2}{3} = \dfrac{y+1}{4} = \dfrac{z-3}{1}$

7 $\overline{w} = t(5,7,7) + (1-t)(3,-1,2),\ 0 \le t \le 1$

8 A ray, namely, the points on the line $y = -\frac{3}{2}x + \frac{7}{2}$ which are to the right of $(-7,14)$.

9 The line through the terminal points of $\overline{u}$ and $\overline{v}$.

10 $(\frac{11}{5},\frac{6}{5},-\frac{3}{5})$, $(\frac{7}{5},\frac{7}{5},-\frac{1}{5})$, $(\frac{3}{5},\frac{8}{5},\frac{1}{5})$, $(\frac{1}{5},\frac{9}{5},\frac{3}{5})$

11 $s(-1,1,0) + t(-1,0,1) \quad 0 \le s \le 1 \quad 0 \le t \le 1$

12 Triangle with vertices $\bar{u}$, $\bar{v}$, (0,0,0)

13 $s(0,-3,-1) + t(1,-3,0)$, $0 \le s \le 1$, $0 \le t \le 1$, $s + t \le 1$

15 $2(x-1) - 1(y-2) - 1(z-1) = 0$

16 $\bar{n} = 2\bar{i} - 3\bar{j} + 4\bar{k}$

17 $\bar{w} = (0,0,\frac{1}{4}) + s(\frac{3}{2},1,0) + t(-2,0,1)$

18 $y - 1 = 0$

19 $2(x+1) + 7(y-1) + 6(z-1) = 0$

20 $1(x-6) - 3(y-1) + 2(z-2) = 0$

22 (0,0,2)

23 $4x + 5y - 8(z-2) = 0$

24 $\frac{1}{13}\sqrt{104}$

25 $2\sqrt{3}$

26 $\frac{1}{14}\sqrt{27^2 + 30^2 + 11^2}$

27 $\sqrt{14}$

28 $\frac{1}{2}\sqrt{34}$

29 $\frac{2}{7}\sqrt{14}$

30 $\frac{1}{29}\sqrt{35^2 + 79^2 + 41^2}$

31 $\frac{1}{3}\sqrt{6}$

32 $\frac{2}{3}\sqrt{6}$

33 $\frac{1}{14}\sqrt{1 + 23^2 + 10^2}$

34 The parallelogram determined by (0, −1) and (5,2).

37 Yes.

39 Yes, no.

40 $\sqrt{3}$, $\sqrt{14}$

BIBLIOGRAPHY

Listed below are a few books that pursue further the topics discussed in this book and related results.

Hoffman, K., and R. Kunze: *Linear Algebra*, Prentice-Hall, Inc., Englewood Cliffs, N.J., 1961.
Includes a proof that the reduced form of a matrix is unique. There are also complete discussions of determinants, polynomial theory, and spectral theory. The authors prove the Cayley-Hamilton theorem and the spectral theorem and, in addition, discuss in detail many deeper results about similar matrices, including a treatment of the Jordan canonical form.

Shields, P.: *Linear Algebra*, Addison-Wesley Publishing Co., Inc., Reading, Mass., 1964.
More elementary and less complete than the above-mentioned book, it does contain a complete discussion of third-order orthogonal matrices and a proof of the spectral theorem that is a direct generalization of the proof given in this text, in Example 3, Section 5, Chapter 3.

Jacobson, N.: *Lectures in Abstract Algebra*, vol. 2, D. Van Nostrand Co., Inc., Princeton, N.J., 1953.
A more general treatment of linear algebra than that of the above books. Included also, is a discussion of infinite-dimensional theory.

Faddeeva, V. N.: *Computational Methods of Linear Algebra*, C. D. Benster, translator, Dover Publications, Inc., New York, 1959.
A discussion of numerical methods for solving systems of equations and for finding characteristic values of a matrix.

Kreider, D. L., R. G. Kuller, D. R. Ostberg, and F. W. Perkins: *Introduction to Linear Analysis*, Addison-Wesley Publishing Co., Inc., Reading, Mass., 1966.
A thorough discussion, using the linear algebra framework, of linear differential equations. This book also includes a treatment of inner products and linear partial differential equations.

Robinson, G.: *Vector Geometry*, Allyn and Bacon, Inc., Boston, 1962.
An elementary, yet quite thorough discussion of vector geometry.

Hummel, J.: *Introduction to Vector Functions*, Addison-Wesley Publishing Co., Inc., Reading, Mass., 1967.
An introduction to the calculus of several variables that uses the linear algebra framework. This is the first of a number of forthcoming books that attempt to present this material at a level suitable for students with a background of one year of calculus.

Ficken, F. A.: *The Simplex Method of Linear Programming*, Holt, Rinehart and Winston, Inc., New York, 1961.
Discusses an important new set of techniques in linear algebra with wide application in the physical and social sciences. Linear programming provides a systematic method for finding maximum and minimum values of linear functions subject to constraints.

LIST OF THEOREMS

THEOREM 1, page 21: A homogeneous system with fewer equations than unknowns always has a non-trivial solution.

THEOREM 2, page 26: A homogeneous system in n variables has a unique solution if and only if its coefficient matrix can be reduced to a matrix whose first n columns are the n by n identity matrix.

THEOREM 3, page 43: If A is a matrix and $\bar{u}$ and $\bar{v}$ are vectors in R^n, then $A(\bar{u} + \bar{v}) = A\bar{u} + A\bar{v}$ and $A(a\bar{u}) = a(A\bar{u})$.

THEOREM 4, page 49: The null space of a matrix with n columns is a subspace of R^n.

THEOREM 5, page 51: The null space of a matrix with fewer rows than columns contains non-zero vectors. The null space of a matrix with n columns is the zero subspace if and only if the first n rows reduce to the identity.

THEOREM 6, page 51: If $A\bar{v} = \bar{c}$, then the solutions to $A\bar{u} = \bar{c}$ are the vectors $\bar{v} + \bar{w}$, where $\bar{w}$ is in the null space of A.

THEOREM 7, page 52: If $A\bar{u} = \bar{0}$ has a unique solution, then for any $\bar{c}$, the equation $A\bar{u} = \bar{c}$ has no more than one solution.

THEOREM 8, page 62: The equation $A\bar{u} = \bar{0}$ has a unique solution if and only if the columns of A are independent.

THEOREM 9, pages 71, 297: If $\bar{u}_1, \bar{u}_2, \ldots, \bar{u}_n$ is a basis for V then any other basis for V contains exactly n vectors.

THEOREM 10, pages 72, 299: A set with n vectors in a space V of dimension n is independent if and only if it spans V.

THEOREM 11, page 72: If A has n rows and n columns, then the columns of A are independent if and only if they span R^n. In particular, if $A\bar{u} = \bar{0}$ has a unique solution then for any $\bar{v}$ in R^n, $A\bar{u} = \bar{v}$ has a unique solution.

THEOREM 12, page 105: If T is a linear transformation from R^n into R^m then there is a *unique* matrix A, with m rows and n columns, such that $T\bar{u} = A\bar{u}$, for all $\bar{u}$ in R^n.

THEOREM 13, pages 144, 300: A square matrix A is invertible if and only if the equation $A\bar{u} = \bar{0}$ has a unique solution.

THEOREM 14, pages 144, 300: If A is a square matrix and $BA = I$, then $AB = I$.

THEOREM 15, page 158: If A has n rows and n columns, then the following are equivalent:

(a) A is invertible.

(b) The only solution to $A\bar{u} = \bar{0}$ is $\bar{u} = \bar{0}$.

(c) The columns of A are independent.

(d) The columns of A are a basis for R^n.

(e) The columns of A span R^n.

THEOREM 16, page 159: A square matrix A is invertible if and only if A^t is invertible. Also $(A^t)^{-1} = (A^{-1})^t$.

THEOREM 17, page 166: A matrix A is invertible if and only if $\det A \neq 0$.

THEOREM 18, page 200: The characteristic values of A are the roots of the characteristic polynomial of A.

THEOREM 19, pages 206, 304: If the characteristic values of A are real and distinct then A is similar to a diagonal matrix.

THEOREM 20, page 215: If A is symmetric then A is similar to a diagonal matrix.

THEOREM 21, page 249: Suppose $p(\lambda)$ is a polynomial and that D is the differentiation operator. If $L = p(D - aI)$ and $L_1 = p(D)$, then $L(e^{ax}y) = e^{ax}L_1y$. In particular the general solution to $Ly = 0$ is

$$e^{ax}(c_1\varphi_1 + c_2\varphi_2 + \cdots + c_n\varphi_n)$$

where $c_1\varphi_1 + c_2\varphi_2 + \ldots + c_n\varphi_n$ is the general solution to $L_1y = 0$.

THEOREM 22, pages 252, 306: Suppose S and T are linear transformations defined on V, each having a finite dimensional null space. Then the dimension of the null space of ST cannot exceed the sum of the dimensions of the null space of S and the null space of T.

THEOREM 23, page 253: The dimension of the null space of a constant coefficient linear differential operator is the order of the operator.

INDEX